Mathematics In Our World

Robert E. Eicholz

Phares G. O'Daffer

Charles R. Fleenor

▲ **Addison-Wesley Publishing Company**

Menlo Park, California · Reading, Massachusetts · London · Amsterdam · Don Mills, Ontario · Sydney

Illustration Acknowledgments

Masami Miyamoto: 82–83, 108–109, 110–111, 265 bottom left, 296–297, 343, 344, 352, 356

Robert Bausch: 86, 100, 101, 131

Dick Cole: 16–17, 112–113, 170–171

Wayne Snyder: 67 top left, 106 top left, center right, 107 top left, bottom, 194–195, 221, 240, 306–307

Dottie Lee: 144, 149, 336–337

Photograph Acknowledgments

Elihu Blotnick*: 8, 146

Rene Burri/Magnum Photos: 121 bottom center

Roger Byers/United States Navy: 67 top right, 120

Richard Crone*: 265 center left, 274–275

Culver Pictures: 176

A. Dejean/Sygma: 38 bottom center, 39 top right

George B. Fry III*: 12, 13 left, top center and bottom center, 20, 22, 23, 24, 28, 36 all, 44, 45 all, 48, 67 bottom left, 72 both, 74, 75, 79 all, 84, 85, 88–89, 92, 94–95, 104 all, 106 top left, center left, bottom left and bottom right, 107 center left, 108, 135 center left and bottom right, 142, 147 all, 154–155, 158, 159 both, 164 both, 165, 166 both, 167 both, 172–173, 193 top left and bottom right, 216, 226–227, 228, 232, 238, 242 all, 243 all, 265 top right, 270, 277 top, 280, 282 all, 283, 286 both, 287 both, 298–299, 300, 334–335

Goodyear Tire & Rubber Company: 121 bottom left

Gerhard Gscheidle*: 315

George Hall*: 207

Erich Hartmann/Magnum Photos: 2

Robb Johns*: 152

Heinz Kluetmeier/SPORTS ILLUSTRATED/© Time Inc.: 30–31

Erich Lessing/Magnum Photos: 265 top center, 291 bottom

Bob Mader/Tom Stack & Associates: 121 top left

© *Wally McNamee/Woodfin Camp & Associates:* 38 top right, 39 left

NASA: 1 top, 4, 5, 42, 121 bottom right, 129 bottom right

David Petrali: 14

Bil Plummer*: 13 right

Ken Regan/Camera 5: 1 bottom center, 38 bottom left and bottom right, 39 top center left, top center right and bottom right

Cindy Rymer/Van Cleve Photography: 290–291

Stephen Shames/Black Star: 38 top center

Ghandi H. Shemdin/Van Cleve Photography: 121 top center

Werner Stoy/Camera Hawaii: 10

Norman Owen Tomalin/Bruce Coleman Inc.: 121 top right, 291 top

Tom Tracy*: 98

*Photographs provided expressly for the publisher.

All other illustrations and photographs by Addison-Wesley staff.

Cover: Aerial view of Chicago by George Hall. Aerial view of farms in Quebec by Richard Crone. Cover composite and remaining photographs by Nikolay Zurek. All provided expressly for the publisher.

With Answers ISBN 0-201-09879-2
Without Answers ISBN 0-201-09870-9
BCDEFGHIJKL-BW-8210798

Contents

The Decimal System
Reviewing Addition and Subtraction
Using Your Skills
Geometric Ideas and Constructions

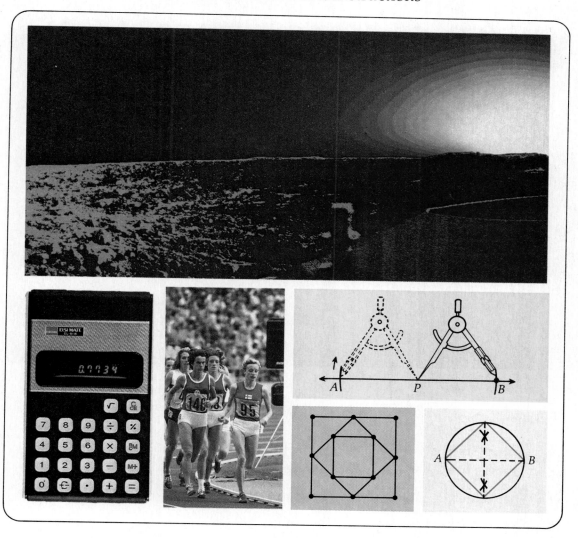

The Decimal System

In a recent year, 7 781 730 people lived in New York City.

1. What digit is in the thousands' place?

2. What digit is in the millions' place?

3. What three digits are in the thousands' period?

4. What digit is in the hundred thousands' place?

The **decimal system**, which we use for naming numbers, uses **place value**.

Millions			Thousands			Units		
5	6	9	4	7	3	8	2	
hundred millions	ten millions	millions	hundred thousands	ten thousands	thousands	hundreds	tens	ones

We write: 56 947 382
We say: Fifty-six **million**, nine hundred forty-seven **thousand**, three hundred eighty-two

The decimal system has a base of ten. This means that each place has a value ten times the place to its right. The decimal system uses only these ten digits: 0, 1, 2, 3, 4, 5, 6, 7, 8, 9.

Read each numeral. Tell what each red digit means.

1. 46 031
2. 29 154
3. 12 019
4. 982 516
5. 990 218
6. 409 385
7. 13 802 003
8. 6 606 111
9. 27 051 364
10. 85 763 149
11. 2 853 461
12. 8 319 104
13. 5 978 216
14. 814 927
15. 12 067 258
16. 78 661 301
17. 6 143 592
18. 3 746 905
19. 5 190 243
20. 4 637 201
21. 5 312 718
22. 6 147 538
23. 2 354 609
24. 90 152 671

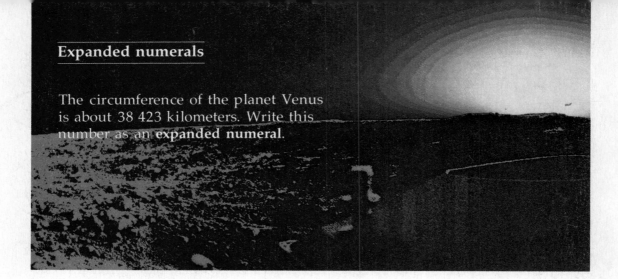

Expanded numerals

The circumference of the planet Venus is about 38 423 kilometers. Write this number as an **expanded numeral**.

$$38\ 423 = (3 \times 10\ 000) + (8 \times 1000) + (4 \times 100) + (2 \times 10) + 3$$
$$38\ 423 = \quad 30\ 000 \quad + \quad 8000 \quad + \quad 400 \quad + \quad 20 \quad + 3$$

standard numeral   expanded numeral

Other examples

$$4836 = (4 \times 1000) + (8 \times 100) + (3 \times 10) + 6$$
$$\quad = \quad 4000 \quad + \quad 800 \quad + \quad 30 \quad + 6$$

$$527\ 049 = (5 \times 100\ 000) + (2 \times 10\ 000) + (7 \times 1000) + (4 \times 10) + 9$$
$$\quad = \quad 500\ 000 \quad + \quad 20\ 000 \quad + \quad 7000 \quad + \quad 40 \quad + 9$$

Copy. Replace each ⦀ with the correct number.

1. $27\ 462 = (2 \times ⦀) + (7 \times ⦀) + (4 \times ⦀) + (6 \times ⦀) + 2$

2. $649\ 816 = (⦀ \times 100\ 000) + (4 \times ⦀) + (9 \times ⦀) + (8 \times ⦀) + (1 \times ⦀) + 6$

3. $730\ 468 = (7 \times ⦀) + (3 \times ⦀) + (⦀ \times 100) + (⦀ \times 10) + 8$

Write the standard numeral.

4. $3000 + 700 + 60 + 4$

5. $50\ 000 + 800 + 7$

6. $(3 \times 100\ 000) + (9 \times 10\ 000) + (6 \times 1000) + (1 \times 100) + (4 \times 10) + 9$

Write an expanded numeral for each standard numeral.

1. 4672
2. 86 943
3. 50 397
4. 387 942
5. 642 803
6. 78 076
7. 9 832 175
8. 7 008 306
9. 50 964
10. 472 965
11. 48 276 000
12. 900 678

Write a standard numeral for each expanded numeral.

13. 6000 + 700 + 40 + 3
14. 3000 + 900 + 70 + 6
15. 8000 + 50 + 7
16. 40 000 + 6000 + 800 + 2
17. 300 000 + 40 000 + 7000 + 600 + 10 + 8
18. 5 000 000 + 900 000 + 4000 + 200 + 80 + 3

For items 19 through 23, write a standard numeral for each number.

19. four hundred sixty-seven thousand, nine hundred forty-six
20. eight million, four hundred sixty-three thousand
21. seven hundred twenty-five thousand, three hundred two

22. The circumference of the planet Mars: twenty-one thousand, three hundred thirty-five kilometers

23. The circumference of the earth: forty thousand, seventy-five kilometers

1. Write the largest number possible using the digits 2 through 8. Write the smallest number possible using the digits 2 through 8. Find their sum.

2. Find this product.

   1 234 569
   ×   9

3. Which number is larger, the sum or the product?

Powers of ten

This is a unit cube. 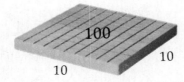 1

There are **10** unit cubes
in a rod.

We write: **10¹**
We say: ten to the first power

$$10$$

There are **10 × 10**
unit cubes in a layer.

We write: **10²**
We say: ten to the second
power or ten squared

There are **10 × 10 × 10**
unit cubes in a block.

We write: **10³**
We say: ten to the
third power
or ten cubed

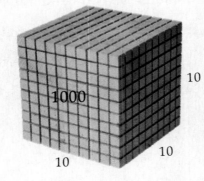

Numbers such as 10^1, 10^2, 10^3, 10^4, and so on are called
powers of ten. 10 is called the **base**. The small raised
numerals, 1, 2, 3, and 4, are called **exponents**.

Write a standard numeral for each ▥.

1. $10^1 =$ ▥

2. $10^2 = 10 \times 10 =$ ▥

3. $10^3 = 10 \times 10 \times 10 =$ ▥

4. $10^4 = 10 \times 10 \times 10 \times 10 =$ ▥

5. $10^5 = 10 \times 10 \times 10 \times 10 \times 10 =$ ▥

6. $10^6 = 10 \times 10 \times 10 \times 10 \times 10 \times 10 =$ ▥

Write each power of ten as a standard numeral.

Example: $10^4 = 10\ 000$

1. 10^2 2. 10^1 3. 10^3 4. 10^5 5. 10^7 6. 10^9

7. 10^6 8. 10^4 9. 10^8 10. 10^{10} 11. 10^4 12. 10^5

Write each standard numeral as a power of ten.

Example: $1000 = 10^3$

13. 100   14. 10 000   15. 100 000   16. 1000

17. 1 000 000   18. 1 000 000 000   19. 100 000 000   20. 10

Write each standard numeral as an expanded numeral using powers of ten.

Example: $5736 = (5 \times 1000) + (7 \times 100) + (3 \times 10) + 6$

$= (5 \times 10^3) + (7 \times 10^2) + (3 \times 10^1) + 6$

21. 965   22. 8763   23. 52 946   24. 378 965

25. 7 643 216   26. 407   27. 8042   28. 36 750

29. 460 987   30. 709 312   31. 9 800 600   32. 590 000

Write each as a standard numeral.

33. $(3 \times 10^3) + (6 \times 10^2) + (4 \times 10^1) + 2$

34. $(8 \times 10^3) + (3 \times 10^1) + 5$

35. $(9 \times 10^5) + (3 \times 10^3) + (6 \times 10^2) + 8$

Have you lived 5×10^3 days?
Have you lived 6×10^6 minutes?

Find out how much more or less
than each you have lived.

Rounding whole numbers

Mapmakers, called cartographers, often make maps that show the heights of mountains and valleys. For some maps they round the actual heights to the nearest ten, hundred, thousand, or more. Mt. Everest is 8848 m high. What is this height rounded to the nearest thousand?

Finding the answer

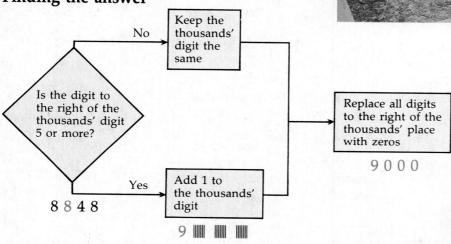

8848 rounded to the nearest thousand is 9000.

Other examples

Round 35 486 to the nearest ten thousand.

35 486

The thousands' digit is 5 or more. 35 486 rounded to the nearest ten thousand is 40 000.

Round 6724 to the nearest hundred.

6724

The tens' digit is less than 5. 6724 rounded to the nearest hundred is 6700.

Round to the nearest thousand.

1. 5437   2. 8794   3. 6500   4. 12 437   5. 58 968

6. 27 500   7. 9995   8. 105 387   9. 245 702   10. 89 503

Round to the nearest ten thousand.

1. 17 499
2. 16 876
3. 52 524
4. 13 500

5. 67 259
6. 706 923
7. 29 598
8. 847 386

9. 409 816
10. 518 094
11. 7 012 568
12. 3 647 899

Round to the nearest hundred.

13. 746
14. 9432
15. 13 650
16. 8569

17. 57 523
18. 967
19. 2750
20. 39 468

21. 659 805
22. 301 952
23. 478 102
24. 190 871

Round to the nearest ten.

25. 784
26. 635
27. 9476
28. 8238

29. 56 295
30. 652
31. 439
32. 7685

33. 905 468
34. 31 999
35. 546 085
36. 82 172

37. The highest mountain in North America is Mount McKinley in Alaska. It is 6194 m high. Round this number to the nearest hundred.

Chinese Abacus—Suan Pan

38. Mount Whitney, in California, is 4418 m high. Round this number to the nearest thousand.

☆ 39. Collect five other facts about mountains. Round each number to the nearest hundred and to the nearest thousand.

The beads pushed toward the middle bar from below represent 1 each, those from above represent 5 each, and each wire has the usual decimal place value. What number do you think is shown on this abacus?

Decimal place value—
tenths and hundredths

Mt. Waialeale on the island of Kauai, Hawaii has been called the wettest place in the world. The average annual rainfall in centimeters during a 30-year period is shown below:

Mt. Waialeale, Kauai, Hawaii

1	2	3	4	6	9
thousands	hundreds	tens	ones	tenths	hundredths

We write: 1234.69

We read: one thousand, two hundred thirty-four and
        sixty-nine hundredths

Write the number of units, tenths and hundredths. Then write the decimal.

Example:

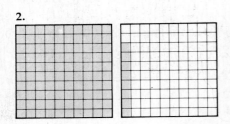

1 unit, 3 tenths, 4 hundredths
Decimal: 1.34

1.

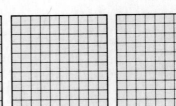

2.

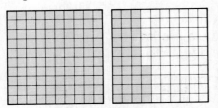

3.

Read each numeral. Tell what each red digit means.

1. 835.97
2. 64.09
3. 5173.92
4. 236.97
5. 53.87
6. 461.39
7. 81.62
8. 7.54
9. 64.71
10. 163.5
11. 42.96
12. 389.01
13. 0.75
14. 381.44
15. 5.30
16. 232.8
17. 51.29
18. 79.78
19. 8.44
20. 22.36
21. 0.46
22. 15.67
23. 67.50
24. 9.81

Write each number as a decimal.

25. Highest recorded temperature on earth: fifty-seven and seven tenths degrees Celsius

26. Heaviest rainfall in one minute: three and twelve hundredths centimeters

27. Heaviest hailstones: seventy-five hundredths of a kilogram

☆ 28. Consult a local weather service or a world almanac and find the average annual rainfall for your city or state.

The normal monthly rainfall in centimeters for Houston, Texas is given by the table.

Month	Rainfall	Month	Rainfall
January	9.07	July	10.46
February	8.99	August	11.05
March	6.81	September	11.81
April	8.99	October	11.29
May	12.95	November	10.24
June	11.48	December	10.26

Find the average monthly rainfall.

Extending place value—thousandths and ten thousandths

Surveyors play an important part in highway development, construction, and map-making. They provide accurate measurements of land surfaces and elevations. Because their figures must be very precise, they often work with numbers such as the one shown below.

5	7	3	2	4	1	8	9
thousands	hundreds	tens	ones	tenths	hundredths	thousandths	ten thousandths

We write: 5732.4189

We read: five thousand, seven hundred thirty-two and four thousand, one hundred eighty-nine ten thousandths

Read each numeral. Tell what each red digit means.

1. 0.12
2. 0.485
3. 0.9182
4. 6.51

5. 2.087
6. 3.0576
7. 0.613
8. 1.064

9. 0.8704
10. 83.009
11. 3.128
12. 0.8153

13. 15.2114
14. 0.356
15. 0.9050
16. 64.0025

17. 0.9812
18. 6.2178
19. 3.7218
20. 3.4401

21. 1.8001
22. 0.696
23. 7.5902
24. 7.0006

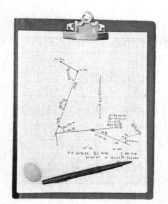

Tell what each red digit means.

1. 1.5821
2. 0.4032
3. 9.136
4. 0.725
5. 2.974
6. 0.4453
7. 3.1519
8. 8.365
9. 3.8001
10. 16.847
11. 26.367
12. 0.1497
13. 531.60
14. 6.058
15. 7.79
16. 4.281
17. 59.72
18. 91.50
19. 354.01
20. 1.9027

Write a decimal for each numeral.

21. seven and four hundred sixty-nine thousandths

22. forty-nine and thirty-eight hundredths

23. twenty-seven hundredths

24. fifty-three and nine thousand, two hundred forty-six ten thousandths

25. eighty-one and fifty-three thousandths

26. ninety-seven and four thousand, three hundred twenty-six ten thousandths

Find the number for a, b, and c in each equation.

$$a \times a = 6084$$
$$b \times b \times b = 32\ 768$$
$$c \times c \times c \times c = 20\ 736$$

Rounding decimals

The highest speed ever recorded for a wheeled vehicle on land is 1016.086 km/h. What is this speed rounded to the nearest hundredth?

Finding the answer

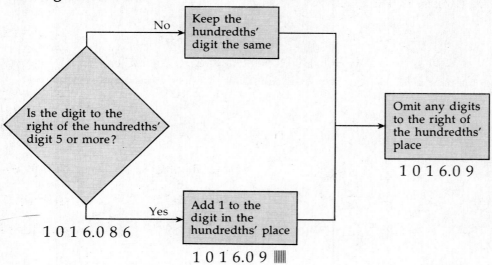

The speed, rounded to the nearest hundredth, is 1016.09 km/h.

Other examples

Round 7.364 to the nearest tenth.

7.364

The hundredths' digit is 5 or more. 7.364 rounded to the nearest tenth is 7.4.

Round 36.247 to the nearest whole number.

36.247

The tenths' digit is less than 5. 36.247 rounded to the nearest whole number is 36.

Round to the nearest hundredth.

1. 9.672　　　2. 12.438　　　3. 0.5154　　　4. 3.968　　　5. 32.0751

6. 0.198　　　7. 15.364　　　8. 5.396　　　9. 0.5739　　　10. 0.4952

Round to the nearest tenth.

1. 5.68	**2.** 3.439	**3.** 25.672	**4.** 19.86
5. 0.5721	**6.** 12.952	**7.** 58.438	**8.** 4.276
9. 54.359	**10.** 7.649	**11.** 4.972	**12.** 36.965
13. 6.01	**14.** 5.147	**15.** 32.091	**16.** 9.113

Round to the nearest whole number.

17. 5.3	**18.** 10.9	**19.** 49.723	**20.** 0.7543
21. 59.825	**22.** 27.38	**23.** 9.546	**24.** 39.72
25. 12.99	**26.** 30.899	**27.** 5.38	**28.** 99.987

Round to the nearest hundredth.

29. 5.387	**30.** 14.295	**31.** 37.684	**32.** 0.796
33. 89.638	**34.** 75.952	**35.** 4.297	**36.** 0.8169
37. 101.241	**38.** 22.195	**39.** 6.184	**40.** 0.1864

41. The highest average lap speed for an auto racer is 344.654 km/h. What is this speed rounded to the nearest tenth?

42. The average speed for the record-setting winner of the Indianapolis auto race in a recent year was 262.261 km/h. What is this speed rounded to the nearest hundredth?

☆ **43.** Find the record speeds for several different auto races. Round the speeds to the nearest tenth.

In a recent year, 10 000 000 automobiles were manufactured in the United States. If factory workers worked for 52 weeks, 5 days a week, and 24 hours a day, about how many autos were produced in a week? In a day? In an hour?

Comparing decimals

One fisherman caught a northern pike with a mass of 20.921 kg. Another fisherman caught a northern pike with a mass of 20.918 kg. One of these fish was caught by Peter Dubuc and was listed as the world record. Which one?

Finding the answer

Compare the whole numbers	→	Compare the tenths	→	Compare the hundredths

20.921	20.921	20.921
20.918	20.918	20.918
same	same	2 is greater than 1

We say:

20.921 is greater than 20.918

20.918 is less than 20.921

We write:

$20.921 > 20.918$

$20.918 < 20.921$

The 20.921 kg northern pike was listed as the world record.

Write > or < for each ◗.

1. 5.7 ◗ 5.4   2. 4.68 ◗ 4.71   3. 0.637 ◗ 0.636

4. 0.5 ◗ 0.49   5. 12.348 ◗ 12.5   6. 6.002 ◗ 6.020

7. 0.946 ◗ 1.712   8. 4.86 ◗ 4.863   9. 0.30 ◗ 0.030

Give the correct symbol, >, =, or <, for each .

1. 0.79 0.97   2. 1.374 1.734   3. 5.862 5.858

4. 0.476 0.472   5. 9.894 9.885   6. 0.706 0.607

7. 5.386 5.0386   8. 0.7 0.39   9. 5.392 4.932

10. 9.99 9.990   11. 6.467 6.5   12. 3.85 3.589

13. 0.6341 0.6345   14. 0.0988 0.999   15. 12.5 12.48

16. 4.777 3.888   17. 0.009 0.01   18. 7.62 7.6201

Write each set of decimals in order from smallest to largest.

19. 4.632, 4.659, 4.617   20. 12.0972, 11.878, 12.165

21. 0.735, 0.729, 0.731   22. 1.6872, 1.6870, 1.6868

23. One rainbow trout caught had a mass of 19.108 kg. Another had a mass of 19.096 kg. One was listed as a world record. Which one was listed?

Suppose an average of 43 balls are used for each major league baseball game. There are 2 leagues, with 12 teams in each league. Each team plays 162 games a year.

1. How many balls are used?

2. Suppose each ball costs $3.25. How much would all the balls cost?

Self-check

Write the standard numeral.

1. $800\ 000 + 90\ 000 + 7000 + 400 + 30 + 5$

2. $(5 \times 10^6) + (4 \times 10^5) + (9 \times 10^4) + (3 \times 10^3) + (2 \times 10^2) + (8 \times 10^1) + 7$

3. Write as an expanded numeral with powers of ten: $2\ 763\ 954$

Write a decimal.

4. Five thousand, nine hundred sixty-three and eight thousand, four hundred twenty-one ten thousandths

5. Forty-six and nine hundred fifty-nine thousandths

6. Round to the nearest thousand: $537\ 678$

7. Round to the nearest tenth: 4.387

Give the correct symbol, $<, =, >$.   8. $4.395 \bullet 4.392$ 9. $8.107 \bullet 8.17$

Answers for Self-check—page 17

Test

Write the standard numeral.

1. $600\ 000 + 80\ 000 + 3000 + 400 + 70 + 5$

2. $(9 \times 10^5) + (3 \times 10^4) + (7 \times 10^3) + (2 \times 10^2) + (5 \times 10^1) + 6$

3. Write as an expanded numeral with powers of ten: $847\ 923$

Write a decimal.

4. Three and eighty-seven hundredths   5. Seven hundred thirty-one thousandths

6. Round to the nearest thousand: $56\ 723$

7. Round to the nearest hundredth: 7.6953

Give the correct symbol, $<, =, >$.   8. $0.9437 \bullet 0.9473$ 9. $6.089 \bullet 6.1$

Base Four Numerals

The decimal numeration system has a base of ten and uses ten digits. Other numeration systems use other bases. The base four system is based on groupings of four and uses only the four digits 0, 1, 2, and 3.

Can you count the cubes, using four digits and a place-value system of base four? Think of each cube as one.

1 four and 0 ones

0	1	2	3	10_{four}
zero	one	two	three	one-zero base four

1 four and 1 one	1 four and 2 ones	1 four and 3 ones	2 fours and 0 ones
11_{four}	12_{four}	13_{four}	20_{four}
one-one base four	one-two base four	one-three base four	two-zero base four

Write a base four numeral and a base ten numeral for each.

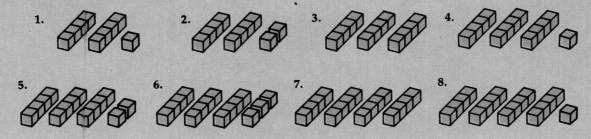

1.   2.   3.   4.

5.   6.   7.   8.

Tell what each base four numeral means in base ten.

9. 11_{four} 10. 210_{four} 11. 123_{four} 12. 1102_{four}

Reviewing Addition and Subtraction

A computer programmer uses carefully thought-out steps to prepare a flow chart for each step on a computer. Study these flow charts and give the outputs.

Zero principle

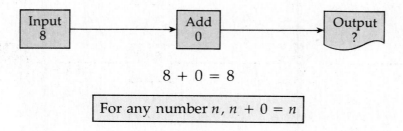

| Input 8 | → | Add 0 | → | Output ? |

$$8 + 0 = 8$$

For any number n, $n + 0 = n$

Commutative principle

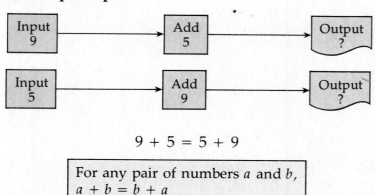

| Input 9 | → | Add 5 | → | Output ? |

| Input 5 | → | Add 9 | → | Output ? |

$$9 + 5 = 5 + 9$$

For any pair of numbers a and b,
$a + b = b + a$

Associative principle

$$(8 + 7) + 6 = 8 + (7 + 6)$$

For any three numbers a, b, and c
$(a + b) + c = a + (b + c)$

Because addition is both commutative and associative, all possible arrangements for adding a, b, and c will give the same sum.

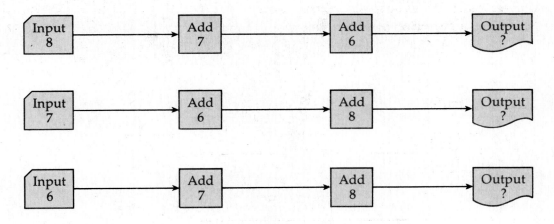

Solve the equations. Use the basic principles.

1. $49 + 0 = p$
   $0 + 49 = q$

2. $23 + 9 = a$
   $9 + 23 = b$

3. $9 + (7 + 6) = c$
   $(9 + 7) + 6 = d$

4. $187 + x = 187$
   $y + 187 = 187$

5. $30 + n = 70$
   $m + 30 = 70$

6. $50 + (20 + 30) = r$
   $(30 + 50) + 20 = s$

7. Write two equations that show the zero principle.

8. Write two equations that show the commutative principle.

9. Write two equations that show the associative principle.

Reviewing whole number addition

Attendance at an art exhibit was recorded for a holiday weekend. 5421 people attended on Saturday, 8759 on Sunday, and 7946 on Monday. What was the total number of people that attended during the three days?

Finding the answer

| Add the ones | → | Add the tens | → | Add the hundreds | → | Add the thousands |

```
    1                1 1              2 1·1            2 1 1
  5 4 2 1          5 4 2 1          5 4 2 1          5 4 2 1
  8 7 5 9          8 7 5 9          8 7 5 9          8 7 5 9
  7 9 4 6          7 9 4 6          7 9 4 6          7 9 4 6
  ───────          ───────          ───────          ───────
        6              2 6            1 2 6        2 2 1 2 6
```

A total of 22 126 people attended during the three days.

Other examples

```
   1 1              1 1  1 1              1  3 2
   9 8 7            5 4 9 3 7            3 4 7 8
 + 3 1 8          + 4 9 8 6 8              2 9 6
 ───────          ───────────          9 6 5 8 2
 1 3 0 5          1 0 4 8 0 5        +       4 5
                                     ───────────
                                     1 0 0 4 0 1
```

Find the sums.

| 1. | 568
+ 349 | 2. | 9643
+ 2867 | 3. | 96 358
+ 8 743 | 4. | 17 845
+ 38 723 | 5. | 56 987
+ 29 643 |

Add.

1.	2.	3.	4.
874	76	438	7623
396	9543	97	796
+ 278	+ 638	+ 376	+ 438

5.	6.	7.	8.
3846	5437	7374	973
975	1324	56	86
2974	507	839	4 398
+ 3081	+ 9658	+ 6834	+ 16 247

9.	10.	11.	12.
593 863	674 389	56 965	794 386
+ 30 786	+ 524 376	+ 395 877	+ 27 387

Solve the equations.

13. $59 + 8 + 3746 + 879 = n$

14. $965 + 35\ 864 + 729 = a$

15. $54\ 965 + 8539 + 346 = c$

16. $8347 + 967 + 84 + 39\ 452 = x$

17. $537\ 964 + 7638 + 97 = y$

18. $1\ 976\ 432 + 7956 + 82\ 965 = n$

19. On Wednesday 549 persons attended an outdoor concert. On Saturday 718 persons attended and on Sunday 956 attended. What was the total number of persons in the three audiences?

20. Attendance at a community play was recorded at 675 for a performance on Thursday, 728 on Friday, and 737 on Saturday. How many attended the play in these three days?

Find the missing numbers in this Magic Square.

9586	?	9626
?	9616	?
?	?	9646

More practice, page 376, Set A

Adding decimals

A pharmacist mixed 2.174 ℓ of one medicine with 1.968 ℓ of another to make a large mixture of cough syrup. How many liters of the cough syrup did the pharmacist make?

Finding the answer

Copy, line up the decimal points	→	Add the thousandths	→	Add the hundredths	→	Add the tenths	→	Add the whole numbers

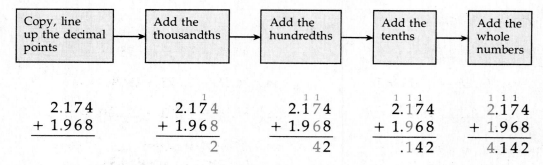

$$\begin{array}{r} 2.174 \\ + 1.968 \\ \hline \end{array}$$

$$\begin{array}{r} 2.17\overset{1}{4} \\ + 1.968 \\ \hline 2 \end{array}$$

$$\begin{array}{r} \overset{1\ 1}{2.174} \\ + 1.968 \\ \hline 42 \end{array}$$

$$\begin{array}{r} \overset{1\ 1\ 1}{2.174} \\ + 1.968 \\ \hline .142 \end{array}$$

$$\begin{array}{r} \overset{1\ 1\ 1}{2.174} \\ + 1.968 \\ \hline 4.142 \end{array}$$

The pharmacist made 4.142 ℓ of cough syrup.

Other examples

$$\begin{array}{r} \overset{1}{2}\overset{1}{4}.09 \\ + 16.57 \\ \hline 40.66 \end{array}$$

$$\begin{array}{r} \overset{1}{0}.7\overset{1}{2}9 \\ + 0.865 \\ \hline 1.594 \end{array}$$

$$\begin{array}{r} \overset{2\ 1\ 1\ 1}{29.307} \\ 6.54 \\ + \quad 8.6984 \\ \hline 44.5454 \end{array}$$

Add.

1. $\begin{array}{r} 5.94 \\ + 6.87 \\ \hline \end{array}$

2. $\begin{array}{r} 0.467 \\ + 5.39 \\ \hline \end{array}$

3. $\begin{array}{r} 6.875 \\ + 27.436 \\ \hline \end{array}$

4. $\begin{array}{r} 0.087 \\ + 9.689 \\ \hline \end{array}$

5. $\begin{array}{r} 2.043 \\ + 0.857 \\ \hline \end{array}$

6. $\begin{array}{r} 4.6817 \\ + 9.3548 \\ \hline \end{array}$

7. $\begin{array}{r} 59.634 \\ + 24.86 \\ \hline \end{array}$

8. $\begin{array}{r} 7.492 \\ + 0.685 \\ \hline \end{array}$

9. $\begin{array}{r} 59.379 \\ + 86.458 \\ \hline \end{array}$

10. $\begin{array}{r} 33.286 \\ + 77.975 \\ \hline \end{array}$

Find the sums.

1. 54.398
    + 27.642

2. 74.076
    + 97.35

3. 8.632
    + 5.0765

4. 49.86
    + 94.68

5. 72.98
    + 35.95

6. 125.97
    + 36.463

7. 57.682
    + 79.234

8. 8.6437
    + 9.7682

9. 6.4059
    + 7.3265

10. 101.907
     + 99.86

11. 4.96
     8.75
     + 7.68

12. 6.597
     8.68
     + 3.046

13. 0.798
     0.697
     + 0.483

14. 54.967
     38.482
     + 9.768

15. 63.497
     57.218
     + 84.956

Solve the equations.

16. $4.56 + 9.4 + 3.768 = n$

17. $0.975 + 4.38 + 6.754 = a$

18. $497.6 + 0.768 + 4.975 = b$

19. $74.96 + 3.875 + 0.684 = n$

20. $27.56 + 9.347 + 16.95 = x$

21. $97.99 + 7.063 + 12.794 = y$

22. A druggist mixed 9.687 ℓ with 4.947 ℓ. How many liters were in the total mixture?

23. 4.096 ℓ of water are mixed with 0.983 ℓ of concentrated medicine. How many liters of medicine are produced?

In each example, can you pay the total amount with the money shown? First decide without adding the decimals. Then use a calculator to find the actual totals.

1. $1.17
    $0.54
    $0.56
    $1.08
    $0.99
    $1.26

2. $1.49
    $1.45
    $2.98
    $1.95
    $1.87

3. $5.75
    $4.20
    $2.16
    $1.26
    $1.19
    $6.32

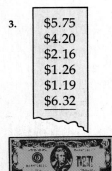

More practice, page 376, Set B

Subtraction—ideas and equations

Here are some ways of thinking about subtraction.

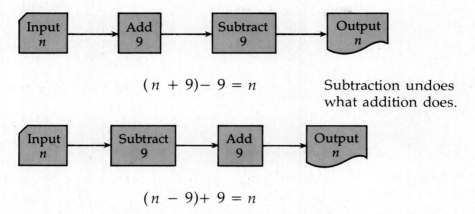

$$(n + 9) - 9 = n$$

Subtraction undoes what addition does.

$$(n - 9) + 9 = n$$

Addition and subtraction of the same number are inverse operations.

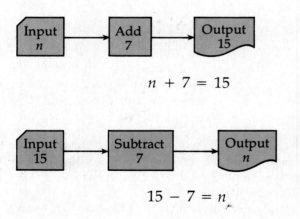

$$n + 7 = 15$$

The missing addend in the first equation is the difference in the second.

$$15 - 7 = n$$

You can find the difference in subtraction by finding the missing addend in addition.

Solve the equations.

1. $17 - 9 = n$

2. $24 - 24 = n$

3. $16 - 0 = n$

4. $(28 - 9) + 9 = n$

5. $(26 + 8) - 8 = n$

6. $(346 + 198) - 198 = n$

7. $n - 0 = 8$

8. $23 - n = 0$

9. $24 - 7 = n$

Solve the equations.

1. $a + 9 = 14$
2. $14 - 9 = a$
3. $t + 18 = 24$
4. $b + 80 = 170$
5. $170 - 80 = b$
6. $x + 38 = 45$
7. $67 - 67 = n$
8. $45 - 9 = r$
9. $32 - 29 = p$
10. $57 - 48 = n$
11. $170 - 50 = q$
12. $140 - 90 = c$
13. $(26 - 5) + 7 = a$
14. $(170 - 40) - 70 = b$
15. $(45 - 9) - 8 = c$
16. $(54 - 9) + 7 = p$
17. $(64 + 8) - 9 = q$
18. $(53 + 9) - 62 = r$
19. $(76 - 8) - 7 = s$
20. $42 - (51 - 9) = t$
21. $67 - (42 - 42) = x$
22. $(28 - 8) - 9 = n$
23. $(140 - 80) - 30 = y$
24. $(270 - 90) + 60 = c$

Find a whole number solution (if possible) for each equation. Then answer the question.

25. $17 - 8 = a$
    $8 - 17 = b$

    Does the commutative principle hold true for subtraction of whole numbers?

26. $(12 - 8) - 3 = a$
    $12 - (8 - 3) = b$

    Does the associative principle hold true for subtraction of whole numbers?

A farmer agreed to sell 16 small pigs, using either of these contracts.

Contract A: $25 per pig

Contract B: 1¢ for the first pig, 2¢ for the second, 4¢ for the third, 8¢ for the fourth, and so on, doubling the number of cents each time.

Which contract would you choose if you wanted to buy the pigs? How much would you save or lose by your choice?

Reviewing whole number subtraction

As the owner of a store, Janet paid $4679 for some items and sold them for $7538. How much did she make on the items?

Finding the answer

Trade a ten Subtract the ones	→	Trade a hundred Subtract the tens	→	Trade a thousand Subtract the hundreds	→	Subtract the thousands

$$
\begin{array}{r}
{\scriptstyle 2\ 18} \\
\$\ 75\cancel{38} \\
-\ 4679 \\
\hline
9
\end{array}
\qquad
\begin{array}{r}
{\scriptstyle 4\ 12\ 18} \\
\$\ 7\cancel{538} \\
-\ 4679 \\
\hline
59
\end{array}
\qquad
\begin{array}{r}
{\scriptstyle 6\ 14\ 12\ 18} \\
\$\ \cancel{7538} \\
-\ 4679 \\
\hline
859
\end{array}
\qquad
\begin{array}{r}
{\scriptstyle 6\ 14\ 12\ 18} \\
\$\ \cancel{7538} \\
-\ 4679 \\
\hline
\$\ 2859
\end{array}
$$

Janet made $2859 on the items.

Other examples

$$
\begin{array}{r}
{\scriptstyle 4\ 11\ 13\ 16} \\
\cancel{5246} \\
-\ 2789 \\
\hline
2457
\end{array}
\qquad
\begin{array}{r}
{\scriptstyle 6\ 9\ 9\ 18} \\
\cancel{7008} \\
-\ 4679 \\
\hline
2329
\end{array}
\qquad
\begin{array}{r}
{\scriptstyle 6\ 14\ 9\ 10} \\
\cancel{7500} \\
-\ 4679 \\
\hline
2821
\end{array}
\qquad
\begin{array}{r}
{\scriptstyle 3\ 9\ 15\ 10} \\
\cancel{4060} \\
-\ 2586 \\
\hline
1474
\end{array}
$$

Subtract.

1.	2.	3.	4.	5.
525 − 289	702 − 567	482 − 296	620 − 479	4816 − 2379

Subtract.

1. 6005 − 2376	2. 8213 − 4376	3. 9004 − 5012	4. 5007 − 4196	5. 3815 − 1796
6. 3500 − 1765	7. 5600 − 2349	8. 2714 − 1876	9. 8401 − 4562	10. 7105 − 3440
11. 5070 − 3849	12. 2530 − 1687	13. 8060 − 2594	14. 9040 − 6872	15. 8422 − 5633
16. 7000 − 3427	17. 6243 − 5685	18. 5846 − 1976	19. 9000 − 6385	20. 6683 − 4974
21. 6524 − 2039	22. 7400 − 2685	23. 4030 − 1734	24. 8000 − 2907	25. 5050 − 3948

26. As a grain elevator operator, Ted needed to find the net mass of some grain on a truck. What was it?

Gross mass (mass of truck plus grain): 9004 kg
Tare (mass of truck): − 2468 kg
Net mass (gross mass minus tare):

☆ 27. A total of 800 kg were to be allowed on a particular shipment. A cargo agent's record book showed that 670 kg were already on board. Which of the following three packages could be taken?
 Package 1: 141 kg
 Package 2: 93 kg
 Package 3: 35 kg

Suppose you earned $4.50 per hour, 8 hours a day, 5 days a week, 49 weeks a year, from your 18th birthday to your 25th birthday. How much money would you earn? Guess first. Then calculate the answer.

More practice, page 377, Set A

Subtracting decimals

How much greater is the race lap record speed than the record average speed for the race?

Indianapolis Auto Race	
Record average race speed	262.261 km/h
Race lap record speed	308.041 km/h
Practice lap record speed	320.273 km/h

Heinz Kluetmeier/SPORTS ILLUSTRATED, © Time Inc.

Finding the answer

Copy. Line up the decimal points	Subtract the thousandths	Subtract the hundredths	Subtract the tenths	Subtract the whole numbers

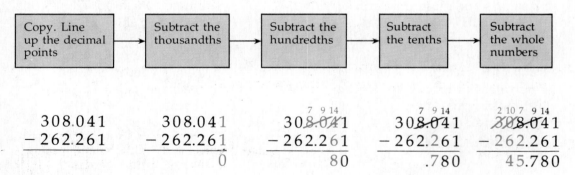

The race lap record speed is 45.780 km/h greater.

Other examples

$$
\begin{array}{r} 7\ 10 \\ 7.8\cancel{0} \\ -\ 3.27 \\ \hline 4.53 \end{array}
\qquad
\begin{array}{r} 5\ 15 \\ 0.8\cancel{6}\cancel{5} \\ -\ 0.427 \\ \hline 0.438 \end{array}
\qquad
\begin{array}{r} 8\ 9\ 9\ 10 \\ 29.0\cancel{0}\cancel{0} \\ -\ 14.826 \\ \hline 14.174 \end{array}
\qquad
\begin{array}{r} 2\ 12\ 7\ 16 \\ 3\cancel{2}.8\cancel{6} \\ -\ 17.78 \\ \hline 15.08 \end{array}
$$

Subtract.

1.	84.6 − 29.8	**2.**	0.672 − 0.186	**3.**	9.68 − 4.39	**4.**	329.7 − 167.9
5.	5.862 − 3.487	**6.**	56.72 − 38.46	**7.**	19.471 − 7.836	**8.**	40.70 − 26.36
9.	5.63 − 2.48	**10.**	583.6 − 29.9	**11.**	0.697 − 0.248	**12.**	8.721 − 4.834
13.	12.139 − 8.647	**14.**	25.86 − 16.95	**15.**	10.076 − 0.947	**16.**	20.00 − 12.95
17.	50.06 − 37.69	**18.**	53.40 − 27.86	**19.**	1.000 − 0.697	**20.**	200.00 − 176.29

Solve the equations.

21. $5.76 − 3.042 = n$ 22. $29.587 − 16.948 = n$

23. $9.075 − 4.68 = n$ 24. $182.943 − 49.685 = n$

25. How much greater is the practice lap record speed
than the race lap record speed at the Indianapolis Race?
(See table of records on page 30.)

Calculator problems

Complete a table like this
for the problems below.

	Estimated answer	Calculated answer	Difference between estimated and calculated answers
26.			
27.			
28.			
29.			
30.			

26.	18.792 − 7.478	**27.**	59.843 − 22.678	**28.**	75.134 − 52.69	**29.**	400.096 − 49.765	**30.**	93.768 − 47.495

More practice, page 377, Set B

Practicing your skills

Find the sums.

1. $\begin{array}{r} 25 \\ + 69 \end{array}$	2. $\begin{array}{r} 87 \\ + 43 \end{array}$	3. $\begin{array}{r} 456 \\ + 98 \end{array}$	4. $\begin{array}{r} 702 \\ + 861 \end{array}$	5. $\begin{array}{r} 2568 \\ + 432 \end{array}$
6. $\begin{array}{r} 1806 \\ + 1519 \end{array}$	7. $\begin{array}{r} 3842 \\ + 9751 \end{array}$	8. $\begin{array}{r} 2619 \\ + 3378 \end{array}$	9. $\begin{array}{r} 1750 \\ + 4749 \end{array}$	10. $\begin{array}{r} 2865 \\ + 7588 \end{array}$
11. $\begin{array}{r} 26 \\ 19 \\ + 33 \end{array}$	12. $\begin{array}{r} 149 \\ 73 \\ + 452 \end{array}$	13. $\begin{array}{r} 2809 \\ 503 \\ + 7396 \end{array}$	14. $\begin{array}{r} 6829 \\ 5931 \\ + 1099 \end{array}$	15. $\begin{array}{r} 2817 \\ 4436 \\ + 5093 \end{array}$
16. $\begin{array}{r} 3.45 \\ + 72.91 \end{array}$	17. $\begin{array}{r} 84.87 \\ + 5.094 \end{array}$	18. $\begin{array}{r} 24.57 \\ + 149.09 \end{array}$	19. $\begin{array}{r} 2.019 \\ + 0.9854 \end{array}$	20. $\begin{array}{r} 4.336 \\ + 9.708 \end{array}$

21. $4.36 + 1.53$

22. $13.7 + 1.09 + 8$

23. $0.72 + 0.874 + 0.3477$

24. $12.8 + 28.4$

25. $0.9 + 0.16 + 0.027$

26. $5008 + 46.02 + 642.80$

27. $9.82 + 13.2 + 0.8$

28. $6.007 + 32.85 + 3.65$

29. $0.909 + 0.999 + 0.091$

Find the differences.

30. $\begin{array}{r} 6537 \\ - 4788 \end{array}$	31. $\begin{array}{r} 1385 \\ - 859 \end{array}$	32. $\begin{array}{r} 5372 \\ - 1645 \end{array}$	33. $\begin{array}{r} 1539 \\ - 947 \end{array}$	34. $\begin{array}{r} 4552 \\ - 1104 \end{array}$
35. $\begin{array}{r} 4994 \\ - 2936 \end{array}$	36. $\begin{array}{r} 7483 \\ - 1135 \end{array}$	37. $\begin{array}{r} 1834 \\ - 299 \end{array}$	38. $\begin{array}{r} 4604 \\ - 3856 \end{array}$	39. $\begin{array}{r} 7445 \\ - 3768 \end{array}$
40. $\begin{array}{r} 8273 \\ - 5578 \end{array}$	41. $\begin{array}{r} 6004 \\ - 3286 \end{array}$	42. $\begin{array}{r} 4102 \\ - 2548 \end{array}$	43. $\begin{array}{r} 9000 \\ - 7111 \end{array}$	44. $\begin{array}{r} 7081 \\ - 5399 \end{array}$
45. $\begin{array}{r} 17.61 \\ - 7.83 \end{array}$	46. $\begin{array}{r} 890.0 \\ - 256.4 \end{array}$	47. $\begin{array}{r} 0.594 \\ - 0.389 \end{array}$	48. $\begin{array}{r} 4.058 \\ - 1.209 \end{array}$	49. $\begin{array}{r} 63.00 \\ - 48.99 \end{array}$

Calculator problems

Write an estimate. Then calculate the answer.

Add.

1.	2.	3.	4.	5.
233	218	675	4358	2279
946	673	937	6854	1087
237	748	979	3798	8715
634	546	803	9271	1594
+ 145	+ 936	+ 677	+ 1685	+ 3239

6.	7.	8.	9.	10.
743 314	328 237	986 347	832 624	514 209
358 257	426 741	389 763	315 687	860 113
729 648	153 888	144 392	790 257	495 027
837 109	867 192	528 705	898 265	293 641
+ 784 476	+ 706 058	+ 689 541	+ 407 498	+ 308 118

11. 3428.75 + 25 019.052 + 1476.194

12. 0.4132 + 5.1097 + 0.6389

Subtract.

13.	14.	15.	16.	17.
0.9728	1.7362	352.368	2.33	25
− 0.1854	− 0.9085	− 47.819	− 1.8654	− 15.202

18.	19.	20.	21.	22.
0.145	3.17	22.01	5.28	72
− 0.098	− 1.0052	− 18.905	− 3.7634	− 25.841

23. 421.782 − 10.948

24. 8.03 − 6.2791

25. 73.9 − 45.68

26. 37.2 − 25.845

27. 61.705 − 38.9954

Arrange the digits
3, 4, 5, 6, 7, 8, 9
in the hexagons so that
the sums of the digits in
any three hexagons in a row
are the same.

More practice, page 378

Self-check

Choose the correct letter to name the principle shown by each equation.

1. $8 + 0 = 8$ a. commutative principle

2. $3 + (5 + 4) = (3 + 5) + 4$ b. associative principle

3. $9 + 4 = 4 + 9$ c. zero principle

Add or subtract.

4.	5.	6.	7.	8.
9374	7085	5627	8005	6207
+ 8696	1968	− 3998	− 4176	− 4964
	+ 8243			

Solve the equations.

9. $4.32 + 91.08 + 7.6 = t$ 10. $18.01 + 0.758 + 1.9026 = s$

11. $15.7 − 3.85 = a$ 12. $24.6 − 6.09 = b$ 13. $0.75 − 0.5972 = c$

Answers for Self-check—page 33

Test

Choose the correct letter to name the principle shown by each equation.

1. $7 + 8 = 8 + 7$ a. associative principle

2. $6 + (4 + 7) = (6 + 4) + 7$ b. zero principle

3. $12 + 0 = 12$ c. commutative principle

Add or subtract.

4.	5.	6.	7.	8.
8265	8196	7843	9003	5402
+ 9707	2877	− 4964	− 2876	− 3682
	+ 9354			

Solve the equations.

9. $7.03 + 23.147 + 6.52 = b$ 10. $17.205 + 6.138 + 9.0045 = t$

11. $1.72 − 0.563 = s$ 12. $33.7 − 25.54 = n$ 13. $0.805 − 0.6275 = k$

Math lab

Calculator Riddles

To solve the riddles, first work each problem. Then turn the calculator upside down to read the answer.

1. What is it that a cowboy trains so that he doesn't need trains?

$$1765.987$$
$$+ 3738.527$$

2. If an angry snake could talk, what would it say?

$$2431.7562$$
$$+ 3082.7952$$

3. What did Big Foot want for his birthday?

$$(5.5 \times 9601.2481) + 238.754$$

4. What did Eli Whitney's mother say the first time she saw him after he had invented the cotton gin?

$$(9859.4875 \div 68.35) + 28.82734$$

☆ 5. Here are the possible letters that can be made with "upside down" numerals.
How many calculator words can you make?
Use the words to invent a riddle of your own.

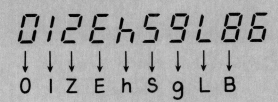

Using Your Skills

People buy insurance to protect themselves against money loss. They can buy life, homeowners, auto, health, and other types of insurance.

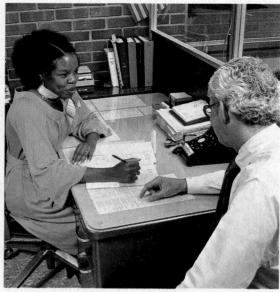

Insurance agents meet with people to explain the advantages of the various types of insurance. Agents also write applications, figure costs, keep records, and help with claims.

Insurance underwriters decide whether or not the insurance should be sold to the customer.

Insurance claim adjustors inspect the property that has been damaged.

Solve these problems. Be sure to **read carefully** to pick out only the facts that are needed to answer the question.

1. For the first year, the insurance on an automobile that cost $5276 was $362.17. The insurance for the second year was $380.54. What was the increase in the cost of the insurance?

2. For a certain car the insurance is $308.67 per year. If a teenager drives the car, the cost is $25.85 more per year. How much would the insurance cost to include the teenage driver?

3. In the first 6 months, an insurance agent earned $4573.45. In the second 6 months he earned $7896.89. Would these earnings be more or less than a salary of $14,000 per year? How much more or less?

4. The cost of health insurance for 6 months is $417.64. How much is the insurance for a year?

5. The cash value of a $5000 life insurance policy was $1345. The cash value of a $10 000 life insurance policy was $2687. How much more was the cash value of the $10 000 policy?

6. An insurance agent visited 585 customers. He sold 76 life insurance policies, 97 fire insurance policies, and 208 auto insurance policies. How many policies did he sell in all?

Problem-solving guidelines
1. Read carefully to find the facts.
2. Look for the question.
3. Decide what to do. (+, −, ×, ÷)
4. Find the answer.
5. Read again. Does your answer make sense?

Olympic records

1. In the 1972 Olympics, Doreen Wilber (USA) scored a record 2424 points in archery. In the 1976 Olympics, Luann Ryon (USA) broke that record by 75 points. What was Luann Ryon's score?

2. In 1976, Evelin Schlaak (E. Ger) set a new record of 69.00 m in the discus throw. The old record was 66.62 m. How much farther was the new record distance?

3. In 1932, Mildred Didrikson (USA) won the Olympic javelin throw with a distance of 43.69 m. In the 1976 Olympics, the javelin was thrown a distance of 65.94 m. How much greater is the 1976 distance than the 1932 distance?

4. Kornelia Ender (E. Ger.) set a new Olympic record of 55.65 s in the 100 m freestyle swim. This time was 2.94 s faster than the old record. What was the time for the old record?

5. The Olympic record for the women's 400 m dash was 49.29 s. The record for the 800 m dash was 1 min 54.94 s. How much more than twice the 400 m record is this?

6. Wilma Rudolph (USA) and Wyomia Tyus (USA) share the Olympic record time of 11.00 s for the women's 100 m dash. The world record for the 100 m dash for women is 10.8 s. How much less is this than the Olympic record?

7. In the 1976 Olympics, Bruce Jenner (USA) scored 8618 points to win the decathalon event. This was 164 points more than the 1972 record. How many points were scored to win the 1972 decathalon?

8. Peter Rocca swam the 100 m backstroke in 56.34 s. John Nabor (USA) set a new record of 55.49 s in this event. How much less was Nabor's time?

9. In 1976, Mac Wilkins (USA) set a new record of 67.50 m in the discus throw. This was 10.01 m less than the record set in the hammer throw. What was the distance in the hammer throw?

10. Edwin Moses (USA) broke the old 400 m hurdles record of 7.82 s by 0.18 s. What was Moses' new record time?

11. Klaus Dibiasa (Italy) was the 1976 Olympic 10 m diving winner. He scored 600.51 points. The silver medal winner scored 23.52 fewer points than Dibiasa, and the bronze medal winner scored 23.38 fewer points than the silver medal winner. How many points did the silver and bronze medal winners score?

12. Jacek Wszola (Poland) set a new high jump record of 2.25 m in 1976. The pole vault record in 1976 was 1.00 m more than double the high jump record. What was the pole vault record?

Keeping records

1. A person with a checking account at a bank should keep a record of the amount of each check written. What is the total amount of the checks recorded here?

Check Paid to:	Amount
Joe's Hardware	$ 24 75
Gooday Tire Store	57 45
Dr. Campbell	76 98
Power and Electric Co.	57 29
Toughview TV, Inc.	27 65
Welcome Drugstore	26 54
R & W Supermarket	43 64
Nickels Department Store	68 00
Total	

2. Find the new balance by subtracting the amount of the check from the old balance.

Balance in account	$ 2076 24
Amount of check	257 45
New balance in account	

3. This is a record that might be kept by a person who owns a small business. Figure the profit for each month and the total profit for the year.

Profit = income − expense

Income – Expense Record			
Month	Income	Expense	Profit
January	$ 8403	$ 7564	
February	7647	6986	
March	10 683	8362	
April	9497	8904	
May	6438	5317	
June	7965	6984	
July	10 436	9205	
August	9 007	8116	
September	11 685	10 050	
October	13 594	12 168	
November	16 872	14 396	
December	18 045	16 858	

Attendance Report	
July 8–July 13	
Day	Paid Attendance
Monday	16 942
Tuesday	24 623
Wednesday	18 076
Thursday	15 029
Friday	27 068
Saturday	35 375

Airline Passenger Report	
Month	Number of Passengers
January	256 823
February	309 610
March	246 397
April	198 463
May	263 978
June	302 846

4. The owners of a major league baseball team kept a record of the total attendance for some recent home games. By how much does this total differ from the record world series six-day attendance of 420 784?

6. Officials of an airline company counted the total number of passengers carried during a six-month period. How much more or less is this than the number in another six-month period, 1 637 097?

Water Consumption Record	
	Kiloliters
Monday	2976
Tuesday	2307
Wednesday	1986
Thursday	2687
Friday	2538
Saturday	3287
Sunday	1287

Machine Use Record	
	Hours
1st year	5689
2nd year	5838
3rd year	6097
4th year	5935
5th year	6178

5. A city water commissioner kept a record of the number of kiloliters of water used by the city in one week. How much more or less is this total than the 38 160 kiloliters that is used by the world's tallest fountain in one day?

7. A factory supervisor kept a record of the number of hours a machine is used each year. How many hours has the machine been used during the 5 years?

☆ 8. How many hours was the machine idle? (Use 365 days in a year.)

Using facts from charts

Area of the
FOUR OCEANS
in millions of square
kilometers (km²)

Ocean	Area
Arctic	14.090
Atlantic	84.463
Indian	73.442
Pacific	165.240

Area of the
FOUR LARGEST ISLANDS
in millions of square
kilometers (km²)

Island	Area
Borneo	0.743
Greenland	2.176
Madagascar	0.587
New Guinea	0.820

A satellite photograph of the earth would show the planet's surface as a pattern of land and water. About 0.71 of the surface is covered by water, while the remaining 0.29 of the surface is land.

**Area of the
SEVEN CONTINENTS
in millions of square
kilometers (km²)**

Continent	Area
Africa	29.785
Asia	43.771
Antarctica	13.727
Australia	7.687
Europe	9.712
North America	24.087
South America	17.612

**Area of the
FIVE LARGEST SEAS
in millions of square
kilometers (km²)**

Sea	Area
Bering	2.268
Caribbean	2.753
Malay	8.143
Mediterranean	2.504
South China	2.968

1. How much greater is the area of North America than the area of South America?

2. What is the total area of the seven continents?

3. How much greater is the area of the smallest continent than the area of the largest island?

4. What is the total area of the four largest islands?

5. How much greater is the area of the Pacific Ocean than the area of the Atlantic Ocean?

6. How much greater is the area of the Atlantic Ocean than the area of the continent of Asia?

7. What is the total area of the four oceans?

8. Which island and sea are closest in area? By how many millions of square kilometers do they differ?

9. How much greater is the area of the smallest ocean than the area of the largest sea?

10. What is the total area of the five largest seas?

11. How much larger than the island of Greenland is the Caribbean Sea?

☆ 12. The total area of the earth's surface (land and water) is 510.066 million km². How much more is this than the total area of the seven continents and the four largest islands?

☆ 13. The total area of the earth that is covered by water is 361.252 million km². How much more is this than the total area of the four oceans and the five largest seas?

Photography problems

If you worked in a photographic equipment store, you would learn about cameras and equipment. Customers would seek your help in using the film and equipment that they buy.

1. The manager bought 100 cameras for $3578. The cameras sold for $6024. How much was the profit?

2. The advertising cost for November was $586.79. For December, it was $747.82. What was the advertising cost for the two-month period?

3. An experienced sales clerk earns $11 425 a year. A new clerk earns $8875. What are the combined earnings of 2 experienced sales clerks and 1 new sales clerk?

4. A camera lens costs $165.45. The cost was reduced by $16.59 for a sale. What was the sale price?

5. A sales clerk's salary was $9375 per year. If the clerk is given a raise of $589 a year, what is the new salary?

6. The store's expenses for a certain period are:

   Redecorating: $4087
   Advertising: $1295
   All other expenses: $26 955

   How much money must the store receive to end up with a profit of $3850?

7. A movie camera sold for $79.74. It was originally priced at $114.50. How much less was the sale price?

Find the total cost of each purchase.

1.

Slide projector	$89.75
Screen	37.95
2 Slide trays	9.65
Total	

2.

Telephoto lens	$179.75
Lens case	14.25
Lens cloth	1.95
Total	

3.

Developing trays	$ 4.49
Enlarging easel	15.99
Print washer	7.12
Darkroom light	7.79
Total	

4.

Camera	$21.99
Camera case	8.45
Film	3.29
Flashbulbs	1.95
Total	

5.

Tripod	$24.95
250 watt light	14.39
Light clamp	4.75
Total	

6.

Electronic flash unit	$21.85
Gadget bag	16.99
Total	

Answers for Self-check   1. $403.44   2. $39.15   3. 8.54 m   4. 7.927 million km²   5. $7105.18

Self-check

Solve the problems.

1. The cost of insurance for the first six months was $194.79. For the second six months it was $208.65. How much was the insurance in all?

2. A camera cost $26.75, film cost $3.45, and a set of filters cost $8.95. What was the total cost?

3. A recent men's long jump record was 8.90 m. A recent triple jump record was 17.44 m. How much farther is the triple jump record?

4. The USSR has a land area of 58.014 million km². Canada has a land area of 25.837 million km² and the USA has a land area of 24.250 million km². How much larger is the USSR than Canada and the USA together?

5. A small business had expenses as follows:

   January: $7628.59
   February: $7847.64
   March: $9495.54

   Income for the three months was $32 076.95. How much was the profit?

Answers for Self-check—page 45

Test

1. The Missouri-Mississippi river is 6020 m long. The Yangtze river in China is 5980 m long. How much longer is the Missouri-Mississippi?

2. How much do all of these cost?

   Slide projector: $49.75
   Screen: 19.89
   Slide viewer: 10.45

3. The women's record for a 400 m race was 49.29 s. The second place winner ran the race in 50.62 s. How many more seconds did the second place winner take?

4. Lake Superior: 82.413 thousand km²
   Lake Huron: 59.596 thousand km²
   Lake Ontario: 19.477 thousand km²
   Lake Michigan: 58.016 thousand km²
   Lake Erie: 25.719 thousand km²

   What is the total area of the five Great Lakes?

5. Two clerks each made $8670 a year. These salaries together are how much more than the manager's salary of $13 975?

Math lab

Tracing Networks

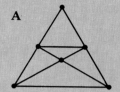 A   B 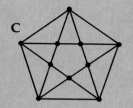   C 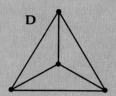   D

Each figure above is a **network**.
Which ones can you trace without lifting your pencil
from the paper or tracing over any line twice?

The famous Swiss mathematician Leonhard Euler (1707–1783)
found a way to solve these kinds of network problems.
He proved the following:

A network can be traced if

- the network has exactly 2 odd
  vertices, or

- the network has no odd vertices.

An odd vertex is a point on the network
with an odd number of paths meeting
at that point.

2 paths–
even
    3 paths–
odd
    4 paths–
even
    5 paths–
odd

Use Euler's rule to decide which of the networks below can be traced.

     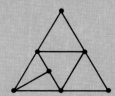   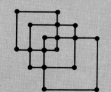   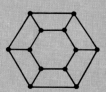

Draw some networks of your own. Make some which can be
traced and some which cannot.

Geometric Ideas and Constructions

The geometry of the physical world is all around us. What geometric ideas or shapes can you find in this picture?

point *A*
symbol: *A*

segment *AB*
symbol: $\overline{AB}$

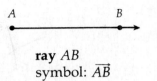

ray *AB*
symbol: $\overrightarrow{AB}$

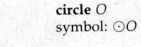

line *AB*
symbol: $\overleftrightarrow{AB}$

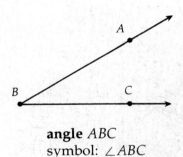

angle *ABC*
symbol: $\angle ABC$

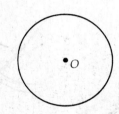

circle *O*
symbol: $\odot O$

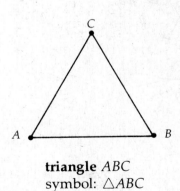

triangle *ABC*
symbol: $\triangle ABC$

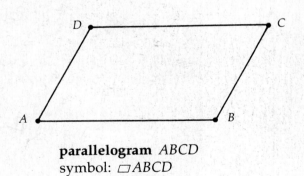

parallelogram *ABCD*
symbol: $\square ABCD$

Draw and label the following figures.

1. point *X*
2. $\overline{PQ}$
3. $\overrightarrow{CD}$
4. $\overleftrightarrow{EF}$
5. $\angle RST$
6. $\odot A$
7. $\triangle PQR$
8. $\square WXYZ$

Constructing congruent figures

Congruent figures have the same size and shape.
They are exact copies of each other. The
following constructions with straightedge
and compass will help you understand the
idea of congruence.

Copying a segment

Step 1

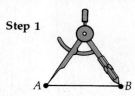

Open your compass the
length of the given
segment.

Step 2

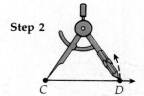

Draw a ray from C.
Use the same compass
opening to mark D.

We write: $\overline{CD} \cong \overline{AB}$
We say: Segment CD
is congruent to
segment AB.

Copying an angle

Step 1

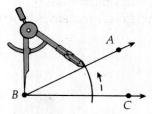

Mark an arc on the
given angle.

Step 2

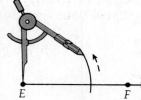

Draw $\overrightarrow{EF}$, and use the
same compass opening
as in step 1 to draw an arc
as shown.

Step 3

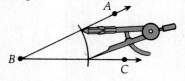

Measure the opening of
the given angle with the
compass.

Step 4

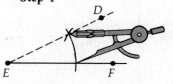

Mark the same opening
for $\angle DEF$. Draw $\overrightarrow{ED}$ as
shown by the dotted line.

We write: $\angle DEF \cong \angle ABC$
We say: Angle DEF **is**
congruent to
angle ABC.

Copying a triangle

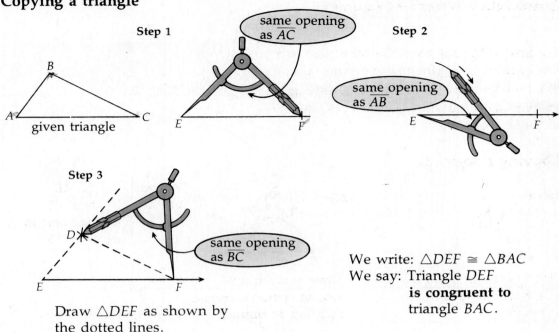

Step 1

Step 2

B

A ⌐ C
given triangle

same opening
as $\overline{AC}$

same opening
as $\overline{AB}$

E   F   E   F

Step 3

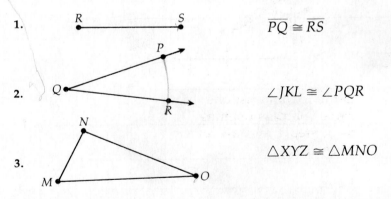

D

same opening
as $\overline{BC}$

E   F

Draw $\triangle DEF$ as shown by
the dotted lines.

We write: $\triangle DEF \cong \triangle BAC$
We say: Triangle DEF
is congruent to
triangle BAC.

Trace the given segment, angle, or triangle. Then copy each figure using a
compass and straightedge. Label your figures so that the given statements are true.

1.   R ●————————● S $\overline{PQ} \cong \overline{RS}$

2.   Q   P $\angle JKL \cong \angle PQR$
                    R

3.   N   O $\triangle XYZ \cong \triangle MNO$
      M

4. Draw $\overline{GH}$. Construct copies of the segment to make $\overline{RS}$ that is twice as
    long as $\overline{GH}$.

5. Draw $\angle JKL$. Construct copies of the angle to construct $\angle PQR$ that is twice as
    large as $\angle JKL$.

☆ 6. Copy a triangle by copying one of its angles and two of its sides.

Measuring segments and angles

A centimeter ruler can be used to measure the length of a segment in centimeters and millimeters. We write $m(\overline{AB})$ to mean "the measure or length of segment AB."

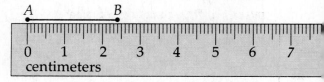

$m(\overline{AB})$ = 2.4 cm
$m(\overline{AB})$ = 24 mm

Estimate the length of each segment. Then measure the length and compare it with your estimate. Show the results in a table like the one below.

1. $A \bullet\!\!-\!\!\!-\!\!\!-\!\!\bullet B$

2. $C \bullet\!\!-\!\!\!-\!\!\!-\!\!\!-\!\!\!-\!\!\!-\!\!\!-\!\!\bullet D$

3. $E \bullet\!\!-\!\!\!-\!\!\!-\!\!\bullet F$

4. $G \bullet\!\!-\!\!\!-\!\!\!-\!\!\!-\!\!\!-\!\!\bullet H$

5. $I \bullet\!\!-\!\!\!-\!\!\!-\!\!\!-\!\!\bullet J$

6. $K \bullet\!\!-\!\!\!-\!\!\!-\!\!\!-\!\!\!-\!\!\bullet L$

7. $M \bullet\!\!-\!\!\!-\!\!\!-\!\!\bullet N$

8. $O \bullet\!\!-\!\!\!-\!\!\!-\!\!\!-\!\!\!-\!\!\bullet P$

9. $Q \bullet\!\!-\!\!\!-\!\!\!-\!\!\!-\!\!\!-\!\!\!-\!\!\bullet R$

10. $S \bullet\!\!-\!\!\!-\!\!\!-\!\!\!-\!\!\!-\!\!\bullet T$

Segment	Your estimate	Actual measure	Difference
1. $\overline{AB}$	▓▓▓ mm	▓▓▓ mm	▓▓▓ mm
2. $\overline{CD}$	▓▓▓ mm	▓▓▓ mm	▓▓▓ mm
3. $\overline{EF}$	▓▓▓ mm	▓▓▓ mm	▓▓▓ mm

A protractor can be used to find the measure of an angle in degrees. We write $m(\angle ABC)$ to mean "the measure of angle ABC."

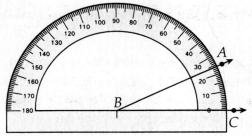

We write: $m(\angle ABC) = 24°$
We say: The measure of angle ABC is twenty-four degrees.

Give the measure of each angle in degrees.

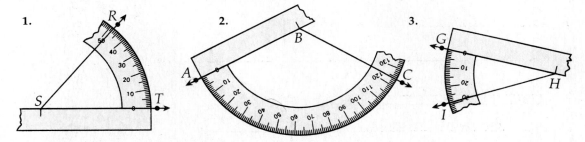

1.

2.

3.

Estimate the degree measure of each angle. Then measure the angle and compare it with your estimate.

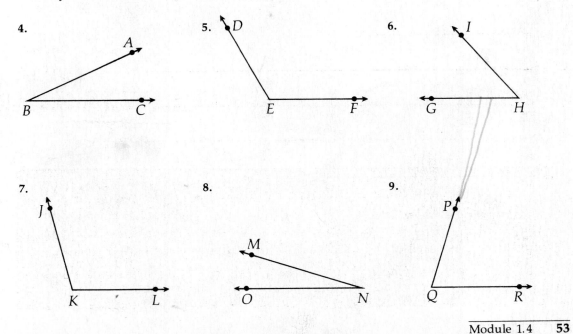

4.

5.

6.

7.

8.

9.

Measuring triangles and quadrilaterals

Complete a table like this for each of the triangles below. Then give the missing words or numerals to complete each sentence.

Part of triangle	measure
$\angle ABC$	▦ °
$\angle BCA$	▦ °
$\angle CAB$	▦ °
$\overline{AB}$	▦ mm
$\overline{BC}$	▦ mm
$\overline{CA}$	▦ mm

_____ triangle

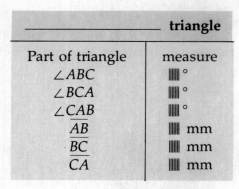

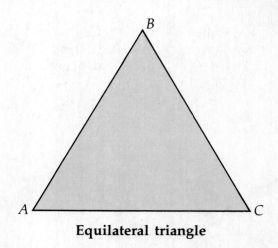

Equilateral triangle

1. An equilateral triangle has ▦ sides of equal measure and ▦ angles, each with measure ▦°.

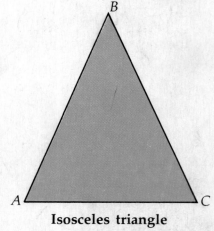

Isosceles triangle

2. An isosceles triangle has ▦ sides of equal measure and ▦ angles with equal measure.

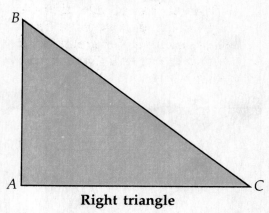

Right triangle

3. A right triangle has a largest angle with measure ▦°. The sum of the measures of the other two angles is ▦°.

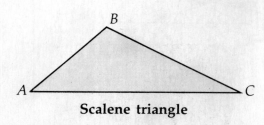

Scalene triangle

4. A scalene triangle has ▦ sides with different measures and ▦ angles with different measures.

5. The sum of the measures of the three angles of any triangle is ▦°.

Complete a table like this for each of the quadrilaterals below. Then give the missing words or numerals to complete each sentence.

Type of Quadrilateral _____	
Part of quadrilateral	Measure
$\angle ABC$	▦ °
$\angle BCD$	▦ °
$\angle CDA$	▦ °
$\angle DAB$	▦ °
$\overline{AB}$	▦ mm
$\overline{BC}$	▦ mm
$\overline{CD}$	▦ mm
$\overline{DA}$	▦ mm

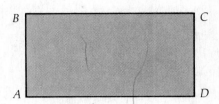

Rectangle

1. A rectangle has ▦ right angles and ▦ pairs of congruent sides.

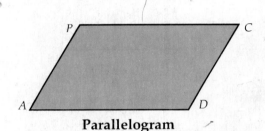

Parallelogram

2. A parallelogram has ▦ congruent angle(s) less than 90° and ▦ congruent angles greater than 90°. It has ▦ pair(s) of congruent sides.

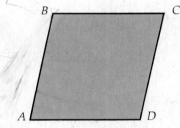

Rhombus

4. A rhombus has ▦ sides that are congruent to each other. It has ▦ congruent angles greater than 90° and ▦ congruent angles less than 90°.

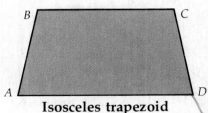

Isosceles trapezoid

3. An isosceles trapezoid has ▦ congruent angles less than 90° and ▦ congruent angles greater than 90°. It has ▦ pair(s) of congruent sides.

5. Find the sum of the angles of each of the above quadrilaterals. Then complete this sentence:
   The sum of the measures of all four angles of any quadrilateral is ▦ °.

✪ Constructing perpendicular and parallel lines

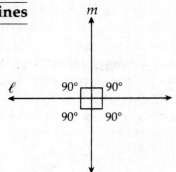

Lines m and ℓ are perpendicular to
each other if they intersect and the
angles formed are right angles.
We write: $m \perp \ell$
We say: m is perpendicular to ℓ.

Constructing perpendicular lines

Construct $m \perp \ell$ through point P on ℓ.

Step 1

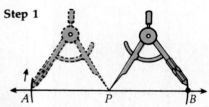

Mark points A and B on ℓ
so $\overline{AP} \cong \overline{PB}$.

Construct $m \perp \ell$ through point P
not on ℓ.

Step 1

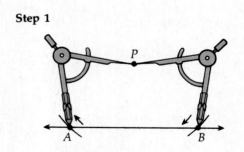

Mark $\overline{AB}$ on ℓ.

Step 2

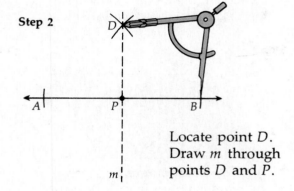

Locate point D.
Draw m through
points D and P.

Step 2

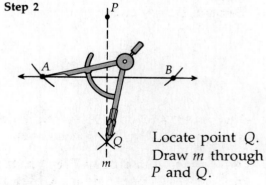

Locate point Q.
Draw m through
P and Q.

1. Draw a line t. Mark a point R not on t.
   Construct a line s through R so that $s \perp t$.

2. Draw a line k. Mark a point M on k.
   Construct a line j through M so that $j \perp k$.

Two lines ℓ and m in the same plane are parallel if they do not intersect.
We write: $\ell \parallel m$
We say: Line ℓ is parallel to line m.

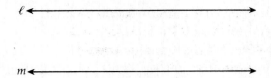

Constructing parallel lines

Construct $\ell \parallel m$ through P.

Step 1

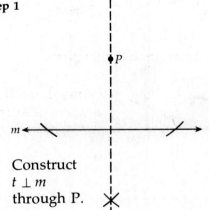

Construct
$t \perp m$
through P.

Step 2

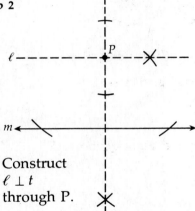

Construct
$\ell \perp t$
through P.

1. Draw line r and point A not on r. Construct a line ℓ so that $\ell \parallel r$ through point A.

2. Draw line m and a point P not on m. Construct a line n that goes through P and is parallel to m.

☆ 3. Draw a line t and mark points A and B on t about 5 cm apart. Construct line ℓ through A so that $\ell \perp t$. Construct line m through B so that $m \perp t$. What can you say about lines m and ℓ?

✪ Bisecting segments and angles

The perpendicular bisector of $\overline{AB}$ is a
line ℓ through the midpoint M of $\overline{AB}$
that forms right angles with $\overline{AB}$.
Line ℓ is the perpendicular bisector of $\overline{AB}$.

Use your ruler and protractor to see
that each of the two statements below
the picture is correct.

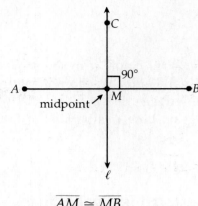

$$\overline{AM} \cong \overline{MB}$$
$$m(\angle BMC) = 90°$$

Constructing the perpendicular bisector of a segment

Step 1
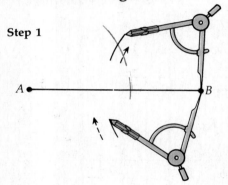

Step 2
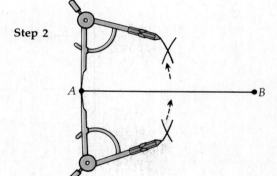

Step 3
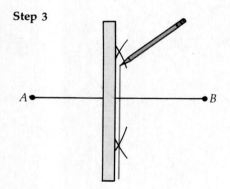

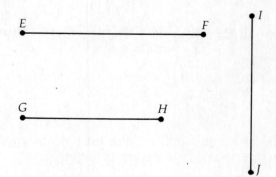

1. Trace $\overline{EF}$, $\overline{GH}$, and $\overline{IJ}$ above. Construct the perpendicular bisector of each one.

2. Draw $\triangle ABC$ with sides 4, 6, and 8 cm long. Construct the perpendicular bisector of each side.

The bisector of $\angle ABC$ is a $\overrightarrow{BD}$ such that $\angle ABD \cong \angle DBC$. Use your protractor to check this congruence.

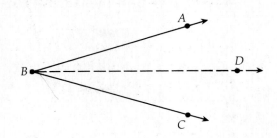

Bisecting an angle

Step 1

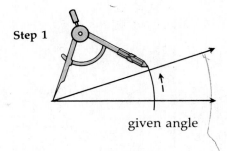

given angle

Step 2

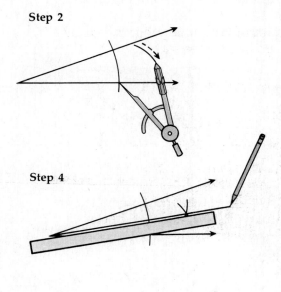

Step 3

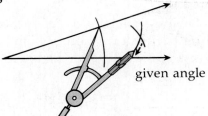

given angle

Step 4

Trace each angle. Then construct the bisector of each one.

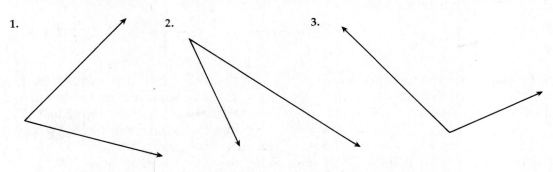

1.

2.

3.

4. Draw an angle and bisect it. Then bisect each half.

✪ Constructing and measuring regular polygons

equilateral
triangle

square

regular
pentagon

regular
hexagon

regular
octagon

In a regular polygon, all sides have the same length and
all angles have the same number of degrees.

Construct the following.

1.

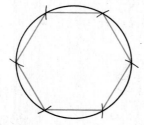

Divide a circle into 6 congruent
parts. Use the length of the
radius *r* for the compass opening.

2.

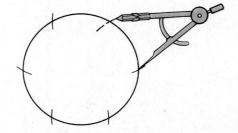

Divide a circle into 6 congruent
parts. Join every other point to
form an equilateral triangle.

3.

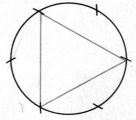

Divide a circle into 6 congruent
parts. Join the 6 points to form
a regular hexagon.

4.

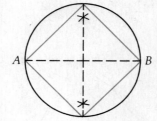

Divide a circle into 4 congruent
parts by constructing the perpendicular bisector of a diameter $\overline{AB}$.
Join the 4 points to form a square.

5. Draw a circle with a radius of 28 mm. Then use a length of 33 mm
   to divide the circle into 5 congruent parts. Join the 5 points to
   form a pentagon.

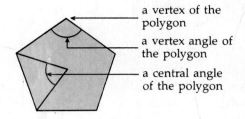

a vertex of the polygon

a vertex angle of the polygon

a central angle of the polygon

Type of polygon: _____

1.	Number of sides	▥
2.	Length of each side	▥ mm
3.	Perimeter (total length of all sides)	▥ mm
4.	Measure of central angle	▥ °
5.	Sum of measures of all central angles	▥ °
6.	Measure of vertex angle	▥ °
7.	Sum of measures of all vertex angles	▥ °

Complete a table like this for each polygon below. (You may wish to trace the polygons and extend the sides to make the angle measurement easier.)

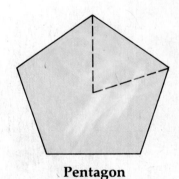

Pentagon

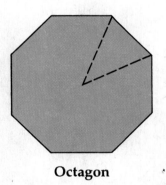

Octagon

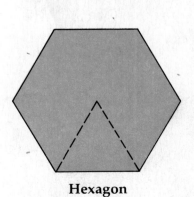

Hexagon

Complete the following statements.

8. In any regular polygon, the measure of a central angle is ▥° divided by the number of sides.

9. In any regular polygon, the measure of a central angle plus the measure of a vertex angle is ▥°.

✪ Discovering new ideas

You can discover interesting geometric relationships by carefully drawing a figure and measuring it. Try these.

1. Trace these quadrilaterals. The midpoints of two sides are given. Find the midpoints of the other two sides. Connect the four midpoints in order. What type of figure is formed? Do you think this figure would be formed for any type of quadrilateral?

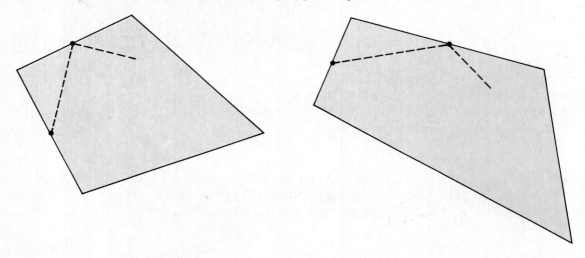

2. Trace these triangles. Find the midpoints M and N of sides $\overline{AB}$ and $\overline{BC}$. Draw and measure $\overline{MN}$. Then measure $\overline{AC}$. $m(\overline{AC})$ is about ▥ times as long as $m(\overline{MN})$. Do you think this would be true for any triangle?

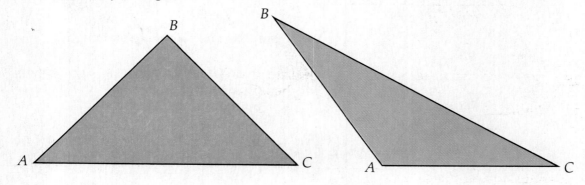

3. Trace angles 1 and 2 for each polygon. Extend the sides of these angles and measure the angles. What do you find? Do you think this will be true for any regular polygon?

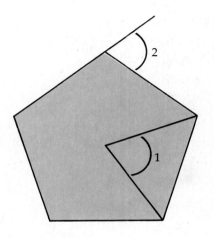 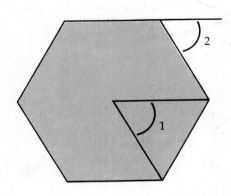

4. Consider these parallel lines and the line *t* that intersects them. Measure angles 3 and 6. What do you find? Do you think this will be true for any pair of parallel lines and an intersecting line?

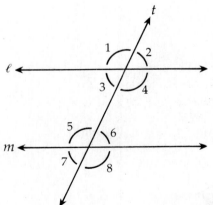 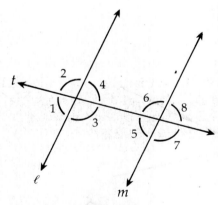

5. How many pairs of congruent angles can you find when two parallel lines are cut by a line *t*? List them using the numbers in the figures above.

Answers for Self-check   3. 4. 5 cm   4. 35°

Self-check

Trace these figures for use in the following exercises.

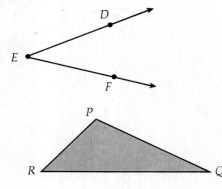

1. Construct $\angle JKL \cong \angle DEF$.

2. Construct $\triangle XYZ \cong \triangle PQR$.

3. Use a ruler to find $m\,(\overline{RQ})$.

4. Use a protractor to find $m(\angle DEF)$.

☆ 5. Construct the perpendicular bisector of $\overline{RQ}$.

☆ 6. Bisect $\angle DEF$.

☆ 7. Choose a point P on $\overleftrightarrow{AB}$. Construct $\ell \perp \overleftrightarrow{AB}$ through P.

☆ 8. Draw a line k and a point P not on k. Construct a line $\ell \parallel k$ through P.

Answers for Self-check—page 63

Test

Trace these figures for use in the following exercises.

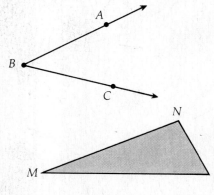

1. Construct $\angle DEF \cong \angle ABC$.

2. Construct $\triangle GHI \cong \triangle MNO$.

3. Use a ruler to find $m\,(\overline{MO})$.

4. Use a protractor to find $m(\angle ABC)$.

☆ 5. Construct the perpendicular bisector of $\overline{MO}$.

☆ 6. Bisect $\angle ABC$.

☆ 7. Choose a point R on $\overleftrightarrow{PQ}$. Construct $m \perp \overleftrightarrow{PQ}$ through R.

☆ 8. Draw a line ℓ and a point P not on ℓ. Construct a line $m \parallel \ell$ through P.

Polygon Puzzles

1. Trace the three small hexagons and cut along all the solid and dotted lines. Use the thirteen pieces to form the large hexagon.

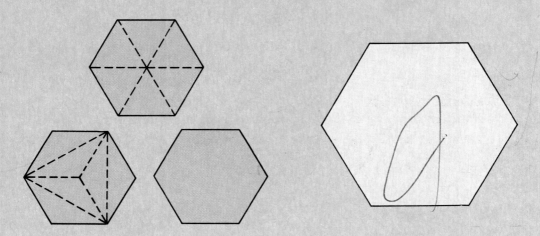

2. Trace the three small stars and cut along all the solid and dotted lines. Use the sixteen pieces to form the large star.

Unit 1 review

Write the standard numeral.

1. $(6 \times 10^5) + (3 \times 10^4) + (7 \times 10^3) + (5 \times 10^2) + (2 \times 10^1) + 9$

2. $(8 \times 10^6) + (6 \times 10^4) + (2 \times 10^3) + (4 \times 10^1) + 7$

3. $(9 \times 10^5) + (4 \times 10^4) + (6 \times 10^2) + (3 \times 10^1) + 1$

4. $(2 \times 10^5) + (7 \times 10^4) + (3 \times 10^1)$

5. $(5 \times 10^7) + (6 \times 10^6) + (7 \times 10^5) + (1 \times 10^3) + (2 \times 10^2) + 4$

Write each standard numeral as an expanded numeral with powers of ten.

6. 702 413

7. 82 145

8. 943 286

9. 265 107

10. 517 328

11. 410 020

Round to the nearest whole number.

12. 75.671

13. 81.309

14. 29.094

15. 701.95

16. 59.914

17. 146.78

Add or subtract.

18.
```
  7322
+ 9146
```

19.
```
  9133
- 2414
```

20.
```
  5754
- 4818
```

21.
```
  7065
- 3458
```

22.
```
  9271
  3486
+ 5792
```

23.
```
  1008
  7645
+ 3187
```

24.
```
  3298
  4675
+ 1972
```

25.
```
  45 726
  31 489
+ 27 368
```

26. $0.819 + 2.46 + 17.508$

27. $32.04 - 14.786$

28. $3.145 + 26.73 + 64.279$

29. $0.9043 - 0.4137$

30. $2.01 + 13.524 + 72.9$

31. $22.01 - 9.843$

Unit **2**

Multiplying Whole Numbers
Multiplying Decimals
Estimation
Using Your Skills
Measuring Length and Area

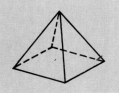

Multiplying Whole Numbers

Time yourself in finding these sums.

1. 2 + 2 + 2 + 2 + 2 + 2   2. 7 + 7 + 7 + 7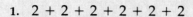

3. 6   4. 4   5. 3   6. 9
    6   4   3   9
    6   4   3   9
    6   4   3   + 9
    6   4   3
    6   + 4   3
  + 6   3
                                  3
                                + 3

7. 8   8. 1   9. 5   10. 23
    8   1   5   23
    8   1   5   23
    8   1   5   + 23
    8   1   5
    8   1   5
    8   1   5
    8   1   + 5
  + 8   1
                   1
                   1
                 + 1

Give yourself a score.

Less than 1 minute . . . . .Lightning calculator
Between 1 and 2 minutes . . . . . .Average
More than 2 minutes . . . . .Snail's pace

What might you do to improve?

When the same addend is repeated, you can use multiplication instead of addition.

$$3 + 3 + 3 + 3 + 3 + 3 \qquad\qquad 7 + 7 + 7 + 7$$

6 threes	4 sevens
$6 \times 3 = 18$	$4 \times 7 = 28$

factors   product   factors   product

Find the products.

1. 5×7	2. 3×9	3. 8×4	4. 6×2	5. 9×9
6. 9×6	7. 8×3	8. 7×5	9. 8×5	10. 4×4
11. 7×4	12. 7×2	13. 9×8	14. 9×9	15. 3×8
16. 6×6	17. 7×8	18. 6×4	19. 9×7	20. 2×9
21. 0×9	22. 4×6	23. 3×7	24. 5×5	25. 8×8
26. 2×5	27. 8×6	28. 3×4	29. 1×1	30. 7×3
31. 1×8	32. 6×8	33. 4×9	34. 9×5	35. 2×8
36. 7×7	37. 5×4	38. 5×9	39. 5×8	40. 8×7
41. 6×9	42. 7×6	43. 8×0	44. 6×7	45. 3×3
46. 2×3	47. 4×8	48. 8×9	49. 9×3	50. 9×4
51. 9×2	52. 6×3	53. 4×3	54. 6×5	55. 7×9
56. 5×3	57. 4×7	58. 8×2	59. 5×2	60. 4×5

Basic principles of multiplication

How many rocks are there
in the collection?

3 rows of 4

$3 \times 4 = 12$

$3 \times 4 = 4 \times 3$

This example illustrates the
commutative principle of multiplication:

For any pair of numbers a and b, $a \times b = b \times a$.

4 columns of 3

$4 \times 3 = 12$

How many collection boxes are there?

$(2 \times 3) \quad \times \quad 4 \quad = 6 \times 4 = 24$

number on   number
the bottom   of layers
layer

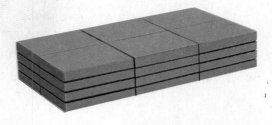

$2 \quad \times \quad (3 \times 4) \quad = 2 \times 12 = 24$

number   number in
of rows   one row

$(2 \times 3) \times 4 = 2 \times (3 \times 4)$

This example illustrates the **associative principle** of multiplication:

For any three numbers a, b, and c, $a \times (b \times c) = (a \times b) \times c$.

Because multiplication is both commutative and associative, all possible
arrangements for multiplying a, b, and c will give the same product.
For example, $5 \times (7 \times 4) = (4 \times 5) \times 7$.

This equation illustrates the property of 1: $1 + 1 + 1 + 1 + 1 + 1 = 6$

$6 \times 1 = 6$

For every number a, $a \times 1 = a$.

4 twos   4 threes   4 fives

4 twos and 4 threes = 4 fives

$$(4 \times 2) + (4 \times 3) = 4 \times (2 + 3)$$

The **distributive principle** of multiplication:

> For any numbers a, b, and c,
> $(a \times b) + (a \times c) = a \times (b + c)$.

Solve the equations. Think about the basic principles.

1. $7 \times 4 = 4 \times n$
2. $6 \times k = 9 \times 6$
3. $7 \times 1 = r$
4. $2 \times 9 = 9 \times t$
5. $8 \times 3 = s \times 8$
6. $z \times 1 = 12$
7. $9 \times b = 8 \times 9$
8. $11 \times 7 = v \times 11$
9. $15 \times c = 15$
10. $2 \times q = 7 \times 2$
11. $6 \times m = 0 \times 6$
12. $h \times 5 = 5 \times 9$
13. $(7 \times 3) \times 5 = 7 \times (s \times 5)$.
14. $8 \times (2 \times 6) = (8 \times 2) \times p$
15. $(4 \times 2) \times 9 = a \times (2 \times 9)$
16. $(7 \times 3) + (7 \times 5) = d \times (3 + 5)$
17. $(9 \times h) + (9 \times 6) = 9 \times (2 + 6)$
18. $(9 \times 20) + (9 \times 5) = 9 \times (20 + w)$
19. $(5 \times j) + (5 \times 7) = 5 \times 37$
20. $(4 \times 7) + (4 \times 3) = e$
21. $4 \times (7 + 3) = q$

The value of JANUARY is 90 when A = 1, B = 2, C = 3, and so on, to Z = 26. Which month of the year has the greatest value? Which has the least?

Multiplying whole numbers

A daily paper is delivered to 76 customers on one paper route. How many papers are delivered to the customers in 312 days?

Finding the answer

Multiply by the ones	→	Multiply by the tens	→	Add the products

```
   312          312          312
 ×  76        ×  76        ×  76
 ----         ----         -----
 1872         1872         1 872
             2184         21 84
                          ------
                          23 712
```

In 312 days, 23 712 papers are delivered.

Other examples

```
  5 274         486          708
 ×     6       ×  85        ×  29
 -------       -----        -----
 31 644       2 430        6 372
              38 88        14 16
              ------       ------
              41 310       20 532
```

Find the products.

1. 94
   × 7

2. 628
   ×   3

3. 3297
   ×   6

4. 5508
   ×   9

5. 7349
   ×   8

6. 35
   × 29

7. 86
   × 48

8. 216
   × 37

9. 583
   × 58

10. 906
    × 62

Multiply.

1. 56 ×23	2. 84 ×49	3. 78 ×37	4. 66 ×19	5. 90 ×43
6. 272 ×34	7. 126 ×58	8. 309 ×77	9. 512 ×81	10. 600 ×26
11. 733 ×52	12. 417 ×65	13. 924 ×96	14. 857 ×88	15. 206 ×99
16. 125 ×32	17. 143 ×77	18. 823 ×15	19. 953 ×57	20. 566 ×94

21. $23 \times 18 \times 31$

22. $7 \times 25 \times 19$

23. $23 \times 22 \times 24$

24. $63 \times 31 \times 8$

25. $50 \times 27 \times 42$

26. $17 \times 32 \times 40$

27. Jack delivers a Sunday paper to 26 customers 52 days a year. How many Sunday papers does he deliver in a year?

☆ 28. Find the cost of a copy of a daily newspaper. How much would it cost to buy a copy a day for one year?

The length of a double page of a newspaper is about 70 cm. Suppose the paper has an average of 25 double pages daily. If these pages were placed end to end, how far would they reach?

About how far would a year's delivery of this paper reach?

More practice, page 379, Set A

Multiplying larger numbers

An average of 266 persons a day take a 9:00 a.m. flight from San Francisco to Honolulu. How many persons take this flight in a year (365 days)?

Finding the answer

Multiply by the ones	Multiply by the tens	Multiply by the hundreds	Add the products

$$
\begin{array}{r} 365 \\ \times 266 \\ \hline 2190 \end{array}
\qquad
\begin{array}{r} 365 \\ \times 266 \\ \hline 2190 \\ 2190 \end{array}
\qquad
\begin{array}{r} 365 \\ \times 266 \\ \hline 2190 \\ 2190 \\ 730 \end{array}
\qquad
\begin{array}{r} 365 \\ \times 266 \\ \hline 2\ 190 \\ 21\ 90 \\ 73\ 0 \\ \hline 97\ 090 \end{array}
$$

97 090 persons take the flight in a year.

Other examples

$$
\begin{array}{r} 317 \\ \times 255 \\ \hline 1\ 585 \\ 15\ 85 \\ 63\ 4 \\ \hline 80\ 835 \end{array}
\qquad
\begin{array}{r} 8424 \\ \times\ 390 \\ \hline 758\ 160 \\ 2\ 527\ 2 \\ \hline 3\ 285\ 360 \end{array}
\qquad
\begin{array}{r} 578 \\ \times 406 \\ \hline 3\ 468 \\ 231\ 2 \\ \hline 234\ 668 \end{array}
$$

Find the products.

1. $\begin{array}{r} 276 \\ \times\ 59 \\ \hline \end{array}$
2. $\begin{array}{r} 163 \\ \times 154 \\ \hline \end{array}$
3. $\begin{array}{r} 367 \\ \times 208 \\ \hline \end{array}$
4. $\begin{array}{r} 1696 \\ \times\ 81 \\ \hline \end{array}$
5. $\begin{array}{r} 5704 \\ \times\ 463 \\ \hline \end{array}$

Multiply.

1.	289 × 6	**2.**	1574 × 8	**3.**	2913 × 5	**4.**	42 818 × 7	**5.**	126 733 × 4
6.	2604 × 23	**7.**	7557 × 46	**8.**	8293 × 68	**9.**	4767 × 57	**10.**	9070 × 98
11.	824 × 276	**12.**	747 × 109	**13.**	276 × 250	**14.**	578 × 111	**15.**	416 × 302
16.	1774 × 290	**17.**	3189 × 345	**18.**	7073 × 802	**19.**	9131 × 657	**20.**	4700 × 306

21. The average speed of a jet plane on a flight from San Francisco to Honolulu was 771 km/h. If the flight took 5 hours, what was the distance flown?

☆ **22.** An airline pilot makes a *round trip* flight from San Francisco to Honolulu six times in one month. How many kilometers does he fly in the month? (Use the results of exercise 21.)

Calculator problems

23.	2179 × 648	**24.**	4149 × 5677	**25.**	23 677 × 946	**26.**	30 487 × 708	**27.**	6109 × 9061

Find the products.

$$1 \times 1 = \text{▓}$$
$$11 \times 11 = \text{▓}$$
$$111 \times 111 = \text{▓}$$
$$1111 \times 1111 = \text{▓}$$
$$11\ 111 \times 11\ 111 = \text{▓}$$
$$111\ 111 \times 111\ 111 = \text{▓}$$

Find some more products in this pattern.

More practice, page 379, Set B

Exponents

$$4 = 4^1$$

Read 4^1 as
four to the first power.

$$4 \times 4 = 4^2$$

Read 4^2 as
four to the second power
or *four squared.*

$$4 \times 4 \times 4 = 4^3$$

Read 4^3 as
four to the third power
or *four cubed.*

When the same factor is repeated, we can use **exponential notation**.

$$3 \times 3 \times 3 \times 3 \times 3 = 3^5 \longleftarrow \text{exponent}$$

$\underbrace{}$

five factors of 3   base

A centered dot can be used instead of $\times$ to show multiplication.

$$7 \times 7 \times 7 \times 7 = 7 \cdot 7 \cdot 7 \cdot 7 = 7^4$$

Write each number using exponents.

1. 5 to the fifth power
2. 2 to the fourth power
3. 10 cubed
4. 3 to the sixth power
5. 9 to the second power
6. 7 squared
7. 4 to the tenth power
8. 2 to the eighth power
9. 13 squared

Tell which number is the base and which is the exponent.

10. 3^7
11. 2^5
12. 7^6
13. 10^4
14. 11^5

Write the product using exponents.

Example: $2 \cdot 2 \cdot 2 \cdot 2 = 2^4$

1. $7 \cdot 7 \cdot 7$
2. $5 \cdot 5 \cdot 5 \cdot 5 \cdot 5$
3. $9 \cdot 9$

4. $3 \cdot 3 \cdot 3 \cdot 3 \cdot 3 \cdot 3$
5. $15 \cdot 15$
6. $10 \cdot 10 \cdot 10 \cdot 10$

7. $8 \cdot 8 \cdot 8 \cdot 8 \cdot 8 \cdot 8 \cdot 8$
8. $4 \cdot 4 \cdot 4 \cdot 4 \cdot 4 \cdot 4$
9. $6 \cdot 6 \cdot 6$

10. $100 \cdot 100 \cdot 100 \cdot 100$
11. $9 \cdot 9 \cdot 9 \cdot 9$
12. $2 \cdot 2 \cdot 2 \cdot 2 \cdot 2 \cdot 2$

Write the factors for each number.

Example: $8^4 = 8 \cdot 8 \cdot 8 \cdot 8$

13. 3^4
14. 2^5
15. 6^2
16. 9^3
17. 10^6

18. 4^3
19. 8^7
20. 2^6
21. 7^5
22. 13^3

Find the product.

Example: $5^3 = 5 \cdot 5 \cdot 5 = 125$

23. 7^2
24. 2^6
25. 3^4
26. 5^4
27. 10^3

28. 13^2
29. 8^3
30. 3^5
31. 6^3
32. 8^2

Find n in each equation.

☆ 33. $3^n = 27$

☆ 34. $2^n = 128$

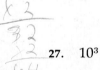

☆ 35. $5^n = 625$

Find the number for n in each equation.
$6^2 + 8^2 = n^2$
$5^2 + 12^2 = n^2$
$8^2 + 15^2 = n^2$
$7^2 + 24^2 = n^2$

☆ 36. $10^n = 10\ 000\ 000$

Self-check

Choose the principle shown by each equation.

1. $7 \times 4 = 4 \times 7$
2. $(5 \times 8) + (5 \times 2) = 5 \times (8 + 2)$
3. $9 \times (2 \times 4) = (9 \times 2) \times 4$

a. associative principle
b. distributive principle
c. commutative principle

Find the products.

4. $\begin{array}{r} 49 \\ \times\, 23 \\ \hline \end{array}$
5. $\begin{array}{r} 128 \\ \times\, 57 \\ \hline \end{array}$
6. $\begin{array}{r} 8147 \\ \times\quad 37 \\ \hline \end{array}$
7. $\begin{array}{r} 314 \\ \times\, 293 \\ \hline \end{array}$
8. $\begin{array}{r} 828 \\ \times\, 306 \\ \hline \end{array}$

9. 5^3
10. 2^4
11. 9^2
12. 6^3
13. 3^3

Rewrite using exponents.

14. 3 to the sixth power
15. 8 cubed
16. $4 \cdot 4 \cdot 4 \cdot 4 \cdot 4 \cdot 4$

Answers for Self-check—page 77

Test

Choose the principle shown by each equation.

1. $6 \times 3 = 3 \times 6$
2. $(7 \times 2) \times 6 = 7 \times (2 \times 6)$
3. $(4 \times 5) + (4 \times 8) = 4 \times (5 + 8)$

a. distributive principle
b. commutative principle
c. associative principle

Find the products.

4. $\begin{array}{r} 67 \\ \times\, 49 \\ \hline \end{array}$
5. $\begin{array}{r} 174 \\ \times\, 35 \\ \hline \end{array}$
6. $\begin{array}{r} 3622 \\ \times\quad 57 \\ \hline \end{array}$
7. $\begin{array}{r} 594 \\ \times\, 372 \\ \hline \end{array}$
8. $\begin{array}{r} 738 \\ \times\, 509 \\ \hline \end{array}$

9. 3^4
10. 10^3
11. 2^6
12. 8^2
13. 4^4

Rewrite using exponents.

14. 5 to the fourth power
15. 10 squared
16. $9 \cdot 9 \cdot 9 \cdot 9$

Math lab

Locating Centers of Gravity

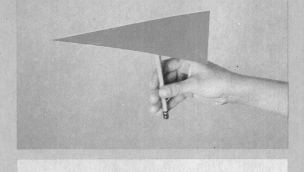

The center of gravity, or **centroid**, of a geometric region is the point at which the region will balance on the point of a pencil.

Follow the directions to find the center of gravity of a triangular region.

1. Cut out a triangular region from a piece of poster board. Measure each side and mark the midpoint.

2. With a segment, connect the midpoint of each side to the opposite vertex of the triangle.

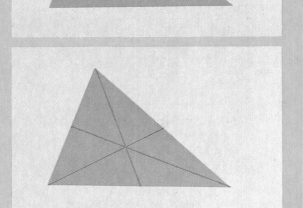

3. The intersection of the three segments is the center of gravity of the region.

Make a pin hole at the center of gravity.
Does your triangle balance?
Make some holes at other points.
Does your triangle balance at any of the other points?

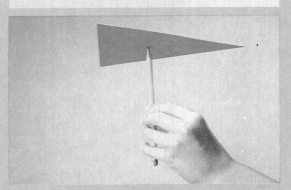

Multiplying Decimals

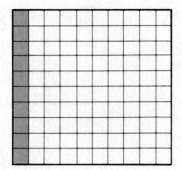

1 tenth is shaded pink.

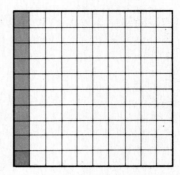

1 tenth of 1 tenth is shaded red.

1 tenth of 1 tenth is 1 hundredth.

$$0.1 \times 0.1 = 0.01$$

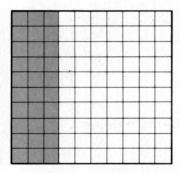

3 tenths is shaded pink.

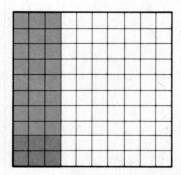

2 tenths of 3 tenths is shaded red.

2 tenths of 3 tenths is 6 hundredths.

$$0.2 \times 0.3 = 0.06$$

Give the product as a decimal.

1.

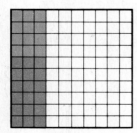

6 tenths of 3 tenths

$0.6 \times 0.3 = n$

2.

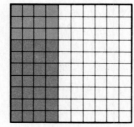

7 tenths of 4 tenths

$0.7 \times 0.4 = m$

3.

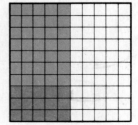

3 tenths of 5 tenths

$0.3 \times 0.5 = k$

Thinking about the number of places a decimal has may help you multiply decimals.

0-place decimals	1-place decimals	2-place decimals	3-place decimals
9	0.7	0.13	0.237
25	3.1	0.09	7.409
347	14.5	3.47	23.660
whole numbers	tenths	hundredths	thousandths

Study each example. Then give the missing numbers.

1. $0.3 \times 0.4 = 0.12$
   A 1-place decimal times a 1-place decimal gives a ▥-place decimal.

2. $0.2 \times 0.08 = 0.016$
   A 1-place decimal times a 2-place decimal gives a ▥-place decimal.

3. $0.05 \times 0.07 = 0.0035$
   A 2-place decimal times a 2-place decimal gives a ▥-place decimal.

4. $6 \times 0.7 = 4.2$
   A whole number times a 1-place decimal gives a ▥-place decimal.

5. $4 \times 0.06 = 0.24$
   A whole number times a 2 place decimal gives a ▥-place decimal.

Find these products.

6. 0.2×0.4

7. 0.3×0.9

8. 0.7×0.5

9. 0.3×0.08

10. 0.09×0.4

11. 0.1×0.07

12. 0.06×0.09

13. 0.4×0.07

14. 0.08×0.09

15. 8×0.3

16. 9×0.5

17. 0.7×3

18. 5×0.06

19. 0.09×7

20. 4×0.08

Multiplying with decimals

Sound travels about 0.33 kilometer per second (km/s) in air. If you hear the thunder from a flash of lightning 6.5 s after the flash, how far away was the lightning?

Finding the answer

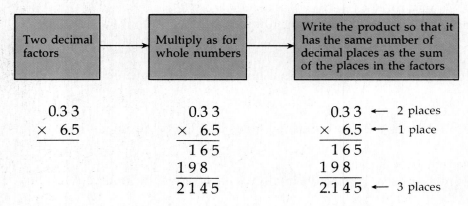

Two decimal factors	→	Multiply as for whole numbers	→	Write the product so that it has the same number of decimal places as the sum of the places in the factors

```
   0.3 3              0.3 3              0.3 3  ←  2 places
 ×  6.5             ×  6.5             ×  6.5  ←  1 place
                      1 6 5              1 6 5
                      1 9 8              1 9 8
                      2 1 4 5            2.1 4 5  ←  3 places
```

The lightning was 2.145 km or a little more than 2 km away.

Other examples

```
   3.78             0.659              41.37
 ×  0.6           ×  0.8            ×     12
   2.268            0.5272             82 74
                                       413 7
                                      496.44
```

Multiply.

1.	62.4 × 2.8	2.	742 × 0.18	3.	5.7 × 0.9	4.	7.06 × 1.5	5.	4.62 × 21

6.	50.4 × 3.9	7.	6.04 × 3.75	8.	239 × 0.54	9.	7.19 × 3.42	10.	291 × 0.007

11.	49.6 × 3.14	12.	0.616 × 0.8	13.	452 × 0.76	14.	8.71 × 6.4	15.	95.3 × 1.04

Find the products.

1. $\begin{array}{r} 7.2 \\ \times\ 0.7 \\ \hline \end{array}$	**2.** $\begin{array}{r} 0.36 \\ \times\ \ 29 \\ \hline \end{array}$	**3.** $\begin{array}{r} 1.67 \\ \times\ \ \ 8 \\ \hline \end{array}$	**4.** $\begin{array}{r} 3.09 \\ \times\ 6.1 \\ \hline \end{array}$	**5.** $\begin{array}{r} 257 \\ \times\ 0.05 \\ \hline \end{array}$
6. $\begin{array}{r} 88.1 \\ \times\ \ 0.9 \\ \hline \end{array}$	**7.** $\begin{array}{r} 4.8 \\ \times\ 2.6 \\ \hline \end{array}$	**8.** $\begin{array}{r} 0.125 \\ \times\ \ \ \ 6 \\ \hline \end{array}$	**9.** $\begin{array}{r} 55.4 \\ \times\ \ 17 \\ \hline \end{array}$	**10.** $\begin{array}{r} 6.2 \\ \times\ 3.8 \\ \hline \end{array}$
11. $\begin{array}{r} 5.38 \\ \times\ 0.27 \\ \hline \end{array}$	**12.** $\begin{array}{r} 0.907 \\ \times\ \ \ 8.3 \\ \hline \end{array}$	**13.** $\begin{array}{r} 2.718 \\ \times\ \ \ 9.2 \\ \hline \end{array}$	**14.** $\begin{array}{r} 18.98 \\ \times\ \ 0.06 \\ \hline \end{array}$	**15.** $\begin{array}{r} 0.81 \\ \times\ 7.7 \\ \hline \end{array}$
16. $\begin{array}{r} 4.95 \\ \times\ 4.9 \\ \hline \end{array}$	**17.** $\begin{array}{r} 11.02 \\ \times\ \ \ 8.5 \\ \hline \end{array}$	**18.** $\begin{array}{r} 587 \\ \times\ 0.035 \\ \hline \end{array}$	**19.** $\begin{array}{r} 46.5 \\ \times\ \ 20 \\ \hline \end{array}$	**20.** $\begin{array}{r} 0.938 \\ \times\ \ \ 56 \\ \hline \end{array}$
21. $\begin{array}{r} 19.76 \\ \times\ \ 7.1 \\ \hline \end{array}$	**22.** $\begin{array}{r} 600 \\ \times\ 0.67 \\ \hline \end{array}$	**23.** $\begin{array}{r} 51.5 \\ \times\ 6.04 \\ \hline \end{array}$	**24.** $\begin{array}{r} 0.83 \\ \times\ 0.97 \\ \hline \end{array}$	**25.** $\begin{array}{r} 79.47 \\ \times\ \ \ 3.8 \\ \hline \end{array}$

26. Sound travels about 4.8 km/s through a steel rail. How far would sound travel in 3.6 s through a steel rail?

☆ **27.** Sound travels 0.33 km/s in air. An echo from a cliff is heard 4 s after the original sound is made. How far away is the cliff?

More practice, page 380, Set A

Placing zeros in products

Gold can be made into very thin sheets called gold leaf. It takes only 0.00024 g of gold to cover 1 square centimeter with gold leaf.

A picture frame has 384 cm² of surface to be covered with gold leaf. How many grams of gold will be needed?

Finding the answer

$$\begin{array}{r} 384 \quad \longleftarrow \text{ 0 places} \\ \times\, 0.00024 \quad \longleftarrow \text{ 5 places} \\ \hline 1536 \\ 768 \\ \hline 0.09216 \quad \longleftarrow \text{ 5 places} \end{array}$$

A zero must be placed in the product to form a 5-place decimal.

To cover the frame, 0.09216 g of gold will be needed.

Other examples

$$\begin{array}{r} 0.008 \\ \times \quad 0.4 \\ \hline 0.0032 \end{array} \qquad \begin{array}{r} 0.06 \\ \times\, 0.09 \\ \hline 0.0054 \end{array} \qquad \begin{array}{r} 0.005 \\ \times \quad 3 \\ \hline 0.015 \end{array}$$

Multiply.

1. $\begin{array}{r} 0.004 \\ \times \quad 0.6 \end{array}$
2. $\begin{array}{r} 0.08 \\ \times\, 0.07 \end{array}$
3. $\begin{array}{r} 0.34 \\ \times \quad 0.2 \end{array}$
4. $\begin{array}{r} 0.003 \\ \times \quad 0.08 \end{array}$
5. $\begin{array}{r} 0.7 \\ \times\, 0.09 \end{array}$

6. $\begin{array}{r} 0.0076 \\ \times \quad 0.09 \end{array}$
7. $\begin{array}{r} 0.033 \\ \times \quad 0.17 \end{array}$
8. $\begin{array}{r} 0.028 \\ \times\, 0.035 \end{array}$
9. $\begin{array}{r} 0.019 \\ \times \quad 0.6 \end{array}$
10. $\begin{array}{r} 0.35 \\ \times\, 0.041 \end{array}$

Find the products.

1. 0.05
   × 0.3

2. 0.0024
   × 0.04

3. 1.7
   × 0.0008

4. 68
   × 0.0006

5. 0.36
   × 0.001

6. 0.71
   × 0.09

7. 0.028
   × 0.05

8. 0.0086
   × 0.8

9. 3.2
   × 0.07

10. 0.27
    × 0.04

11. 0.36
    × 0.13

12. 2.7
    × 0.025

13. 14.6
    × 0.04

14. 0.51
    × 0.028

15. 0.079
    × 0.034

16. 1.025
    × 0.066

17. 3.94
    × 0.059

18. 6.01
    × 0.78

19. 0.034
    × 0.062

20. 463
    × 0.0096

21. 8.72
    × 0.053

22. 0.0742
    × 67

23. 0.918
    × 0.422

24. 12.15
    × 0.013

25. 9.39
    × 0.0028

26. Gold leaf is sold in sheets which have an area of 79 cm². Each square centimeter has about 0.00024 g of gold in it. How much gold is in a sheet of gold leaf?

☆ 27. Find the number of square centimeters on the front cover of a book. Find the number of grams of gold needed to cover it with gold leaf.

In a recent year, gold was worth $4.18 a gram. How many grams of gold would it take to balance your mass? How much would that amount of gold be worth?

More practice, page 380, Set B

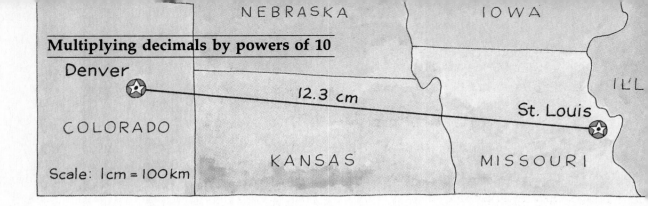

The scale of the map is 1 cm = 100 km. The map distance between Denver and St. Louis is 12.3 cm. How many kilometers is it from Denver to St. Louis?

Finding the answer

$12.3 \times 100 = 1230.$

> To multiply by 100, move the decimal point two places to the right

It is 1230 km from Denver to St. Louis.

You can find products mentally when one factor is 10, 100, or 1000.

Other examples

$3.428 \times 10 = 34.28$ move 1 place to the right

$3.428 \times 100 = 342.8$ move 2 places to the right

$3.428 \times 1000 = 3428.$ move 3 places to the right

Multiply each number by 10.

1. 2.71	2. 0.86	3. 31.42	4. 0.081	5. 9.4
6. 0.006	7. 21.79	8. 0.728	9. 746.2	10. 1.014

Multiply each number by 100.

11. 7.476	12. 0.913	13. 82.47	14. 0.0077	15. 9.2
16. 0.083	17. 0.0009	18. 1.5	19. 16.56	20. 8.728

Multiply each number by 1000.

21. 3.142	22. 0.9163	23. 12.75	24. 0.0048	25. 17.8

You can also find products mentally when one factor is 0.1, 0.01, or 0.001.

$12.3 \times 0.1 = 1.23$ 1 place to the left

$12.3 \times 0.01 = 0.123$ 2 places to the left

$12.3 \times 0.001 = 0.0123$ 3 places to the left

Multiply each number by 0.1.

1. 2.87	2. 34.5	3. 726	4. 0.9	5. 62.75
6. 0.04	7. 142.5	8. 6276	9. 0.007	10. 8.044

Multiply each number by 0.01.

11. 175.6	12. 9.7	13. 23.6	14. 0.5	15. 276.97
16. 0.78	17. 0.043	18. 200	19. 2746.1	20. 847.3

Multiply each number by 0.001.

21. 7468.3	22. 29,744	23. 59.7	24. 6.28	25. 0.97
26. 47.63	27. 5094	28. 927.5	29. 3000	30. 679.24

Find the products.

31. 72.46×10	32. 8.9×1000
33. 62.4×0.1	34. 81.75×100
35. 66.8×0.01	36. 0.714×10
37. 377.3×0.001	38. 0.0915×100
39. 0.42×1000	40. 0.3×100
41. 12.46×0.1	42. 9764.3×0.001

Place operation signs, +, −, ×, or ÷, between the sixes so that each equation will be correct. Use parentheses where necessary.

6 ⬤ 6 ⬤ 6 ⬤ 6 = 8
6 ⬤ 6 ⬤ 6 ⬤ 6 = 13
6 ⬤ 6 ⬤ 6 ⬤ 6 = 210
6 ⬤ 6 ⬤ 6 ⬤ 6 = 48
6 ⬤ 6 ⬤ 6 ⬤ 6 = 1
6 ⬤ 6 ⬤ 6 ⬤ 6 = 3

Rounding products

A certain fabric costs $2.35 per meter.
What is the cost of 3.25 m of the fabric,
rounded to the nearest cent?

Finding the answer

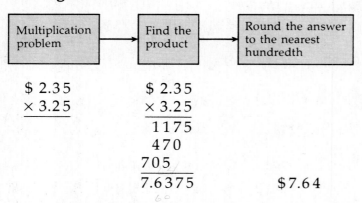

| Multiplication problem | → | Find the product | → | Round the answer to the nearest hundredth |

$$
\begin{array}{r}
\$\,2.35 \\
\times\ 3.25 \\
\hline
\end{array}
\qquad
\begin{array}{r}
\$\,2.35 \\
\times\ 3.25 \\
\hline
1175 \\
470 \\
705 \\
\hline
7.6375
\end{array}
\qquad
\$7.64
$$

The cost is $7.64, rounded to the nearest cent.

Other examples

Multiply 3.819 by 65. Round the
answer to the nearest whole number.

$$
\begin{array}{r}
3.819 \\
\times\ \ \ 65 \\
\hline
19095 \\
22914 \\
\hline
248.235
\end{array}
\longrightarrow 248
$$

Multiply 17.8 by 3.7. Round the
answer to the nearest tenth.

$$
\begin{array}{r}
17.8 \\
\times\ \ 3.7 \\
\hline
1246 \\
534 \\
\hline
65.86
\end{array}
\longrightarrow 65.9
$$

1. Round the product
   to the nearest
   cent.

   $$
   \begin{array}{r}
   \$\,0.13 \\
   \times\ 27.6 \\
   \hline
   \end{array}
   $$

2. Round the product
   to the nearest whole
   number.

   $$
   \begin{array}{r}
   8.9 \\
   \times\ 3.6 \\
   \hline
   \end{array}
   $$

3. Round the product
   to the nearest tenth.

   $$
   \begin{array}{r}
   4.67 \\
   \times\ 0.58 \\
   \hline
   \end{array}
   $$

Round each answer to the nearest cent.

1.	$ 12.79 × 0.06	2.	$ 8.23 × 0.04	3.	$ 128.37 × 0.08	4.	$ 42.95 × 0.07	5.	$ 66.50 × 0.09
6.	$ 7.64 × 1.7	7.	$ 9.16 × 0.25	8.	$ 86.44 × 0.015	9.	$ 8.74 × 3.9	10.	$ 0.136 × 27

Round each answer to the nearest whole number.

11.	2.3 × 5.6	12.	8.19 × 43	13.	76 × 3.8	14.	3.07 × 1.9	15.	0.987 × 68
16.	6.4 × 0.77	17.	27.46 × 6.4	18.	57.8 × 3.1	19.	379 × 9.5	20.	3.27 × 8.6

Round each answer to the nearest tenth.

21.	3.8 × 7.6	22.	3.09 × 0.9	23.	12.42 × 8	24.	57.8 × 4.3	25.	0.74 × 2.5
26.	6.44 × 5.9	27.	9.38 × 0.6	28.	0.74 × 0.27	29.	6.09 × 1.7	30.	0.688 × 1.34

31. If oil costs 98¢ per liter and gasoline costs 15.9¢ per liter, how much for 5 ℓ of oil and 27.6 ℓ of gasoline?

☆ 32. Find the cost of gasoline at a local gasoline station. How much would it cost to fill a car tank that holds 45.6 ℓ?

How thick are the pages of a book? Put enough pages together to give a thickness of 1 centimeter. Count the number of pages. Divide 1 cm by the number of pages to get the thickness of 1 page.

Answers for Self-check 1. 0.06   2. 0.028   3. 0.0012   4. 0.0042   5. 2.28   6. 6.96   7. 5.766
8. 25.333   9. 0.0333   10. 0.00192   11. 0.010602   12. 0.00944   13. 53.5   14. 0.96   15. 716.3
16. 271.9   17. 3.24   18. 1.784   19. 0.0934   20. 0.008   21. $1.70   22. $249.58   23. $246.71

Self-check

1. 0.2×0.3

2. 0.04×0.7

3. 0.6×0.002

4. 0.07×0.06

5.
$$\begin{array}{r} 3.8 \\ \times\, 0.6 \\ \hline \end{array}$$

6.
$$\begin{array}{r} 2.9 \\ \times\, 2.4 \\ \hline \end{array}$$

7.
$$\begin{array}{r} 0.62 \\ \times\, 9.3 \\ \hline \end{array}$$

8.
$$\begin{array}{r} 5.39 \\ \times\, 4.7 \\ \hline \end{array}$$

9.
$$\begin{array}{r} 0.037 \\ \times\quad 0.9 \\ \hline \end{array}$$

10.
$$\begin{array}{r} 0.016 \\ \times\quad 0.12 \\ \hline \end{array}$$

11.
$$\begin{array}{r} 0.279 \\ \times\, 0.038 \\ \hline \end{array}$$

12.
$$\begin{array}{r} 0.0016 \\ \times\qquad 5.9 \\ \hline \end{array}$$

13. 5.35×10

14. 0.0096×100

15. 0.7163×1000

16. 27.19×10

17. 32.4×0.1

18. 178.4×0.01

19. 93.4×0.001

20. 0.8×0.01

Round the product to the nearest cent.

21.
$$\begin{array}{r} \$\,37.75 \\ \times\, 0.045 \\ \hline \end{array}$$

22.
$$\begin{array}{r} \$\,32.84 \\ \times\quad 7.6 \\ \hline \end{array}$$

23.
$$\begin{array}{r} \$\,29.37 \\ \times\quad 8.4 \\ \hline \end{array}$$

Answers for Self-check—page 89

Test

1. 0.7×0.6

2. 0.09×0.5

3. 0.06×0.04

4. 0.002×0.8

5.
$$\begin{array}{r} 7.2 \\ \times\, 0.6 \\ \hline \end{array}$$

6.
$$\begin{array}{r} 5.4 \\ \times\, 7.1 \\ \hline \end{array}$$

7.
$$\begin{array}{r} 0.77 \\ \times\, 5.8 \\ \hline \end{array}$$

8.
$$\begin{array}{r} 93.6 \\ \times\, 4.9 \\ \hline \end{array}$$

9.
$$\begin{array}{r} 0.056 \\ \times\quad 0.8 \\ \hline \end{array}$$

10.
$$\begin{array}{r} 0.29 \\ \times\, 0.017 \\ \hline \end{array}$$

11.
$$\begin{array}{r} 0.816 \\ \times\, 0.045 \\ \hline \end{array}$$

12.
$$\begin{array}{r} 0.073 \\ \times\, 0.084 \\ \hline \end{array}$$

13. 7.48×10

14. 31.8×100

15. 0.7194×1000

16. 0.917×100

17. 128.5×0.1

18. 3.8×0.01

19. 96.43×0.001

20. 0.93×0.1

Round the product to the nearest tenth.

21.
$$\begin{array}{r} 0.169 \\ \times\quad 42 \\ \hline \end{array}$$

22.
$$\begin{array}{r} 17.2 \\ \times\, 8.6 \\ \hline \end{array}$$

23.
$$\begin{array}{r} 6.27 \\ \times\, 0.95 \\ \hline \end{array}$$

Math lab

Napier's Bones

John Napier (1550–1617) was a Scottish mathematician who invented one of the world's first calculators. Napier's calculator is called **Napier's Bones** and can be used to find products.

You can make and use Napier's Bones. Make these ten strips. Each strip should be 3 cm by 27 cm.

Here is the way to use Napier's Bones to find 729 × 6.

Place the strips headed 7, 2, and 9 side by side. Place the blue strip beside these three strips. Find the squares next to 6 on the blue strip.

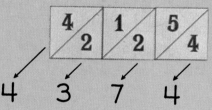

Add the numbers diagonally to find the product.

729 × 6 = 4374

Find these products using Napier's Bones.

1. 32 × 8
2. 78 × 9
3. 638 × 7
4. 779 × 6
5. 2647 × 9
6. 1987 × 5
7. 3624 × 8
8. 9237 × 7

Estimation

Making an estimate before solving a problem will help you decide whether the answer you find is reasonable.

Choose the best estimate for each problem.

Shop-rite

$0.69
0.39
0.32
1.72
0.93
0.12
1.28
0.77

What is the total?

Estimates:

A $10   B $2   C $6

2. It takes James about 15 minutes to walk to school from his home. One month he walked to school and back home 22 times. About how many hours did he spend walking to and from school?

Estimates:

A 5 hours   B 11 hours   C 20 hours

3. If you can save 25¢ each week, how much could you save in one year?

Estimates:

A $13   B $25   C $50

4. If your scores on four tests were 83, 78, 90, and 95, what would be your average score?

Estimates:

A 75   B 85   C 95

To make estimates, numbers are often rounded to **one-digit** accuracy.

Examples:

278: Round to 300   0.058: Round to 0.06
4376: Round to 4000   88.43: Round to 90
3.17: Round to 3   0.00489: Round to 0.005
0.728: Round to 0.7   0.98: Round to 1

Round each number to one-digit accuracy.

1. 316	2. 4.87	3. 0.69	4. 17.27	5. 2958
6. 0.811	7. 509	8. 0.1374	9. 0.0793	10. 92
11. 29.46	12. 6192	13. 0.0785	14. 0.977	15. 887
16. 327.6	17. 0.392	18. 4.19	19. 0.068	20. 87.54
21. 70.82	22. 6874	23. 567.6	24. 0.0038	25. 218

Round the number in each sentence to one-digit accuracy.

26. The trans-Alaska oil pipeline is 1284 km long.

27. The Simplon II rail tunnel, connecting Switzerland and Italy, is 19.82 km long.

28. The Apollo X astronauts reached a speed of 39 897 km/h.

29. There were 924 108 telephones in Miami, Florida, in a recent year.

30. A large jet airplane has a length of 70.5 m.

31. Sound travels 331 m/s.

32. The area of Yosemite Park is 308 106 hectares.

33. The oceans cover about 0.71 of the earth's surface.

34. Takkakaw Falls, British Columbia, is 380.4 m high.

35. In a recent year Utah had a population of 1 059 273.

Estimating sums and differences

Estimate the total cost of these items.

Onion dip	**49¢**
Cole slaw	**59¢**
Fruit drinks	**41¢**
Hash browns	**43¢**
Biscuits	**19¢**

Finding the answer

Problem	→	Round each number and add	→	Write the estimate

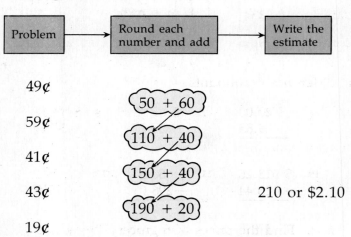

49¢

59¢

41¢

43¢

19¢

50 + 60

110 + 40

150 + 40

190 + 20

210 or $2.10

The estimated total is $2.10.

Other examples

224
389
+ 273
———
900

200 + 400
600 + 300

6128
− 2889
———
3000

6000 − 3000

Estimate the total.

1.	609	2.	76	3.	$ 9.75
	274		88		2.33
	+ 422		34		+ 7.98
			+ 52		

Estimate the difference.

4.	$ 50.00	5.	$ 72.36
	− 39.95		− 28.77

Estimate the total amounts.

1.
Grapefruit	49¢
Apricots	58¢
Peas	23¢
Juice	79¢

2.
Crackers	54¢
Mixed vegetables	35¢
Potatoes	99¢
Bread	39¢
Vinegar	57¢

3.
Detergent	$1.05
Cheese	1.79
Milk	2.72
Round steak	3.27

4.
Fried chicken	$2.39
Enchiladas	1.19
Apple pie	1.79
Sponge cake	1.07
Sugar	1.89

Estimate the difference in amounts.

5.
$$\begin{array}{r} \$\ 0.73 \\ -\ 0.29 \\ \hline \end{array}$$

6.
$$\begin{array}{r} \$\ 20.00 \\ -\ 9.85 \\ \hline \end{array}$$

7.
$$\begin{array}{r} \$\ 69.95 \\ -\ 38.27 \\ \hline \end{array}$$

8.
$$\begin{array}{r} \$\ 93.66 \\ -\ 34.19 \\ \hline \end{array}$$

9.
$$\begin{array}{r} \$\ 72.15 \\ -\ 59.84 \\ \hline \end{array}$$

10.
$$\begin{array}{r} \$\ 513.26 \\ -\ 125.44 \\ \hline \end{array}$$

11.
$$\begin{array}{r} \$\ 688.54 \\ -\ 296.09 \\ \hline \end{array}$$

12.
$$\begin{array}{r} \$\ 5943 \\ -\ 1998 \\ \hline \end{array}$$

13. Estimate the cost of each list. Which total is greater? Check your estimate.

A
Bread	59¢
Milk	68¢
Butter	96¢
Eggs	73¢

B
Apples	89¢
Green beans	67¢
Lettuce	33¢
Potatoes	69¢

☆ 14. Find the prices of 6 grocery items from an advertisement. Estimate the total cost. Find the difference between your estimate and the exact cost.

 Draw a 4 by 4 grid.

Now fill each square of the grid with one of these 16 numbers.

4 zeros, 3 threes, 3 twos, 3 ones, 3 fours

Do not use the same number twice in any one row, column, or diagonal.

More practice, page 381, Set A

Special products

When the factors are multiples of 10, 100, or 1000, you can often find the products mentally.

$$6 \cdot 70 = (6 \cdot 7) \cdot 10 = 420$$
$$6 \cdot 700 = (6 \cdot 7) \cdot 100 = 4200$$
$$6 \cdot 7000 = (6 \cdot 7) \cdot 1000 = 42\,000$$
$$60 \cdot 70 = (6 \cdot 7) \cdot 100 = 4200$$
$$60 \cdot 700 = (6 \cdot 7) \cdot 1000 = 42\,000$$
$$600 \cdot 700 = (6 \cdot 7) \cdot 10\,000 = 420\,000$$

Find the products mentally.

1. $7 \cdot 30$	2. $8 \cdot 60$	3. $9 \cdot 50$	4. $6 \cdot 20$	5. $5 \cdot 40$
6. $3 \cdot 90$	7. $7 \cdot 70$	8. $2 \cdot 60$	9. $9 \cdot 90$	10. $4 \cdot 70$
11. $8 \cdot 400$	12. $6 \cdot 200$	13. $2 \cdot 500$	14. $3 \cdot 800$	15. $7 \cdot 300$
16. $4 \cdot 8000$	17. $2 \cdot 9000$	18. $6 \cdot 6000$	19. $8 \cdot 7000$	20. $5 \cdot 3000$
21. $30 \cdot 80$	22. $50 \cdot 70$	23. $40 \cdot 20$	24. $90 \cdot 40$	25. $70 \cdot 80$
26. $60 \cdot 40$	27. $50 \cdot 20$	28. $70 \cdot 70$	29. $20 \cdot 90$	30. $80 \cdot 40$
31. $70 \cdot 200$	32. $90 \cdot 600$	33. $30 \cdot 200$	34. $80 \cdot 600$	35. $50 \cdot 700$
36. $200 \cdot 400$	37. $600 \cdot 800$	38. $700 \cdot 900$	39. $300 \cdot 600$	40. $500 \cdot 600$

Find the products mentally.

1. $7 \cdot 50$
2. $40 \cdot 80$
3. $30 \cdot 700$
4. $20 \cdot 9$
5. $600 \cdot 3$

6. $6 \cdot 8000$
7. $9 \cdot 400$
8. $70 \cdot 90$
9. $60 \cdot 200$
10. $50 \cdot 30$

11. $400 \cdot 7$
12. $30 \cdot 300$
13. $80 \cdot 90$
14. $4000 \cdot 3$
15. $90 \cdot 20$

16. $20 \cdot 800$
17. $10 \cdot 700$
18. $50 \cdot 60$
19. $600 \cdot 7$
20. $40 \cdot 40$

21. $9 \cdot 600$
22. $80 \cdot 30$
23. $7 \cdot 5000$
24. $600 \cdot 800$
25. $20 \cdot 300$

26. $90 \cdot 5$
27. $70 \cdot 300$
28. $90 \cdot 900$
29. $50 \cdot 80$
30. $6 \cdot 4000$

Find the squares.

31. 20^2
32. 50^2
33. 70^2
34. 90^2
35. 40^2

36. 300^2
37. 80^2
38. 600^2
39. 100^2
40. 30^2

Solve the equations.

41. $90 \cdot n = 2700$
42. $4 \cdot k = 12\,000$
43. $r \cdot 50 = 200$

44. $60 \cdot s = 540$
45. $t \cdot 8 = 160$
46. $40 \cdot a = 240$

Solve these equations.

$(1089 \times 9) \div 1 = n$
$(2178 \times 8) \div 2 = n$
$(3267 \times 7) \div 3 = n$
$(4356 \times 6) \div 4 = n$
$(5445 \times 5) \div 5 = n$
$(6534 \times 4) \div 6 = n$

Find the pattern in these equations.
Then write and solve the next three
equations in the pattern.

Estimating whole number products

A building is 52 stories tall.
The front of the building has
48 windows on each story.
Estimate the number of windows
on the front of the building.

Finding the answer

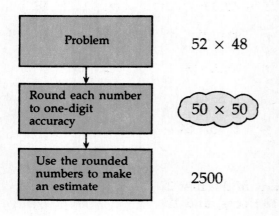

Problem	52×48
Round each number to one-digit accuracy	50×50
Use the rounded numbers to make an estimate	2500

There are about 2500 windows on the front of the building.

Other examples

$$383 \rightarrow \boxed{400 \times 7}$$
$$\times\ 7$$
$$2800$$

$$517 \rightarrow \boxed{500 \times 40}$$
$$\times\ 38$$
$$20\ 000$$

$$624 \rightarrow \boxed{600 \times 200}$$
$$\times 198$$
$$120\ 000$$

Estimate each product.

1. 68
    × 9

2. 23
    × 37

3. 209
    × 31

4. 53
    × 68

5. 73
    × 18

6. 776
    × 6

7. 4127
    × 9

8. 84
    × 89

9. 425
    × 67

10. 211
    × 71

Estimate each product.

1. 27×84
2. 9×39
3. 326×7
4. 41×63

5. 59×9
6. 213×8
7. 67×23
8. 18×47

9. 521×11
10. 74×77
11. 487×19
12. 92×37

13. 608×27
14. 31×41
15. 6023×7
16. 588×3

17. 17×43
18. 26×73
19. 41×319
20. 84×37

21. $61 \cdot 59$
22. $5 \cdot 726$
23. $72 \cdot 194$
24. $337 \cdot 296$

25. $71 \cdot 48$
26. $34 \cdot 68$
27. $83 \cdot 475$
28. $296 \cdot 504$

29. $722 \cdot 188$
30. $643 \cdot 315$
31. $9 \cdot 10 \cdot 11$
32. $8 \cdot 79 \cdot 4$

33. $18 \cdot 22 \cdot 93$
34. $9 \cdot 21 \cdot 29$
35. $8 \cdot 5 \cdot 41$
36. $27 \cdot 34 \cdot 8$

37. $54 \cdot 9 \cdot 7$
38. $3 \cdot 976 \cdot 6$
39. $11 \cdot 52 \cdot 81$
40. $99 \cdot 98 \cdot 19$

☆ 41. A certain building has 32 windows on each of the first 22 floors, 15 windows on each of the next 18 floors, and 12 windows on each of the remaining 6 floors. About how many windows does it have in all?

Find the number for each letter. Then find the secret message.

1. $2^4 = A$
2. $308 - 279 = C$
3. $2 \cdot 3 \cdot 5 \cdot 7 = D$
4. $13^2 - 12^2 = E$
5. $(70 + 7) - (60 + 6) = F$
6. $4001 - 3999 = H$
7. $(7 \times 7) - 8 = L$
8. $3^2 - 2^3 = N$
9. $17 + 18 + 19 = O$
10. $3^3 - 14 = P$
11. $(3 \times 17) + 9 = R$
12. $(3 \times 9) + 17 = T$
13. $429 + 387 - 777 = U$
14. $2^2 \cdot 3^2 = W$

$\overline{13}\ \overline{25}\ \overline{54}\ \overline{13}\ \overline{41}\ \overline{25}$

$\overline{36}\ \overline{2}\ \overline{54}\ \ \overline{210}\ \overline{54}\ \overline{1}\ \overline{44}$

$\overline{29}\ \overline{54}\ \overline{39}\ \overline{1}\ \overline{44}\ \ \overline{36}\ \overline{54}\ \overline{1}\ \overline{44}$

$\overline{29}\ \overline{54}\ \overline{39}\ \overline{1}\ \overline{44}.$

$\overline{16}\ \overline{1}\ \overline{16}\ \overline{44}\ \overline{54}\ \overline{41}\ \overline{25}$

$\overline{11}\ \overline{60}\ \overline{16}\ \overline{1}\ \overline{29}\ \overline{25}$

Estimating decimal products

The length of a side of a square is 0.7071 times the length of the diagonal of the square.

Estimate the length of one side of a square room if the diagonal is 6.1 m.

Finding the answer

| Problem | Round each number to one-digit accuracy | Use the rounded numbers to make the estimate |

0.7071 × 6.1   0.7 × 6   4.2

The side of the square is about 4.2 m.

Other examples

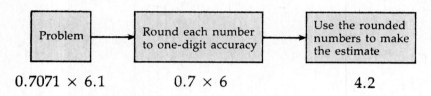

$\begin{array}{r} 6.82 \\ \times\ 2.35 \\ \hline 14 \end{array}$ → 7 × 2

$\begin{array}{r} 29.43 \\ \times\ 0.082 \\ \hline 2.40 \end{array}$ → 30 × 0.08

$\begin{array}{r} 0.59 \\ \times\ 0.72 \\ \hline 0.42 \end{array}$ → 0.6 × 0.7

Choose the best estimate.

1. 3.86 × 2.2

    A 6
    B 8
    C 10

2. 48 × 8.1

    A 400
    B 320
    C 40

3. 0.76 × 5.2

    A 40
    B 0.4
    C 4.0

4. 39.4 × 9.2

    A 400
    B 360
    C 270

5. 0.42 × 0.77

    A 3.2
    B 0.32
    C 0.032

6. 61.4 × 0.072

    A 4.2
    B 0.42
    C 0.042

Estimate each product.

1.	9.1 ⨯ 3.8	2.	6.27 ⨯ 0.73	3.	0.413 ⨯ 0.609	4.	29.3 ⨯ 8.8	5.	7.26 ⨯ 3.9
6.	0.36 ⨯ 5.2	7.	31.6 ⨯ 57.4	8.	9.95 ⨯ 3.87	9.	0.772 ⨯ 0.619	10.	42.7 ⨯ 8.5
11.	1.74 ⨯ 6.6	12.	34.5 ⨯ 0.19	13.	2.7 ⨯ 3.2	14.	28.6 ⨯ 0.77	15.	209 ⨯ 3.1
16.	0.92 ⨯ 0.87	17.	10.76 ⨯ 5.33	18.	57.42 ⨯ 6.83	19.	0.715 ⨯ 0.806	20.	8.125 ⨯ 0.528

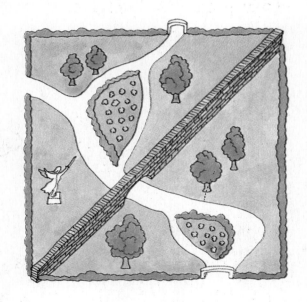

21. The side of a square is 0.7071 times the length of the diagonal of the square. This small city park is a square. A wall across the diagonal of the square is 109 m long. Estimate the length of one side of the park.

☆ 22. Draw a square. Measure the length of the diagonal of the square to the nearest tenth of a centimeter. Estimate the length of the side of the square (use 0.7071). Check your estimate by measuring.

Answers for Self-check 1. 500 2. 60 3. 0.8 4. 9 5. 0.07 6. 360 7. 4200 8. 1500
9. 32 000 10. 480 000 11. 160 12. 5000 13. $110 14. 4000 15. $600 16. 1500 17. 630
18. 4800 19. 32 20. 12

More practice, page 381, Set B

Self-check

Round each number to one-digit accuracy.

1. 523
2. 63.4
3. 0.758
4. 9.344
5. 0.0693

Find the products.

6. 9 · 40
7. 60 · 70
8. 5 · 300
9. 4000 · 8
10. 800 · 600

Estimate the sum or difference.

11.　21
　　38
　　43
　+ 59

12.　8863
　− 3942

13.　$ 39.45
　　22.50
　+ 48.47

14.　6000
　− 1995

15.　$ 496.83
　+ 119.25

Estimate the products.

16. 33 · 47
17. 9 · 72
18. 6 · 813
19.　8.1
　× 3.9
20.　6.3
　× 1.8

Answers for Self-check—page 101

Test

Round each number to one-digit accuracy.

1. 7.82
2. 21.75
3. 0.913
4. 8746
5. 0.0193

Find the products.

6. 30 · 7
7. 90 · 50
8. 8 · 200
9. 6 · 4000
10. 300 · 500

Estimate the sum or difference.

11.　67
　　23
　　31
　+ 59

12.　7104
　− 1833

13.　$ 5.95
　　2.33
　　4.83
　+ 1.27

14.　8239
　− 4953

15.　$ 89.95
　+ 62.50

Estimate the products.

16. 59 · 22
17. 83 · 9
18. 7 · 788
19.　3.7
　× 2.3
20.　7.15
　× 4.7

Math lab

Penny Estimations

Which is the best estimate?
Check your estimate by trying the activity.

1. About how many pennies are
   in a stack of pennies
   as high as a penny
   standing on edge?

   a. less than 8
   b. 8
   c. 9
   d. 10
   e. more than 10

2. If you toss a penny
   100 times, how many
   heads would you expect
   to get?

   a. between 25 and 35
   b. between 35 and 45
   c. between 45 and 55
   d. between 55 and 65

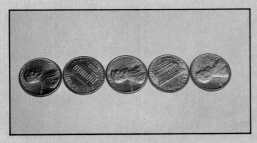

3. How many pennies placed
   side by side would make
   a line of pennies 1 meter
   long?

   a. 32
   b. 53
   c. 74
   d. 95

4. If you give away a penny
   a second, how much money
   would you give away in
   a year?

   a. $3153
   b. $31 536
   c. $315 360
   d. $31 536 000

Using Your Skills

Plumbers are workers who install pipe systems that carry water, steam, air, or other gases or liquids. They also repair pipe systems.

Plumbers must be able to use many different kinds of hand tools and power tools. They must also be able to use welding, soldering, and brazing equipment. Apprentice plumbers often work with master plumbers to learn the trade.

Plumbers and other craftsmen must be able to read and interpret diagrams and blueprints. They must be able to use the data to solve problems which often require more than one step.

Example:

Find distance d, if $D = 3.18$ cm and $h = 0.27$ cm.

Solution: To find d, h must be multiplied by 2 and the product subtracted from D.

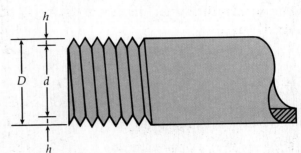

$$\begin{array}{r} 0.27 \\ \times \quad 2 \\ \hline 0.54 \end{array} \qquad \begin{array}{r} 3.18 \\ - 0.54 \\ \hline 2.64 \end{array} \qquad d = 2.64 \text{ cm}$$

Solve these problems.

1. A steel pipe was 2.48 m long. A plumber cut off a piece that was 1.86 m long. What was the length of the remaining piece of pipe?

2. A plumber is installing a drain pipe. The drain must slope downward 0.15 m for each 1 meter of length. How much should the pipe slope downward if the drain pipe is 23 m in length?

3. Find the outside diameter, D, of the pipe in this drawing. 0.6 cm ⊢ 2.5 cm ⊣ 0.6 cm — D —

4. A plumber earned $9.83 an hour. A repair job took 3.5 hours. How much did the plumber earn on this job?

5. A plumber bought a roll of copper tubing that cost $1.88 a meter. The roll contained 12 m of tubing. What was the cost of the tubing?

...ture problems

...diagrams, and pictures often give information that is
...to solve a problem. Use the information given in the
...es below to answer the questions.

1. How much is saved by buying the shoes on sale?

2. How far is a trip from San Antonio to Austin to Houston to San Antonio?

3. How much of a 3 m board will be left when 4 pieces, each 0.63 m long, are cut off?

4. What is the difference in the altitudes of the two planes?

5. How much will 1 dozen lemons cost?

6. How much will 3 double-dip cones and 2 single-dip cones cost?

Writing problems from pictures

Each picture suggests one or more problems. Write and solve a problem using the information in each picture.

1.

Down-filled Sleeping Bags

Regular price $59.95

Sale price $39.99

2.

Maxville 95 km
Oakdale 133 km

3.
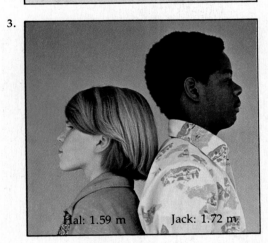

Hal: 1.59 m   Jack: 1.72 m

4.
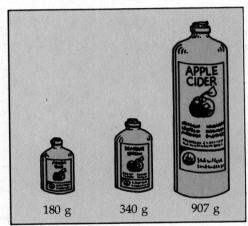

APPLE CIDER

180 g   340 g   907 g

5.

$2.75 Admit one Adult
$2.75 Admit one Adult
$2.75 Admit one Adult
$1.50 Admit one Child
$1.50 Admit one Child

6.

Secretary
$900 a month

Good shorthand and
typing skills needed

Call
123-4567

for appointment

Using a distance formula

Oceanographers use sonar to find the depth of the ocean at any particular spot. Sensitive equipment measures the time it takes for sound from the surface of the ocean to reach the ocean floor. In sea water, sound travels 1460 m (1.46 km) in one second.

Since $d = r \cdot t$, where d = distance, r = rate, and t = time, the ocean depth may be found by using this equation:

Ocean depth = 1460 m/s × time
(in meters)   (in seconds)

Example: It takes sound 0.8 s to reach the ocean bottom at a certain place. How deep is the ocean at that point?

$$
\begin{array}{r}
1460 \\
\times \quad 0.8 \\
\hline
1168.0
\end{array}
$$

The ocean is about 1168 m or 1.168 km deep at that point.

Find the ocean depth for each time given.

1. 1.3 s   2. 0.5 s   3. 0.1 s   4. 2.3 s   5. 3 s

Find the depth in meters for each location.

1. The average depth of the Pacific Ocean
   Time: 2.92 s

2. The greatest depth of the Atlantic Ocean is in the Puerto Rico Trench.
   Time: 5.92 s

3. The greatest depth of the Mediterranean Sea is in the Hellenic Trough.
   Time: 3.53 s

4. The greatest depth of the Arctic Ocean
   Time: 3.73 s

5. An oceanographer found a mountain below the surface of the water. It took 2.05 s for sound to reach the top of the mountain. How far below the surface was the mountain top?

6. The greatest ocean depth is the Challenger Deep near Guam.
   Time: 7.55 s

7. The greatest depth of the Indian Ocean is near Java.
   Time: 5.29 s

8. The Sargasso Sea is part of the Atlantic Ocean.
   Time: 3.29 s

9. The point of greatest depth of the North Sea
   Time: 0.5 s

10. On January 23, 1969, Piccard and Walsh descended to the ocean floor in the Marianas Trench in a special diving sphere. It took 7.4 s for sound to reach from the surface to the sphere. How deep was the diving sphere?

Using a formula—electrical energy

A **watt** (W) is a unit of electrical energy.
A larger unit is the kilowatt (kW).
1000 watts = 1 kilowatt.

Electrical meters, like the one shown, measure, in kilowatt-hours (kW·h), the amount of electricity used.

Amount of electricity (in watt-hours)
= watts × time (in hours)

A 100-watt light bulb burning for 10 hours will use:

100 watts × 10 hours = 1000 watt-hours
= 1 kilowatt-hour (kW·h)

A 60-watt light bulb burning for 20 hours will use:

60 watts × 20 hours = 1200 watt-hours
= 1.2 kW·h

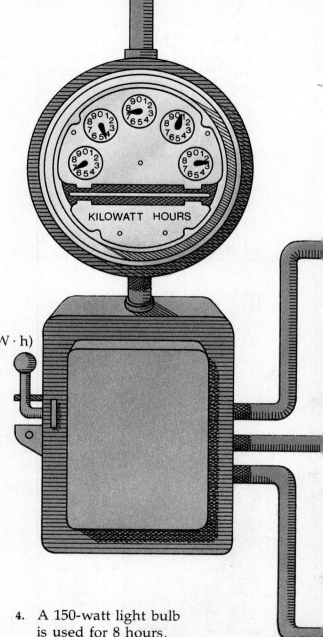

KILOWATT HOURS

Find the number of kilowatt-hours.

1. A 100-watt light bulb is used for 20 hours.

2. A 25-watt light bulb is used for 40 hours.

3. A light fixture has four 50-watt bulbs which burn for 4 hours.

4. A 150-watt light bulb is used for 8 hours.

5. A 75-watt light bulb is used for 18 hours.

6. A room is lighted by two 150-watt light bulbs and two 60-watt light bulbs. The lights are on for 4 hours.

Study this problem.

In a year's time, a family might use about 400 kW · h of energy for a black and white television set. If electricity costs 3.05¢ per kW · h, how much does it cost to run the television set for one year?

Solution:
$$\begin{array}{r} 3.05¢ \\ \times\ 400 \\ \hline 1220.00¢ \end{array}$$

The yearly cost is 1220¢ or $12.20

Find the yearly cost of electricity for each appliance. Round the answer to the nearest cent.

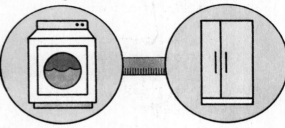

1. Washing machine

125 kW · h per year
3.05¢ per kW · h

2. Refrigerator

75 kW · h per year
3.05¢ per kW · h

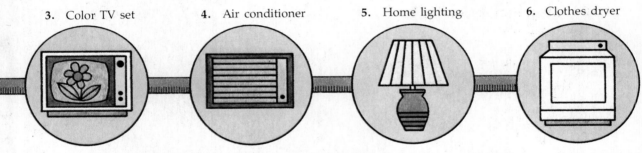

3. Color TV set

540 kW · h per year
3.05¢ per kW · h

4. Air conditioner

3000 kW · h per year
2.96¢ per kW · h

5. Home lighting

1870 kW · h per year
2.96¢ per kW · h

6. Clothes dryer

1500 kW · h per year
3.22¢ per kW · h

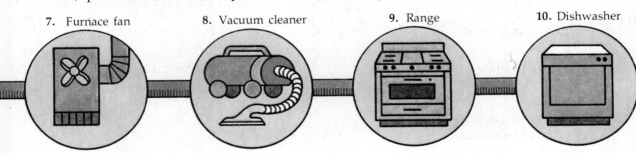

7. Furnace fan

480 kW · h per year
3.22¢ per kW · h

8. Vacuum cleaner

45 kW · h per year
3.34¢ per kW · h

9. Range

1500 kW · h per year
3.34¢ per kW · h

10. Dishwasher

350 kW · h per year
3.34¢ per kW · h

⊛ Scientific notation

Dinosaurs first appeared on earth about 220 000 000 years ago. A number as large as this is often written in scientific notation.

Standard numeral

Scientific notation

$$220\,000\,000 = 2.2 \times 10^8$$

a number between 1 and 10   a power of ten

What is the standard numeral for 3.6×10^7?

$$3.6 \times 10^7 = 3.6 \times 10\,000\,000$$
$$= 36\,000\,000$$

Write a standard numeral for each.

1. 5×10^4 2. 7×10^6 3. 1.2×10^9 4. 6.2×10^3 5. 8.5×10^5

6. 3.1×10^3 7. 9.4×10^7 8. 8×10^8 9. 1.7×10^4 10. 4.6×10^{10}

Give the standard numeral.

1. Trilobite fossil
   6×10^8 years ago

2. Coal
   6.5×10^7 years ago

3. Pterodactyl
   1.8×10^8 years ago

4. Early horse
   4×10^7 years ago

5. Fossil cephalopod
   4×10^8 years ago

6. Fern trees
   3.1×10^8 years ago

7. Coral
   1.1×10^9 years ago

8. Mammoth
   3×10^6 years ago

9. 2.6×10^6 10. 4.1×10^3

11. 8.2×10^5 12. 1.9×10^2

13. 7.5×10^8 14. 3.9×10^5

15. 5.3×10^7 16. 2.5×10^9

Answers for Self-check   1. 6.95 cm   2. 3942.0 m   3. 4 kW·h   4. $26.72   5. 30 000   6. 800
7. 1700   8. 290 000

Self-check

1.

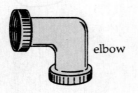

Find distance d.

2. Sound travels through sea water at a rate of 1460 m/s. How far would sound travel in sea water in 2.7 seconds?

3. A 100-watt light bulb burned for 40 hours. How many kilowatt-hours is this?

4. A 100-watt light bulb which burns continuously for a year would use about 876 kW·h of electricity. If electricity costs 3.05¢ per kW·h, what would be the cost of the electricity for the light bulb?

Write the standard numeral for each.

☆ **5.** 3×10^4 ☆ **6.** 8×10^2

☆ **7.** 1.7×10^3 ☆ **8.** 2.9×10^5

Answers for Self-check—page 113

Test

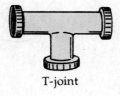

elbow

T-joint

1. Elbows cost 49¢ each. T-joints cost 39¢ each. What is the cost of 4 elbows and 3 T-joints?

2. Sound travels through sea water at a rate of 1460 m/s. How far would sound travel in sea water in 1.9 seconds?

3. A 150-watt light bulb burned for 20 hours. How many kilowatt-hours is this?

4. An electric clock uses only 17 kW·h of electricity a year. Find the cost of the electricity for the clock, if the cost of 1 kW·h is 3.05¢.

Write the standard numeral for each.

☆ **5.** 4×10^5 ☆ **6.** 9×10^2

☆ **7.** 1.3×10^4 ☆ **8.** 7.5×10^6

Block Patterns

Make patterns for four cubes and letter the faces exactly as shown.
Cut out the patterns. Fold and tape the edges together to form cubes.

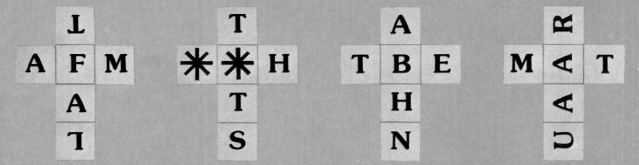

Now try to stack the four cubes so that
1. the word MATH appears on one side of the stack,
2. the other three sides each form a 3 or 4 letter word, and
3. all four sides together spell out a sentence.

Measuring Length and Area

Each square on the grid below is 1 centimeter (cm) long.
Find the path along the red lines from start to finish.
How many centimeters long is the path?

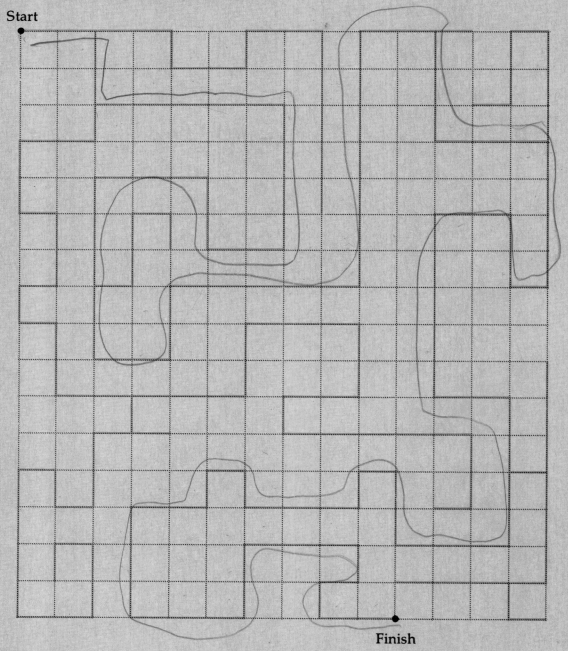

Start

Finish

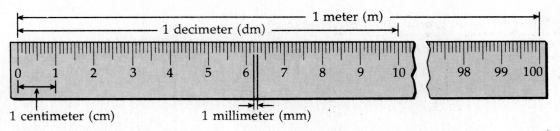

1 centimeter (cm) 1 millimeter (mm)

The basic unit of length in the metric system is the **meter** (m).

Other metric units of length are related to the meter.

Unit	Prefix	Meaning of Prefix	Symbol
millimeter	milli	one thousandth of	mm
centimeter	centi	one hundredth of	cm
decimeter	deci	one tenth of	dm
meter			m
dekameter	deka	ten	dam
hectometer	hecto	one hundred	hm
kilometer	kilo	one thousand	km

A decimeter is one tenth of a meter.   1 dm = 0.1 m
A centimeter is one hundredth of a meter.   1 cm = 0.01 m
A kilometer is one thousand meters.   1 km = 1000 m

Complete each sentence.

1. A millimeter is ___?___ of a meter.

2. A hectometer is ___?___ meters.

Give the missing numbers.

3. 1 mm = ▓ m

4. 1 cm = ▓ m

5. 1 dm = ▓ m

6. 1 dam = ▓ m

7. 1 hm = ▓ m

8. 1 km = ▓ m

9. 1 m = ▓ km

10. 10 dm = ▓ m

11. 100 cm = ▓ m

12. ▓ mm = 1 m

13. 1 mm = ▓ cm

14. 1000 mm = ▓ m

Relationships between units of length

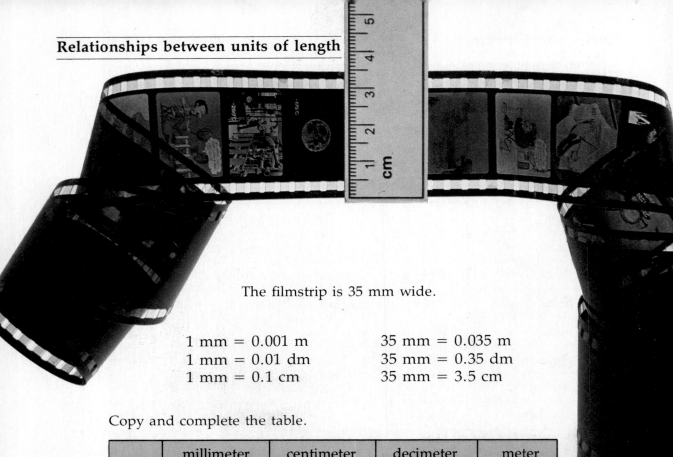

The filmstrip is 35 mm wide.

1 mm = 0.001 m	35 mm = 0.035 m
1 mm = 0.01 dm	35 mm = 0.35 dm
1 mm = 0.1 cm	35 mm = 3.5 cm

Copy and complete the table.

	millimeter	centimeter	decimeter	meter
	94 mm	9.4 cm	0.94 dm	0.094 m
1.	63 mm			
2.	276 mm			
3.		8.5 cm		
4.			0.37 dm	
5.				0.549 m
6.		67 cm		
7.	2000 mm			
8.		52.6 cm		
9.			8.4 dm	
10.				3 m

The filmstrip is 185 cm long.
1 centimeter = 0.01 m
185 cm = 1.85 m
The filmstrip is 1.85 m long.

Give each distance in meters.

1. 163 cm   2. 155 cm   3. 149 cm

4. 171 cm   5. 623 cm   6. 317 cm

7. 84 cm   8. 2754 cm   9. 7 cm

Give each distance in kilometers.

Use 1000 m = 1 km.

10. 5000 m   11. 8300 m   12. 2000 m

13. 800 m   14. 1860 m   15. 25 000 m

16. 6297 m   17. 100 000 m   18. 3618 m

Give each distance in meters.

Use 1000 m = 1 km.

19. 3 km   20. 1.5 km   21. 6.27 km

22. 18 km   23. 0.9 km   24. 0.75 km

25. 0.1 km   26. 70 km   27. 3.62 km

Suppose that metric prefixes were used for money, with the dollar
as the unit. Then a decidollar would be one tenth of a dollar or
10 cents. How much money would each of the following be?

1. 1 centidollar   2. 1 dekadollar   3. 1 hectodollar
4. 1 kilodollar   5. 3 decidollars   6. 56 centidollars
7. 2.5 decidollars   8. 1.67 centidollars   9. 2000 millidollars

Perimeter

The Pentagon building in Arlington, Virginia is the world's largest office building. Each of the 5 outer sides of the Pentagon is 281 m long.

The **distance around** the Pentagon is

$$5 \times 281 = 1405 \text{ m}.$$

The **perimeter** of the Pentagon is 1405 m.

Perimeter of a rectangle = 2 times (*length* + *width*)

$$P = 2(l + w)$$

Find the perimeter of a rectangle when $l = 6.8$ cm and $w = 5.6$ cm.

$$
\begin{aligned}
P &= 2(6.8 + 5.6) \\
&= 2(12.4) \\
&= 24.8
\end{aligned}
$$

The perimeter is 24.8 cm.

Find the perimeter of each.

1.
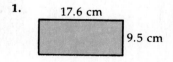
17.6 cm
9.5 cm

2.
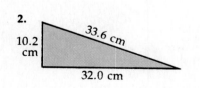
10.2 cm
33.6 cm
32.0 cm

3.
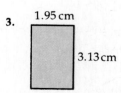
1.95 cm
3.13 cm

Find the perimeter of each triangle.

4. each side: 6.3 cm

5. side 1: 26.4 cm
   side 2: 19.2 cm
   side 3: 10.3 cm

6. side 1: 33.6 cm
   side 2: 32.0 cm
   side 3: 10.2 cm

Find the perimeter of each building.

1. Parthenon
   Athens, Greece
   length: 72 m
   width: 34 m

2. The Great Pyramid
   of Egypt. The base is a
   square, each side of
   which is 236.4 m.

3. World's largest castle
   Berkshire, England
   length: 576 m
   width: 164 m

4. World's largest zeppelin hangar
   Akron, Ohio
   length: 358 m
   width: 99 m

5. Imperial Palace
   Peking, China
   length: 960 m
   width: 750 m

6. Vehicle assembly building for spacecraft
   Cape Canaveral, Florida
   length: 218 m
   width: 158 m

☆ 7. Find the perimeter of your
   classroom or school building.

Does this pattern of equations continue?
Write 6 more equations in the pattern and
check to see if they are correct.

$(0 \times 1 \times 2 \times 3) + 1 = 1 = 1^2$
$(1 \times 2 \times 3 \times 4) + 1 = 25 = 5^2$
$(2 \times 3 \times 4 \times 5) + 1 = 121 = 11^2$
$(3 \times 4 \times 5 \times 6) + 1 = 361 = 19^2$

More practice, page 382, Set A

Area of rectangles and parallelograms

Area of a rectangle equals *length* times *width*.
$A = lw$

$l = 4$ cm, $w = 2$ cm
$A = 2 \cdot 4 = 8$
$A = 8$ cm²

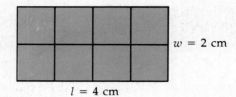

$w = 2$ cm

$l = 4$ cm

The picture can help you to understand why the area of a parallelogram equals *base* times *height*.

$A = bh$
$b = 5$ cm, $h = 3$ cm
$A = 5 \cdot 3 = 15$
$A = 15$ cm²

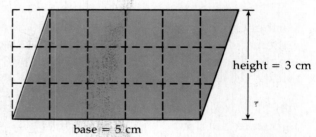

height = 3 cm

base = 5 cm

Find the area of each rectangle.

1. $l = 20$ cm
    $w = 10$ cm

2. $l = 1.8$ m
    $w = 1.2$ m

3. $l = 72$ cm
    $w = 41$ cm

4. $l = 9.3$ km
    $w = 2.5$ km

5. $l = 42$ mm
    $w = 19$ mm

6. $l = 1.48$ m
    $w = 0.75$ m

7. $l = 5.8$ cm
    $w = 5.8$ cm

8. $l = 1.7$ km
    $w = 0.8$ km

Find the area of each parallelogram.

9. $b = 16$ cm
    $h = 9$ cm

10. $b = 3.2$ cm
    $h = 1.5$ cm

11. $b = 2.9$ m
    $h = 1.4$ m

12. $b = 16$ mm
    $h = 7$ mm

13. $b = 6.5$ m
    $h = 1.2$ m

14. $b = 1.2$ cm
    $h = 0.8$ cm

15. $b = 2$ m
    $h = 0.5$ m

16. $b = 3.5$ m
    $h = 2.0$ m

1. What is the area of the table top?

2. The white stripes around the table and through the middle are 2 cm wide. What is the area of the green part of the table?

3. What is the total area of all the white stripes?

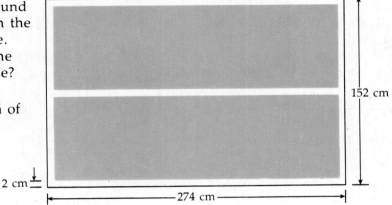

152 cm

2 cm

274 cm

4. A city lot is in the shape of a parallelogram. The base is 38 m and the height is 40 m. What is the area of the lot?

5. A rectangular house on the lot has a length of 25 m and a width of 15 m. What is the area of the house?

6. What is the area of the lot not covered by the house?

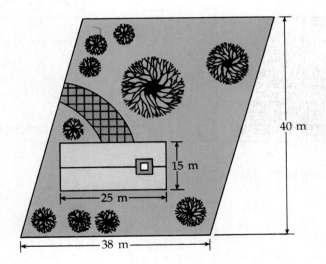

40 m

15 m

25 m

38 m

☆ 7. Floor tiles are sold in squares 30 cm on each side. How much would it cost to tile a rectangular room 7.2 m long and 5.4 m wide if the tiles cost $0.72 each?

☆ 8. Find the area of your classroom in square meters.

More practice, page 382, Set B

Area of triangles

Parallelogram $ABCD$ has been divided into two congruent triangles. $\triangle ABD \cong \triangle CDB$. The area of $\triangle ABD$ is one half of the area of parallelogram $ABCD$.

Area of a parallelogram $= bh$

Area of a triangle $= \frac{1}{2}bh = \frac{bh}{2}$

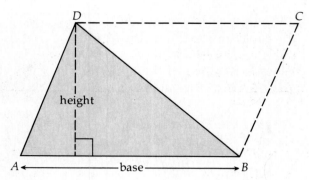

What is the area of a triangle if $b = 8$ cm and $h = 5$ cm?

$A = \frac{8 \times 5}{2} = \frac{40}{2} = 20$

The area is 20 cm².

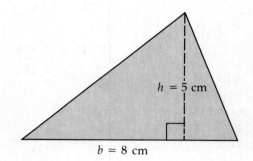

Find the area of each triangle.

1.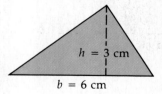

2.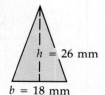

3.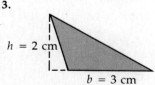

4. $b = 12$ cm $h = 8$ cm	5. $b = 26$ cm $h = 18$ cm	6. $b = 36$ cm $h = 14$ cm	7. $b = 10$ cm $h = 10$ cm
8. $b = 34$ cm $h = 15$ cm	9. $b = 9$ m $h = 6$ m	10. $b = 120$ m $h = 42$ m	11. $b = 95$ m $h = 56$ m

Find the area of each triangle.

1.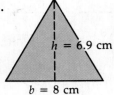
$h = 6.9$ cm
$b = 8$ cm

2.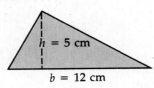
$h = 5$ cm
$b = 12$ cm

3.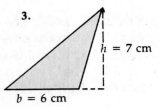
$h = 7$ cm
$b = 6$ cm

4. $b = 32$ cm
$h = 15$ cm

5. $b = 2$ m
$h = 1$ m

6. $b = 25$ m
$h = 10$ m

7. $b = 25$ cm
$h = 14$ cm

8. $b = 33$ mm
$h = 16$ mm

9. $b = 60$ cm
$h = 22$ cm

10. $b = 34$ cm
$h = 9$ cm

11. $b = 50$ cm
$h = 40$ cm

12. $b = 64$ m
$h = 37$ m

☆ **13.**

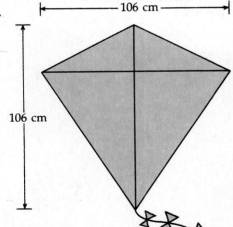

← 106 cm →

106 cm

What is the area of the kite?

☆ **14.**

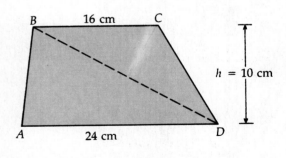

B 16 cm C
$h = 10$ cm
A 24 cm D

Find the area of trapezoid $ABCD$.
Hint: Find the area of $\triangle ABD$ and
the area of $\triangle BCD$.

More practice, page 383, Set A

Surface area

Before buying paint, you need
to know the surface area of the
object to be painted.

What is the total surface area of all the
faces of this rectangular prism in square
centimeters?

Area of face $A = 8 \times 20 = 160$ cm²
Area of face $B = 20 \times 12 = 240$ cm²
Area of face $C = 8 \times 12 = 96$ cm²

Total area of faces A, B, and $C = 496$ cm²

The area of all the faces is twice the area of faces A, B, and C.

The area of all the faces of the prism $= 2 \times 496$ cm² $= 992$ cm².

The **total surface area** of the prism is 992 cm².

Find the total surface area of each rectangular prism.

1.
2 cm
3 cm
4 cm

2.
1 cm
5 cm
10 cm

3.
8 cm
3 cm
3 cm

4.
5 cm
6 cm
8 cm

5.
7 cm
7 cm
2 cm

6.
5 cm
9 cm
12 cm

Find the total surface area of each pyramid.
The pattern for each pyramid is given.

1.

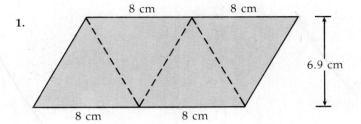

8 cm   8 cm

6.9 cm

8 cm   8 cm

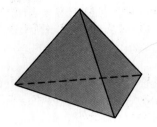

triangular pyramid

2.

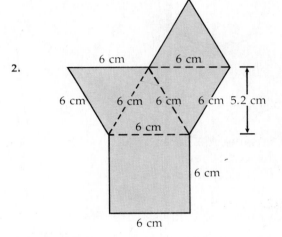

6 cm   6 cm

6 cm   6 cm   6 cm   6 cm   5.2 cm

6 cm

6 cm

6 cm

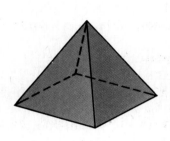

square pyramid

3.

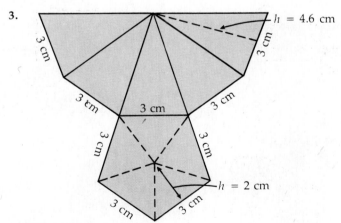

h = 4.6 cm

3 cm

3 cm   3 cm

3 cm   3 cm

3 cm

3 cm   3 cm

h = 2 cm

3 cm   3 cm

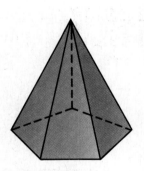

pentagonal pyramid

A regular icosahedron has 20 equilateral
triangles as its faces. Here the base
of each triangle is 3.8 cm long and the
height of each triangle is 3.3 cm.
Find the total surface area of the icosahedron.

Circumference of a circle

The distance around a circle, called the circumference of the circle, is about 3.14 times the diameter of the circle.

By measurement, the diameter of the cup is 8.4 cm and the circumference is 26.4 cm.

By computing
    $8.4 \cdot 3.14 = 26.376$

By measurement, the diameter of the clock is 33.8 cm and the circumference is 106.1 cm.

By computing
    $33.8 \cdot 3.14 = 106.132$

The circumference of any circle is always the same multiple of its diameter. This multiple is shown by the Greek letter π (pi), and has been computed to thousands of decimal places.

To find the circumference of a circle, you can use one of these formulas:

    $C = \pi d$ or $C = 2\pi r$

Other examples

Find the circumference.
Use $\pi = 3.14$.

$C = \pi d$
$C = 3.14 \cdot 6.1$
$C = 19.154 \,\text{cm}$

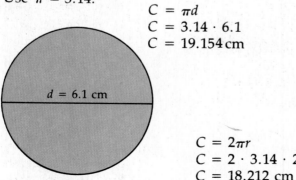

$d = 6.1$ cm

$C = 2\pi r$
$C = 2 \cdot 3.14 \cdot 2.9$
$C = 18.212$ cm

Find the circumference.
Use $\pi = 3.14$.

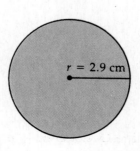

$r = 2.9$ cm

Find the circumference of each circle. Use $\pi = 3.14$.

1.

bicycle wheel
$d = 66$ cm

2.

auto tire
$d = 60$ cm

3.

tractor tire
$d = 1.3$ m

4.

45 rpm record
$d = 17.8$ cm

5.

78 rpm record
$d = 25.4$ cm

6.

33 rpm record
$d = 30.5$ cm

7.

tennis ball
$r = 3.6$ cm

8.

basketball
$r = 12.1$ cm

9.

the earth
$r = 6383$ km

10. A large Douglas fir tree has a diameter of 4.6 m. What is the circumference of the tree to the nearest tenth of a meter?

☆ **11.** Measure the diameter of some circular objects. Find the circumference for each object.

More practice, page 383, Set B

Area of a circle

The area of the circle with radius 4 units
can be estimated by counting the
whole squares inside the circle and
then estimating the area of the partial
squares inside the circle.

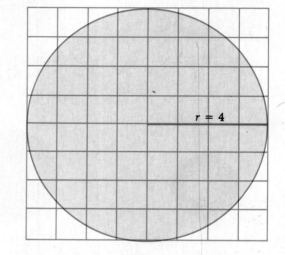

Whole squares   ⟶ 32
Estimated area of   ⟶ 18
partial squares
Total area   ⟶ 50 square units

$r = 4$

Estimate the area of the circle with
radius 3 units.

The area of any circle can be found by
using the formula:

$A = \pi r^2$

Find the area of the circle with radius 4 units.
$A = \pi r^2$
$A = 3.14 \times 4^2$
$A = 3.14 \times 16$
$A = 50.24$ square units

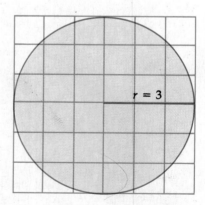

$r = 3$

1. What is the area of the circle with radius 3 units?

2. On graph paper, draw a circle with radius 5 units. Estimate the area by
   counting squares. Find the area by using the formula.

Find the area of each circle.
Use 3.14 for π.

1.

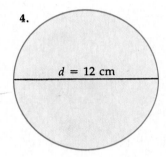

r = 3 cm

2.

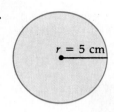

r = 5 cm

3.

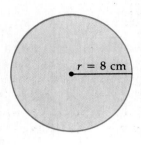

r = 8 cm

4.

d = 12 cm

5.

d = 2 cm

6.

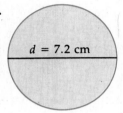

d = 7.2 cm

Find the area of each circle.
Use 3.14 for π.

7. $r = 2$ cm   **8.** $r = 10$ cm   **9.** $r = 11$ cm   **10.** $r = 1$ m

11. $r = 1.5$ m   **12.** $r = 4.4$ m   **13.** $r = 0.8$ cm   **14.** $r = 50$ cm

15. $r = 6$ cm   **16.** $r = 9.2$ cm   **17.** $r = 100$ m   **18.** $r = 2.5$ cm

☆ **19.** A metal washer has an outside diameter
of 2.5 cm. The hole in the center has
a diameter of 1 cm. What is the area
of the washer?

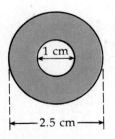

1 cm

2.5 cm

Larry bought a 24 cm pizza and a 32 cm
pizza. Dave bought one 40 cm pizza.
Did Larry buy more, less, or the same
amount of pizza as Dave?

Answers for Self-check   **1.** 100   **2.** 10   **3.** 1   **4.** 1000   **5.** 1000   **6.** 4.63   **7.** 93   **8.** 8.7
9. 1.780   **10.** 58 cm   **11.** 8.0 m   **12.** 10.0 cm²   **13.** 12 m²   **14.** 25.12 cm   **15.** 28.26 cm²

More practice, page 383, Set C

Self-check

Give the missing numbers.

1. 1 m = ▦ cm
2. 1 dm = ▦ cm
3. 10 mm = ▦ cm

4. ▦ m = 1 km
5. 1 m = ▦ mm
6. 463 cm = ▦ m

7. 0.93 m = ▦ cm
8. 87 mm = ▦ cm
9. 1780 m = ▦ km

Find the perimeter.

Find the area.

10.
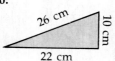
26 cm
10 cm
22 cm

11.
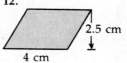
1.7 m
2.0 m
1.9 m
1.1 m
1.3 m

12.

2.5 cm
4 cm

13.

3 m
8 m

14. Find the circumference. Use $\pi = 3.14$.
$d = 8$ cm

15. Find the area. Use $\pi = 3.14$.
$r = 3$ cm

Answers for Self-check—page 131

Test

Give the missing numbers.

1. 100 cm = ▦ m
2. 1 m = ▦ dm
3. 1 cm = ▦ mm

4. 1000 m = ▦ km
5. 1000 mm = ▦ m
6. 273 cm = ▦ m

7. 1500 m = ▦ km
8. 28 mm = ▦ cm
9. 0.5 km = ▦ m

Find the perimeter.

Find the area.

10.
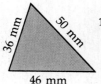
36 mm
50 mm
46 mm

11.
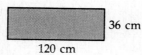
36 cm
120 cm

12.

4 m
4 m

13.

20 mm
25 mm

14. Find the circumference. Use $\pi = 3.14$.
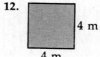
$d = 2.5$ cm

15. Find the area. Use $\pi = 3.14$.

$r = 5$ cm

Betti Numbers of Networks

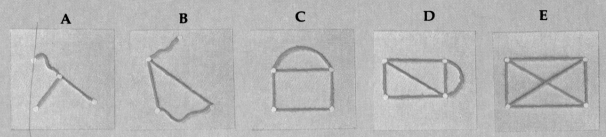

A   B   C   D   E

A **network** is a set of points connected by **paths** which can be straight or curved. The figures above are examples of networks. Models of networks could be made with string or wire.

The **Betti number** of a network is the largest number of cuts that can be made through the paths of the network without causing the network to become separated into 2 or more pieces.

The Betti number for network **A** is 0 because any cut will cause the network to separate into 2 parts.

The Betti number for network **B** is 1. One cut, in the proper place, will not form 2 pieces, but a second cut would.

What are the Betti numbers of networks **C, D,** and **E**?

Try these activities.

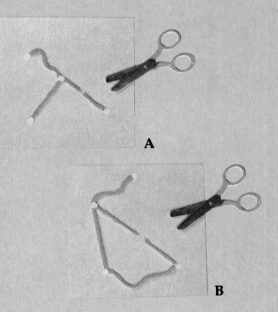

A

B

1. Draw some networks. Find the Betti number of each network.

2. Which capital letter of the alphabet has the largest Betti number?

3. Draw a network that has a Betti number of 5.

Unit 2 review

Identify the principle shown by each equation.

A commutative principle **C** distributive principle
B associative principle **D** property of one

1. $47 \times 56 = 56 \times 47$

2. $4 \times 32 = (4 \times 30) + (4 \times 2)$

3. $5 \times (7 + 12) = (5 \times 7) + (5 \times 12)$

4. $83 \times 106 = 106 \times 83$

5. $12 \times (41 \times 15) = (12 \times 41) \times 15$

6. $117 \times 1 = 117$

Multiply.

7. $\begin{array}{r} 910 \\ \times\ 28 \\ \hline \end{array}$

8. $\begin{array}{r} 318 \\ \times\ 46 \\ \hline \end{array}$

9. $\begin{array}{r} 426 \\ \times\ 93 \\ \hline \end{array}$

10. $\begin{array}{r} 855 \\ \times\ 74 \\ \hline \end{array}$

11. $\begin{array}{r} 767 \\ \times\ 59 \\ \hline \end{array}$

12. $\begin{array}{r} 827 \\ \times\ 966 \\ \hline \end{array}$

13. $\begin{array}{r} 3715 \\ \times\ 118 \\ \hline \end{array}$

14. $\begin{array}{r} 1239 \\ \times\ 764 \\ \hline \end{array}$

15. $\begin{array}{r} 8423 \\ \times\ 501 \\ \hline \end{array}$

16. $\begin{array}{r} 7542 \\ \times\ 303 \\ \hline \end{array}$

17. $\begin{array}{r} 524 \\ \times\ 0.3 \\ \hline \end{array}$

18. $\begin{array}{r} 1.16 \\ \times\ 2.5 \\ \hline \end{array}$

19. $\begin{array}{r} 49.7 \\ \times\ 0.47 \\ \hline \end{array}$

20. $\begin{array}{r} 38.2 \\ \times\ 0.16 \\ \hline \end{array}$

21. $\begin{array}{r} 53.6 \\ \times\ 9.8 \\ \hline \end{array}$

22. $\begin{array}{r} 0.012 \\ \times\ 0.8 \\ \hline \end{array}$

23. $\begin{array}{r} 4.037 \\ \times\ 1.5 \\ \hline \end{array}$

24. $\begin{array}{r} 85.61 \\ \times\ 0.09 \\ \hline \end{array}$

25. $\begin{array}{r} 0.701 \\ \times\ 3.8 \\ \hline \end{array}$

26. $\begin{array}{r} 5.118 \\ \times\ 0.007 \\ \hline \end{array}$

Round each number to one-digit accuracy.

27. 0.099

28. 401

29. 5.124

30. 6.82

31. 79.99

32. 0.258

33. 0.00396

34. 0.987

35. 1.987

36. 101.987

Find the squares.

37. 7^2

38. 3^2

39. 12^2

40. 20^2

41. 50^2

Division of Whole Numbers
Division of Decimals
Using Your Skills
Number Theory

Division of Whole Numbers

1. 24 oranges
    Put 6 in each bag. $24 \div 6 = ?$
    How many bags?
    How many oranges are left over?

2. 24 oranges
    Put 8 in each bag. $24 \div 8 = ?$
    How many bags?
    How many oranges are left over?

3. 24 oranges
    Put 4 in each bag. $24 \div 4 = ?$
    How many bags?
    How many oranges are left over?

4. 24 oranges
    Put 5 in each bag. $24 \div 5 = ?$
    How many bags?
    How many oranges are left over?

1. 24 oranges
   Put one in each bag. $24 \div 1 = ?$
   How many bags?
   How many oranges are left over?

> For any number n, $n \div 1 = n$

2. 24 oranges
   Put 24 in each bag. $24 \div 24 = ?$
   How many bags?
   How many oranges are left over?

> For any number n, except 0, $n \div n = 1$

Division and multiplication are related operations.

$24 \div 6 = 4$ because $4 \times 6 = 24$.

$35 \div 5 = 7$ because $7 \times 5 = 35$.

Complete each sentence with the related multiplication equation.

3. $18 \div 3 = 6$ because ____?____ .
4. $49 \div 7 = 7$ because ____?____ .
5. $12 \div 4 = 3$ because ____?____ .
6. $100 \div 5 = 20$ because ____?____ .
7. $0 \div 8 = 0$ because ____?____ .
8. $0 \div 10 = 0$ because ____?____ .

Exercises 7 and 8 illustrate this property of division:

> For any number n, except 0, $0 \div n = 0$

The two examples below show why we do not divide any number by 0.

$24 \div 0 = ?$ $? \times 0 = 24$

There is no number times 0 that equals 24.

$0 \div 0 = ?$ $? \times 0 = 0$

Any number times 0 equals 0.

> Dividing by zero is impossible.

Missing factors and quotients

Thinking about a missing factor can help you find a quotient.

$28 \div 4 = 7$ because $7 \times 4 = 28$

You have found this quotient,

$$28 \div 4 = n$$
$$n \times 4 = 28$$

when you find this missing factor.

Solve the division equations.

1. $n \times 5 = 35$

$35 \div 5 = n$

2. $n \times 6 = 48$

$48 \div 6 = n$

3. $n \times 9 = 54$

$54 \div 9 = n$

4. $n \times 4 = 36$

$36 \div 4 = n$

5. $n \times 8 = 40$

$40 \div 8 = n$

6. $n \times 7 = 63$

$63 \div 7 = n$

7. $n \times 8 = 72$

$72 \div 8 = n$

8. $n \times 5 = 45$

$45 \div 5 = n$

9. $n \times 8 = 64$

$64 \div 8 = n$

10. $24 \div 3 = e$

11. $30 \div 6 = h$

12. $12 \div 3 = t$

13. $32 \div 4 = k$

14. $42 \div 6 = a$

15. $49 \div 7 = c$

16. $20 \div 4 = b$

17. $56 \div 7 = m$

18. $27 \div 9 = n$

19. $16 \div 8 = s$

20. $72 \div 9 = d$

21. $25 \div 5 = f$

22. $15 \div 3 = g$

23. $21 \div 7 = j$

24. $30 \div 5 = p$

25. $42 \div 7 = q$

26. $63 \div 9 = r$

27. $56 \div 8 = t$

28. $81 \div 9 = v$

29. $48 \div 8 = v$

30. $45 \div 9 = w$

31. $32 \div 8 = x$

32. $54 \div 6 = n$

33. $36 \div 6 = a$

34. $35 \div 7 = y$

35. $40 \div 5 = z$

36. $28 \div 7 = b$

Find the quotients.

1. $40 \div 5 = n$
2. $27 \div 9 = q$
3. $30 \div 5 = b$
4. $32 \div 8 = f$

5. $30 \div 6 = v$
6. $72 \div 8 = m$
7. $54 \div 6 = x$
8. $16 \div 4 = i$

9. $48 \div 8 = u$
10. $63 \div 9 = c$
11. $28 \div 4 = s$
12. $45 \div 9 = g$

13. $36 \div 6 = p$
14. $56 \div 8 = a$
15. $35 \div 7 = l$
16. $40 \div 8 = j$

17. $42 \div 7 = r$
18. $24 \div 6 = z$
19. $28 \div 7 = w$
20. $81 \div 9 = k$

21. $42 \div 6 = h$
22. $25 \div 5 = e$
23. $27 \div 3 = d$
24. $36 \div 9 = y$

25. $54 \div 9 = j$
26. $21 \div 7 = a$
27. $24 \div 4 = t$
28. $64 \div 8 = b$

29. $72 \div 9 = b$
30. $48 \div 6 = x$
31. $35 \div 5 = n$
32. $36 \div 4 = t$

33. $32 \div 4 = r$
34. $24 \div 8 = c$
35. $21 \div 3 = k$
36. $24 \div 3 = m$

37. $18 \div 6 = s$
38. $20 \div 4 = y$
39. $16 \div 8 = p$
40. $20 \div 5 = j$

÷ 8	
41. 48	‖‖‖
42. 64	‖‖‖
43. 32	‖‖‖
44. 72	‖‖‖
45. 56	‖‖‖

÷ 7	
46. 49	‖‖‖
47. 35	‖‖‖
48. 63	‖‖‖
49. 42	‖‖‖
50. 56	‖‖‖

÷ 9	
51. 27	‖‖‖
52. 45	‖‖‖
53. 54	‖‖‖
54. 81	‖‖‖
55. 72	‖‖‖

Suppose you walk 1 km in 12 minutes.
If you walked 8 hours each day, how far
could you walk in a week (7 days)?

Special quotients

Knowing the basic facts will help you
find special quotients.

Study this pattern.

$24 \div 6 = 4$
$240 \div 6 = 40$
$2400 \div 6 = 400$
$24\,000 \div 6 = 4000$

Complete this pattern.

$35 \div 7 = $ ▓
$350 \div 7 = $ ▓
$3500 \div 7 = $ ▓
$35\,000 \div 7 = $ ▓

You can check special quotients by multiplying.

$630 \div 7 = 90$ $90 \times 7 = 630$

$630 \div 70 = 9$ $9 \times 70 = 630$

Find the quotients. Check your answers.

1. $48 \div 6 = a$
   $480 \div 6 = b$
   $4800 \div 6 = c$

2. $40 \div 5 = a$
   $400 \div 5 = b$
   $4000 \div 5 = c$

3. $32 \div 8 = a$
   $320 \div 8 = b$
   $3200 \div 8 = c$

4. $63 \div 9 = a$
   $630 \div 9 = b$
   $6300 \div 9 = c$

5. $49 \div 7 = a$
   $490 \div 7 = b$
   $4900 \div 7 = c$

6. $36 \div 4 = a$
   $360 \div 4 = b$
   $3600 \div 4 = c$

7. $720 \div 80 = a$
   $7200 \div 80 = b$
   $72\,000 \div 80 = c$

8. $240 \div 30 = a$
   $2400 \div 30 = b$
   $24\,000 \div 30 = c$

9. $540 \div 60 = a$
   $5400 \div 60 = b$
   $54\,000 \div 60 = c$

10. $420 \div 70 = a$
    $4200 \div 70 = b$
    $42\,000 \div 70 = c$

11. $200 \div 40 = a$
    $2000 \div 40 = b$
    $20\,000 \div 40 = c$

12. $810 \div 90 = a$
    $8100 \div 90 = b$
    $81\,000 \div 90 = c$

13. $350 \div 50 = a$
    $3500 \div 50 = b$
    $35\,000 \div 50 = c$

14. $180 \div 90 = a$
    $1800 \div 90 = b$
    $18\,000 \div 90 = c$

15. $270 \div 30 = a$
    $2700 \div 30 = b$
    $27\,000 \div 30 = c$

Find the quotients. Check your answers.

1. $160 \div 40 = s$ 2. $560 \div 80 = t$ 3. $360 \div 40 = r$

4. $2800 \div 70 = q$ 5. $45\,000 \div 90 = k$ 6. $350 \div 70 = a$

7. $4200 \div 60 = g$ 8. $540 \div 9 = h$ 9. $4000 \div 80 = n$

10. $63\,000 \div 70 = b$ 11. $3000 \div 60 = l$ 12. $3500 \div 50 = f$

13. $6400 \div 80 = m$ 14. $210 \div 30 = j$ 15. $3600 \div 60 = p$

16. $72\,000 \div 90 = d$ 17. $480 \div 8 = e$ 18. $1800 \div 90 = v$

19. $24\,000 \div 80 = x$ 20. $450 \div 50 = w$ 21. $3200 \div 40 = y$

22. $270 \div 30 = z$ 23. $56\,000 \div 70 = r$ 24. $36\,000 \div 90 = u$

25. $320 \div 40 = x$ 26. $7200 \div 8 = c$ 27. $400 \div 20 = g$

28. $21\,000 \div 300 = b$ 29. $180 \div 30 = d$ 30. $1500 \div 500 = e$

31. $8000 \div 40 = z$ 32. $64\,000 \div 800 = a$ 33. $9000 \div 30 = f$

34. $270 \div 3 = y$ 35. $160 \div 40 = r$ 36. $3000 \div 100 = v$

37. $4200 \div 700 = t$ 38. $6000 \div 3000 = s$ 39. $7000 \div 700 = u$

Calculator problems

Estimate each quotient by rounding. Then find the answers on a calculator.
How close were your estimates?

Example: $4497 \div 5 = b$ Estimate: $4500 \div 5 = 900$

40. $5419 \div 6 = d$ 41. $3589 \div 39 = a$ 42. $3989 \div 79 = r$

43. $2810 \div 71 = s$ 44. $2995 \div 59 = h$ 45. $2069 \div 39 = c$

46. $8099 \div 88 = j$ 47. $4897 \div 71 = g$ 48. $4204 \div 58 = t$

49. $3989 \div 81 = e$ 50. $1487 \div 49 = k$ 51. $3140 \div 61 = m$

52. $5627 \div 72 = r$ 53. $8143 \div 89 = g$ 54. $7333 \div 93 = p$

55. $1848 \div 29 = f$ 56. $2495 \div 48 = s$ 57. $5993 \div 31 = n$

1-digit divisors

By being careful, a family of four used only 6547 ℓ of water a week. About how many liters did they use a day?

Finding the answer

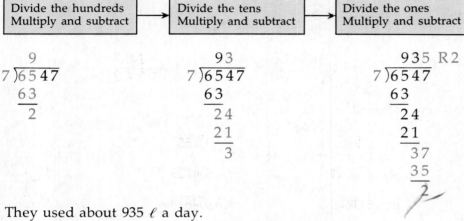

Divide the hundreds Multiply and subtract	→	Divide the tens Multiply and subtract	→	Divide the ones Multiply and subtract

```
     9                    93                   935 R2
7)6547               7)6547               7)6547
  63                   63                   63
 ───                  ───                  ───
   2                   24                   24
                      21                   21
                      ───                  ───
                        3                   37
                                           35
                                           ──
                                            2
```

They used about 935 ℓ a day.

Other examples

```
    63 R2                 457                 308 R5
4)254                3)1371               6)1853
  24                   12                   18
  ──                   ──                   ──
  14                   17                   53
  12                   15                   48
  ──                   ──                   ──
   2                   21                    5
                       21
                       ──
                        0
```

Find the quotients and remainders.

1. 5)182   2. 7)179   3. 3)141   4. 9)386

5. 6)444   6. 4)1069   7. 6)1762   8. 2)1257

9. 7)2817   10. 3)1773   11. 4)2435   12. 8)4538

13. 9)2557   14. 5)2049   15. 6)1699   16. 4)2907

The flow chart shows how to use short division for 1-digit divisors.

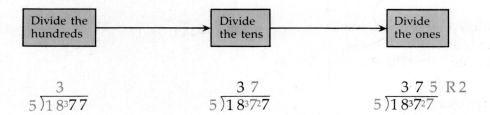

| Divide the hundreds | → | Divide the tens | → | Divide the ones |

$$\begin{array}{r} 3 \\ 5\overline{)1\,8^3 7\,7} \end{array} \qquad \begin{array}{r} 3\;7 \\ 5\overline{)1\,8^3 7^2 7} \end{array} \qquad \begin{array}{r} 3\;7\;5\;R2 \\ 5\overline{)1\,8^3 7^2 7} \end{array}$$

Other examples

$$\begin{array}{r} 2\;4\;3\;R5 \\ 8\overline{)1\;9^3 4^2 9} \end{array} \qquad \begin{array}{r} 5\;1\;6\;R2 \\ 3\overline{)1\;5\;5^2 0} \end{array} \qquad \begin{array}{r} 2\;0\;7 \\ 6\overline{)1\;2\;4\;2} \end{array}$$

Find the quotients and remainders.

1. $6\overline{)316}$ 2. $4\overline{)282}$ 3. $3\overline{)155}$ 4. $8\overline{)393}$

5. $6\overline{)252}$ 6. $4\overline{)2055}$ 7. $8\overline{)4728}$ 8. $2\overline{)2835}$

9. $3\overline{)1520}$ 10. $5\overline{)3215}$ 11. $9\overline{)4623}$ 12. $6\overline{)3290}$

13. $7\overline{)2828}$ 14. $3\overline{)1531}$ 15. $5\overline{)1323}$ 16. $2\overline{)1670}$

17. $7\overline{)2467}$ 18. $5\overline{)3019}$ 19. $9\overline{)1917}$ 20. $7\overline{)3503}$

21. $8\overline{)4050}$ 22. $6\overline{)3114}$ 23. $2\overline{)1018}$ 24. $3\overline{)1802}$

25. A family of 5 used 1170 ℓ of water a day. About how many liters were used per person?

☆ 26. Estimate how many liters of water your family uses in one day. Figure the average number of liters of water one person in your family uses a day.

The table below shows how far an object will fall (not counting wind resistance) in a given number of seconds.

| 4.9×1^2 m in 1 s | 4.9×3^2 m in 3 s |
| 4.9×2^2 m in 2 s | $4.9 \times n^2$ m in n s |

If a skydiver wants to free-fall for 25 s and still open his parachute at 600 m above the ground, how high should the plane be when he jumps? (Discount wind resistance.)

More practice, page 384, Set A

2-digit divisors

Ken made this string sculpture. He used
608 cm of thread. The design has 16 line
segments or chords. How long is each chord?

Finding the answer

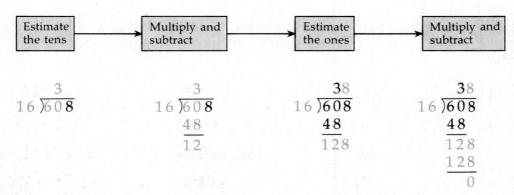

| Estimate the tens | → | Multiply and subtract | → | Estimate the ones | → | Multiply and subtract |

$$
\begin{array}{r}
3 \\
16\overline{)608}
\end{array}
\qquad
\begin{array}{r}
3 \\
16\overline{)608} \\
48 \\
\hline
12
\end{array}
\qquad
\begin{array}{r}
38 \\
16\overline{)608} \\
48 \\
\hline
128
\end{array}
\qquad
\begin{array}{r}
38 \\
16\overline{)608} \\
48 \\
\hline
128 \\
128 \\
\hline
0
\end{array}
$$

Each chord is 38 cm long.

Other examples

$$
\begin{array}{r}
37 \text{ R24} \\
53\overline{)1985} \\
159 \\
\hline
395 \\
371 \\
\hline
24
\end{array}
\qquad
\begin{array}{r}
61 \text{ R15} \\
39\overline{)2394} \\
234 \\
\hline
54 \\
39 \\
\hline
15
\end{array}
\qquad
\begin{array}{r}
374 \text{ R15} \\
28\overline{)10\,487} \\
8\,4 \\
\hline
2\,08 \\
1\,96 \\
\hline
127 \\
112 \\
\hline
15
\end{array}
$$

Find the quotients and remainders.

1. $42\overline{)2238}$ 2. $68\overline{)1878}$ 3. $72\overline{)2580}$ 4. $51\overline{)3423}$

5. $39\overline{)2112}$ 6. $83\overline{)1550}$ 7. $61\overline{)4427}$ 8. $87\overline{)3764}$

9. $24\overline{)1448}$ 10. $36\overline{)1764}$ 11. $56\overline{)13\,626}$ 12. $95\overline{)23\,139}$

13. $84\overline{)43\,119}$ 14. $45\overline{)41\,610}$ 15. $73\overline{)29\,673}$ 16. $92\overline{)55\,525}$

Here is a diagram for checking division.

$$
\begin{array}{r}
46 \\
38\overline{)1775} \\
152 \\
\hline
255 \\
228 \\
\hline
27
\end{array}
$$

Check:
$$
\begin{array}{r}
46 \\
\times\,38 \\
\hline
368 \\
138 \\
\hline
1748 \\
+\quad 27 \\
\hline
1775
\end{array}
$$

Find the quotients and remainders.

Check your answers.

1. $36\overline{)1876}$
2. $52\overline{)3708}$
3. $34\overline{)673}$
4. $83\overline{)3735}$

5. $47\overline{)1268}$
6. $74\overline{)4626}$
7. $54\overline{)4946}$
8. $72\overline{)3603}$

9. $84\overline{)5265}$
10. $25\overline{)2274}$
11. $16\overline{)1364}$
12. $63\overline{)2520}$

13. $49\overline{)2819}$
14. $81\overline{)4006}$
15. $88\overline{)929}$
16. $65\overline{)15\,816}$

17. $41\overline{)25\,720}$
18. $93\overline{)21\,633}$
19. $29\overline{)13\,398}$
20. $15\overline{)7255}$

21. $57\overline{)17\,360}$
22. $70\overline{)38\,019}$
23. $68\overline{)27\,676}$
24. $72\overline{)43\,800}$

25. Joan started with the same string design as Ken. But she added 8 diameters each about 38 cm long. How much more thread did she need?

☆ 26. Construct a circle with a diameter of 15 cm. Construct an equilateral triangle in the circle. If each side of the triangle is about 13 cm, how many triangles could you construct in the circle with 164 cm of thread?

 Find the missing digits.

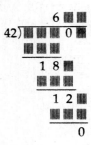

More practice, page 384, Set B

Larger divisors

Dairy farmers keep records of milk production of their cows. In 325 days, one cow produced 4875 kg of milk. What was the average milk production per day for this cow?

Finding the answer

| Estimate the tens | → | Multiply and subtract | → | Estimate the ones | → | Multiply and subtract |

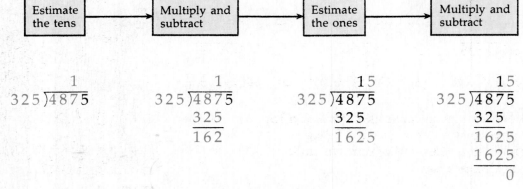

```
      1              1             15             15
325)4875       325)4875      325)4875       325)4875
                   325            325            325
                   162           1625           1625
                                                1625
                                                   0
```

The cow's average milk production was 15 kg per day.

Other examples

```
      53 R87                247                306 R125
318)16 941          596)147 212          278)85 193
    15 90               119 2                 83 4
    1 041                28 01                1 793
      954                23 84                1 668
       87                 4 172                 125
                          4 172
                              0
```

Find the quotients and remainders.

1. 421)26 145   2. 295)10 267   3. 682)43 324   4. 523)43 932

5. 775)335 345   6. 912)350 208   7. 198)139 461   8. 824)516 883

Find the quotients and remainders.

1. $3\overline{)194}$ 2. $8\overline{)236}$ 3. $5\overline{)338}$

4. $7\overline{)2438}$ 5. $2\overline{)1298}$ 6. $9\overline{)2163}$

7. $6\overline{)1849}$ 8. $5\overline{)1114}$ 9. $4\overline{)2412}$

10. $24\overline{)1244}$ 11. $63\overline{)3276}$ 12. $52\overline{)4913}$

13. $47\overline{)10\ 046}$ 14. $71\overline{)4718}$ 15. $18\overline{)1425}$

16. $86\overline{)17\ 514}$ 17. $39\overline{)21\ 177}$ 18. $90\overline{)27\ 690}$

19. $294\overline{)6428}$ 20. $633\overline{)53\ 229}$ 21. $711\overline{)27\ 542}$

22. $528\overline{)19\ 636}$ 23. $166\overline{)6569}$ 24. $385\overline{)36\ 397}$

25. $402\overline{)154\ 368}$ 26. $977\overline{)297\ 008}$ 27. $849\overline{)648\ 342}$

28. A recent record for milk production for a year for one cow was 23 024 kg. About how many kilograms of milk was this per day?

29. A cheese manufacturer used 6525 kg of fresh milk to make 593 kg of cheddar cheese. About how many kilograms of milk did it take to make 1 kilogram of the cheddar cheese?

Think!

A brick is 20 cm long, 9 cm wide, and 5 cm thick. How many different heights can be formed by stacking one, two, or three of these bricks on top of each other?

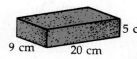

9 cm   20 cm   5 cm

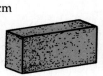

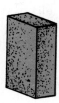

Answers for Self-check   1. 7   2. 9   3. 7   4. 8   5. 80   6. 7   7. 70   8. 80   9. 9   10. 90
11. 4   12. 600   13. 52 R4   14. 27 R7   15. 60 R4   16. 352 R1   17. 308 R6   18. 51 R4
19. 35 R1   20. 40 R32   21. 346 R21   22. 602 R31   23. 54 R123   24. 38 R249   25. 624 R258
26. 307 R147

More practice, page 384, Set C

Self-check

Solve.

1. $42 \div 6 = r$ 2. $36 \div 4 = s$ 3. $49 \div 7 = t$

4. $40 \div 5 = b$ 5. $240 \div 3 = a$ 6. $560 \div 80 = p$

7. $4200 \div 60 = x$ 8. $3200 \div 40 = n$ 9. $810 \div 90 = u$

10. $7200 \div 80 = m$ 11. $120 \div 30 = c$ 12. $36\,000 \div 60 = q$

Find the quotients and remainders.

13. $6\overline{)316}$ 14. $8\overline{)223}$ 15. $5\overline{)304}$ 16. $4\overline{)1409}$ 17. $7\overline{)2162}$

18. $32\overline{)1636}$ 19. $58\overline{)2031}$ 20. $66\overline{)2672}$ 21. $29\overline{)10\,055}$ 22. $41\overline{)24\,713}$

23. $283\overline{)15\,405}$ 24. $465\overline{)17\,919}$ 25. $374\overline{)233\,634}$ 26. $596\overline{)183\,119}$

Answers for Self-check—page 147

Test

Solve.

1. $35 \div 5 = c$ 2. $56 \div 7 = x$ 3. $18 \div 3 = n$

4. $32 \div 4 = a$ 5. $72 \div 9 = f$ 6. $2700 \div 30 = w$

7. $160 \div 40 = d$ 8. $5400 \div 60 = g$ 9. $6300 \div 90 = v$

10. $3500 \div 70 = z$ 11. $490 \div 70 = u$ 12. $28\,000 \div 40 = y$

Find the quotients and remainders.

13. $4\overline{)213}$ 14. $6\overline{)496}$ 15. $3\overline{)152}$ 16. $7\overline{)1511}$ 17. $5\overline{)1524}$

18. $41\overline{)2363}$ 19. $37\overline{)2392}$ 20. $64\overline{)1315}$ 21. $28\overline{)9731}$ 22. $52\overline{)21\,097}$

23. $576\overline{)30\,101}$ 24. $464\overline{)29\,391}$ 25. $385\overline{)160\,427}$ 26. $253\overline{)77\,041}$

Curve Stitching

Many interesting designs can be made using a needle, colored thread, and some geometry. The straight lines made with the thread will form curved-line designs.

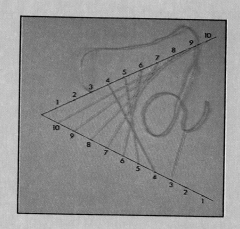

Draw an angle on tagboard. Number one ray from 1 to 10 and the other from 10 to 1. Stitch the curve by connecting numbers 1 to 1, 2 to 2, and so on.

Try a few simple angles before you experiment with more complicated designs.

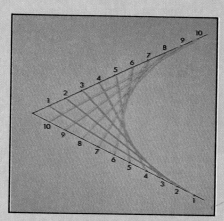

The designs below only suggest possibilities. Create your own designs and color schemes.

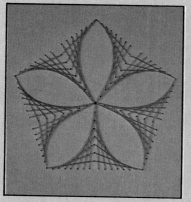
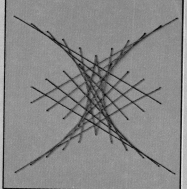
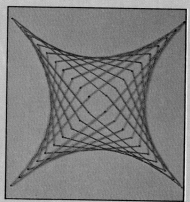

Division of Decimals

Dividing decimals is much like dividing whole numbers. You can check your answers by multiplying.

The same loop of string is used in problems 1 to 4. It is 21.6 cm around.

1. Measure to find the length of each side when the looped string is divided into 2 equal parts.

Which of these quotients is closest to your measure?

$$\frac{1.08 \text{ cm}}{2\overline{)21.6}} \qquad \frac{10.8 \text{ cm}}{2\overline{)21.6}} \qquad \frac{108 \text{ cm}}{2\overline{)21.6}}$$

Multiply to check the quotient you think is correct.

2. Measure to find the length of each side when the loop of string is divided into 3 equal parts.

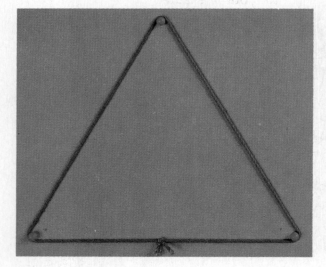

Which of these quotients is closest to your measure?

$$\frac{0.72 \text{ cm}}{3\overline{)21.6}}$$

$$\frac{7.2 \text{ cm}}{3\overline{)21.6}}$$

$$\frac{72 \text{ cm}}{3\overline{)21.6}}$$

Multiply to check the quotient you think is correct.

3. Measure to find the length of each side when the loop of string is divided into 4 equal parts.

Which of these quotients is closest to your measure?

$$\frac{0.54 \text{ cm}}{4)\overline{21.6}}$$ $$\frac{5.4 \text{ cm}}{4)\overline{21.6}}$$ $$\frac{54 \text{ cm}}{4)\overline{21.6}}$$

Multiply to check the quotient you think is correct.

4. Measure to find the length of each side when the loop of string is divided into 6 equal parts.

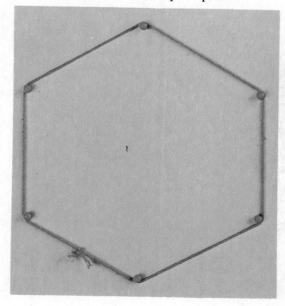

Which of these quotients is closest to your measure?

$$\frac{0.36 \text{ cm}}{6)\overline{21.6}}$$

$$\frac{3.6 \text{ cm}}{6)\overline{21.6}}$$

$$\frac{36 \text{ cm}}{6)\overline{21.6}}$$

Multiply to check the quotient you think is correct.

Dividing a decimal by a whole number

A test car was driven 31.2 km on 4 ℓ of gasoline. How many kilometers per liter of gasoline is this?

Finding the answer

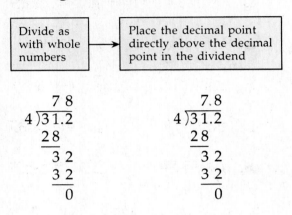

The test car got 7.8 km per liter of gasoline.

Other examples

```
    2.96              0.46                    5.4
6)17.76           37)17.02            243)1312.2
  12                14 8                    1215
  ───               ────                    ────
   5 7                2 22                    97 2
   5 4                2 22                    97 2
   ───                ────                    ────
    36                   0                       0
    36
    ──
     0
```

Find the quotients. Check your answers by multiplying.

1. 5)17.35

2. 3)7.644

3. 6)255.78

4. 28)181.44

5. 27)577.8

6. 62)14.88

7. 241)1542.4

8. 354)187.62

Find the quotients.

1. $5\overline{)36.5}$ 2. $4\overline{)14.8}$ 3. $3\overline{)18.3}$ 4. $7\overline{)40.6}$

5. $9\overline{)220.5}$ 6. $6\overline{)343.2}$ 7. $5\overline{)17.05}$ 8. $6\overline{)21.42}$

9. $7\overline{)22.743}$ 10. $8\overline{)2.72}$ 11. $4\overline{)1426.8}$ 12. $3\overline{)1.458}$

13. $27\overline{)172.8}$ 14. $42\overline{)268.8}$ 15. $36\overline{)1886.4}$ 16. $54\overline{)3364.2}$

17. $63\overline{)147.42}$ 18. $18\overline{)7.02}$ 19. $71\overline{)248.5}$ 20. $52\overline{)25.48}$

21. $78\overline{)252.72}$ 22. $91\overline{)51.87}$ 23. $29\overline{)89.03}$ 24. $85\overline{)276.25}$

25. $425\overline{)977.5}$ 26. $563\overline{)3603.2}$ 27. $291\overline{)989.4}$ 28. $942\overline{)6405.6}$

29. $714\overline{)164.22}$ 30. $302\overline{)706.68}$ 31. $158\overline{)5482.6}$ 32. $831\overline{)382.26}$

33. Another test car was driven 49.8 km on 6 ℓ of gasoline. How many kilometers per liter of gasoline is this?

☆ 34. How far could the test car in exercise 33 go on 4 ℓ of gasoline?

It has been estimated that the average person walks 7 km a day. At that rate, how long would it take you to walk the distance around the earth? Give your answer in years and days.

40 075 km

More about dividing decimals

The outside wall of a school has been chosen for a mural. The wall is 22 m long, and 8 classes will paint equal sections of the mural. How many meters long should each section be?

Finding the answer

Divide the ones	Place the decimal points Annex a zero	Divide the tenths	Annex a zero Divide the hundredths

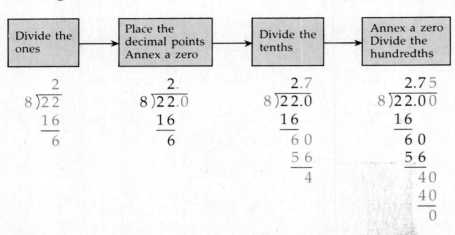

Each section of the mural should be 2.75 m long.

Other examples

```
   0.75              0.16              0.375
4)3.00           25)4.00           4)1.500
  2 8               2 5               1 2
  ───               ───               ──
   20               1 50              30
   20               1 50              28
   ──               ────             ──
    0                  0              20
                                     20
                                     ──
                                      0
```

Find each quotient. Continue annexing zeros and dividing until the remainder is zero.

1. $4\overline{)10}$ 2. $8\overline{)30}$ 3. $4\overline{)31}$ 4. $5\overline{)27}$

5. $16\overline{)30}$ 6. $32\overline{)120}$ 7. $80\overline{)900}$ 8. $128\overline{)80}$

More examples

```
      5.528              0.025               0.0036
25)138.200         16)0.400          125)0.4500
   125                  32                  375
    13 2                80                  750
    12 5                80                  750
       70                0                    0
       50
      200
      200
        0
```

Find the quotients. Continue dividing until the remainder is zero.

1. $4\overline{)37}$

2. $8\overline{)43}$

3. $5\overline{)2.7}$

4. $8\overline{)20.6}$

5. $16\overline{)40}$

6. $25\overline{)8.5}$

7. $32\overline{)1.28}$

8. $20\overline{)64.9}$

9. $25\overline{)1.15}$

10. $16\overline{)52}$

11. $32\overline{)1392}$

12. $40\overline{)268}$

13. $16\overline{)0.72}$

14. $25\overline{)1.35}$

15. $32\overline{)40}$

16. $80\overline{)3000}$

17. $50\overline{)3.2}$

18. $64\overline{)470.4}$

19. $32\overline{)0.16}$

20. $16\overline{)1.088}$

21. $125\overline{)385}$

22. $160\overline{)4}$

23. $128\overline{)315.52}$

24. $125\overline{)8.5}$

25. 4 classes decided to share a 25 m long wall for a mural. How long should the sections for each class be?

☆ 26. Choose and measure an outside wall of your school. If every class in your school were to paint a section of a mural on it, how long would each section be?

Tom is 3 times as old as Sue. In 4 years, Tom will be 2 times as old as Sue. How old are they now?

More practice, page 385, Set A

Rounding the quotient

The mass of 6 ℓ of oil
is 5.6 kg. Find the mass
of 1 ℓ of oil, to the nearest
hundredth of a kilogram.

Finding the answer

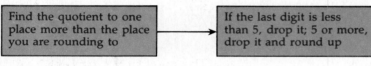

| Find the quotient to one place more than the place you are rounding to | → | If the last digit is less than 5, drop it; 5 or more, drop it and round up |

$$\begin{array}{r} 0.933 \\ 6\overline{)5.600} \end{array} \qquad 0.93$$

The mass, to the nearest hundredth, is 0.93 kg.

Other examples

$$\begin{array}{r} 1.428 \\ 7\overline{)10.000} \end{array}$$ 1.4 (nearest tenth)
1.43 (nearest hundredth)

$$\begin{array}{r} 1.3157 \\ 19\overline{)25.0000} \end{array}$$ 1.3 (nearest tenth)
1.32 (nearest hundredth)
1.316 (nearest thousandth)

Round each quotient to the nearest tenth.

1. $\begin{array}{r} 2.43 \\ 8\overline{)19.44} \end{array}$
2. $\begin{array}{r} 0.78 \\ 26\overline{)20.28} \end{array}$
3. $\begin{array}{r} 5.41 \\ 6\overline{)32.46} \end{array}$
4. $\begin{array}{r} 0.29 \\ 54\overline{)15.66} \end{array}$

Round each quotient to the nearest hundredth.

5. $\begin{array}{r} 0.327 \\ 47\overline{)15.369} \end{array}$
6. $\begin{array}{r} 2.482 \\ 7\overline{)17.374} \end{array}$
7. $\begin{array}{r} 1.345 \\ 35\overline{)47.075} \end{array}$
8. $\begin{array}{r} 0.264 \\ 9\overline{)2.376} \end{array}$

Find the quotients. Round to the nearest tenth.

1. $6\overline{)20}$
2. $9\overline{)14}$
3. $3\overline{)14}$
4. $7\overline{)12}$

5. $14\overline{)26}$
6. $12\overline{)75}$
7. $15\overline{)32}$
8. $13\overline{)37.2}$

9. $23\overline{)62.8}$
10. $56\overline{)375}$
11. $42\overline{)74}$
12. $35\overline{)37}$

13. $31\overline{)82}$
14. $28\overline{)63}$
15. $54\overline{)512}$
16. $49\overline{)320}$

Find the quotients. Round to the nearest hundredth.

17. $7\overline{)9.2}$
18. $3\overline{)7.1}$
19. $6\overline{)8}$
20. $9\overline{)17}$

21. $12\overline{)4.1}$
22. $17\overline{)13}$
23. $18\overline{)19.2}$
24. $19\overline{)21}$

25. $34\overline{)21.4}$
26. $28\overline{)35.4}$
27. $47\overline{)26}$
28. $52\overline{)38}$

29. $68\overline{)143}$
30. $71\overline{)32.8}$
31. $33\overline{)75}$
32. $41\overline{)69.3}$

33. The milk in a 3 ℓ carton has a mass of 3.084 kg. Find the mass of 1 ℓ of milk to the nearest hundredth.

34. The mass of 9 ℓ of gasoline is about 6 kg. Find the mass of 1 ℓ of gasoline to the nearest hundredth.

Which box of cereal is the better buy?

A Cereal 89¢ 454g

B Cereal 69¢ 356g

More practice, page 385, Set B

Dividing a decimal by a decimal

Each candle mold holds 0.08 ℓ
of hot wax. How many candles can
be made from 2.8 ℓ of hot wax?

Finding the answer

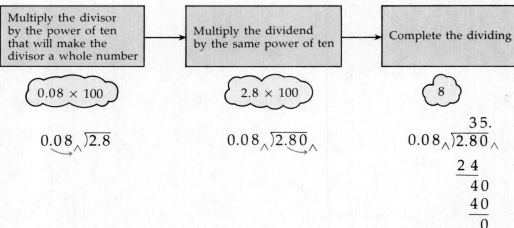

Multiply the divisor by the power of ten that will make the divisor a whole number	Multiply the dividend by the same power of ten	Complete the dividing

0.08×100

$$0.0\underset{\wedge}{8}\,\overline{)2.8}$$

2.8×100

$$0.0\underset{\wedge}{8}\,\overline{)2.8\underset{\wedge}{0}}$$

8

$$\begin{array}{r} 35. \\ 0.0\underset{\wedge}{8}\,\overline{)2.8\underset{\wedge}{0}} \\ \underline{2\,4} \\ 4\,0 \\ \underline{4\,0} \\ 0 \end{array}$$

35 candles can be made.

Other examples

$$\begin{array}{r} 5.61 \\ 3.4_{\wedge}\overline{)19.0_{\wedge}74} \\ \underline{17\,0} \\ 2\,0\,7 \\ \underline{2\,0\,4} \\ 34 \\ \underline{34} \end{array}$$

$$\begin{array}{r} 42.5 \\ 0.032_{\wedge}\overline{)1.360_{\wedge}0} \\ \underline{1\,28} \\ 80 \\ \underline{64} \\ 16\,0 \\ \underline{16\,0} \end{array}$$

$$\begin{array}{r} 0.666 \\ 0.3_{\wedge}\overline{)0.2_{\wedge}000} \\ \underline{1\,8} \\ 20 \\ \underline{18} \\ 20 \\ \underline{18} \\ 2 \end{array}$$ → 0.67 (to the nearest hundredth)

Find the quotients. Round to the nearest hundredth when necessary.

1. $0.03\overline{)0.114}$

2. $6.2\overline{)21.39}$

3. $0.15\overline{)5.31}$

4. $3.7\overline{)28.2}$

5. $0.004\overline{)5.7}$

6. $3.24\overline{)3.42}$

7. $0.134\overline{)2.33}$

8. $52.6\overline{)65}$

Find the quotients. Round to the nearest hundredth when necessary.

1. $0.2\overline{)1.26}$ 2. $0.8\overline{)4.336}$ 3. $0.7\overline{)2.73}$ 4. $0.5\overline{)1855}$

5. $0.3\overline{)5.45}$ 6. $0.4\overline{)7}$ 7. $0.9\overline{)7}$ 8. $0.6\overline{)1.7}$

9. $2.3\overline{)7.82}$ 10. $5.1\overline{)34.17}$ 11. $6.4\overline{)21.888}$ 12. $8.2\overline{)51.66}$

13. $5.9\overline{)32.8}$ 14. $6.8\overline{)0.75}$ 15. $3.7\overline{)83}$ 16. $1.5\overline{)50}$

17. $0.04\overline{)0.152}$ 18. $0.08\overline{)0.488}$ 19. $0.03\overline{)1.92}$ 20. $0.06\overline{)5.484}$

21. $0.07\overline{)0.327}$ 22. $0.02\overline{)5.2}$ 23. $0.05\overline{)0.6}$ 24. $0.09\overline{)0.14}$

25. $0.231\overline{)0.7854}$ 26. $0.152\overline{)0.0912}$ 27. $1.75\overline{)8.925}$ 28. $0.008\overline{)0.712}$

29. $0.036\overline{)5}$ 30. $0.185\overline{)76}$ 31. $0.029\overline{)3.8}$ 32. $0.006\overline{)2.73}$

33. A certain candle mold holds 0.07 ℓ. How many candles can be made from 3.4 ℓ of hot wax?

☆ 34. Fill a container to the brim with water. Submerge a candle in the container and, in another container, catch the water that overflows. The volume of this water is the volume of the candle. Measure it in milliliters. How many of these candles could you make from a liter of wax (1000 ml)?

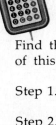

Find the volume of this circular candle.

Step 1. Find $r \times r$

Step 2. Multiply by π (3.14). The product is the area of the circle at the top.

Step 3. Multiply by the length (20 cm). This product is the volume in cubic centimeters (milliliters).

radius (r)
1.2 cm

20 cm

More practice, page 385, Set C

Module 3.2   **159**

Practicing your skills

Add or subtract.

1. 41.7
    + 3.67

2. 4.529
    − 1.764

3. 82.55
    + 54.88

4. 7.036
    − 4.679

5. 18.02
    + 0.986

6. 16.05
    + 42.408

7. 0.324
    − 0.319

8. 249.6
    + 157.8

9. 5.001
    − 2.989

10. 1.698
    + 8.413

Find the sums and differences.

11. 20.1 + 13.46 + 7.08

12. 19.005 − 12.91

13. 45.26 + 112.04 + 56.75

14. 0.7042 − 0.0851

15. 0.193 + 1.34 + 2.909

16. 202.54 − 198.75

17. 62.4 + 84.09 + 104.375

18. 73.02 − 58.846

Find the products.

19. 6.4
    × 1.2

20. 0.27
    × 0.5

21. 62.31
    × 6

22. 5.024
    × 3.8

23. 92.36
    × 0.75

24. 73.8
    × 6.2

25. 1.008
    × 0.12

26. 0.092
    × 0.04

27. 81.57
    × 2.06

28. 3.147
    × 0.8

Find the quotients. Round to the nearest hundredth.

29. $42\overline{)136.5}$

30. $65\overline{)40}$

31. $36\overline{)27}$

32. $67\overline{)12}$

33. $0.36\overline{)5.26}$

34. $71\overline{)39.76}$

35. $2.9\overline{)74.23}$

36. $6.8\overline{)50.32}$

37. $0.64\overline{)5.696}$

38. $54\overline{)69.12}$

39. $235\overline{)84}$

40. $2.8\overline{)54.13}$

41. $1.6\overline{)0.368}$

42. $0.38\overline{)3.591}$

43. $23\overline{)145.36}$

44. $4.3\overline{)251.98}$

Calculator problems

Add.

1.	2.	3.	4.
13 746	26 857	95 479	70 186
92 536	63 149	83 081	54 722
84 175	43 117	26 325	66 534
32 981	57 229	70 649	71 086
+ 26 745	+ 54 483	+ 71 058	+ 81 930

5.	6.	7.	8.
72.345	314.02	49.23	427.68
91.615	189.01	768.14	35.09
80.268	82.5	91.237	942.15
73.499	900.08	503.48	83.667
+ 41.378	+ 764.25	+ 679.209	+ 41.008

Subtract.

9.	10.	11.	12.
401 008	814 956	720 045	536 000
− 245 109	− 573 889	− 381 265	− 208 999

13.	14.	15.	16.
12.892	91.2834	85.006	327.4
− 8.7655	− 72.3785	− 32.8794	− 186.057

Multiply. Round the products to the nearest hundredth.

17.	18.	19.	20.
16.257	754.12	102.36	51.108
× 3.84	× 6.53	× 92.8	× 64.1

21.	22.	23.	24.
2.0135	65.217	44.476	120.63
× 8.426	× 0.035	× 35.8	× 54.28

Divide. Round the quotients to the nearest hundredth.

25. $1.59)\overline{11.3526}$ 26. $0.211)\overline{0.075538}$ 27. $8.44)\overline{5496.36}$

28. $35.8)\overline{0.895}$ 29. $9.46)\overline{61.3872}$ 30. $1.79)\overline{5.62843}$

31. $0.35)\overline{0.26873}$ 32. $5.16)\overline{3.01395}$ 33. $63.5)\overline{42.5837}$

Answers for Self-check   1. 2.6   2. 3.76   3. 6.4   4. 0.27   5. 3.125   6. 0.35   7. 2.4   8. 0.512
9. 0.125   10. 4.29   11. 5.78   12. 1.67   13. 0.71   14. 1.75   15. 2.64   16. 4.72   17. 12.97
18. 57.43   19. 0.68   20. 6.90   21. 13.48

Self-check

Find the quotients.

1. $6\overline{)15.6}$

2. $4\overline{)15.04}$

3. $21\overline{)134.4}$

4. $58\overline{)15.66}$

5. $8\overline{)25}$

6. $20\overline{)7}$

7. $25\overline{)60}$

8. $125\overline{)64}$

9. $32\overline{)4}$

Find the quotients to the nearest hundredth.

10. $7\overline{)30}$

11. $9\overline{)52}$

12. $3\overline{)5}$

13. $88\overline{)62.9}$

14. $34\overline{)59.4}$

15. $17\overline{)44.82}$

16. $0.6\overline{)2.83}$

17. $3.6\overline{)46.7}$

18. $0.03\overline{)1.723}$

19. $7.4\overline{)5}$

20. $3.51\overline{)24.22}$

21. $26.4\overline{)356}$

Answers for Self-check—page 161

Test

Find the quotients.

1. $5\overline{)41.5}$

2. $7\overline{)226.8}$

3. $38\overline{)357.2}$

4. $62\overline{)401.14}$

5. $4\overline{)27}$

6. $16\overline{)6}$

7. $32\overline{)100}$

8. $128\overline{)16}$

9. $45\overline{)9}$

Find the quotients to the nearest tenth.

10. $6\overline{)22}$

11. $3\overline{)4}$

12. $7\overline{)59}$

13. $76\overline{)134.5}$

14. $23\overline{)40}$

15. $56\overline{)293.4}$

16. $2.3\overline{)52.6}$

17. $0.4\overline{)35.1}$

18. $0.06\overline{)4.451}$

19. $0.31\overline{)0.6}$

20. $4.25\overline{)18.62}$

21. $14.2\overline{)351}$

Finding the Day of the Week

Neil Armstrong first walked on the moon on
July 20, 1969. On what day of the week was this?

The rules below show how to find the day of the week
for any date after 1600 A.D.

		July 20, 1969
Step 1	Write the last two digits of the year.	69
Step 2	Find 0.25 times the number in step 1 (omit the decimal part).	17
Step 3	Write the day of the month.	20
Step 4	Write the month's code number. (See table below)	2
Step 5	Write the code number for the number of hundreds in the year. (See table below)	5
Step 6	Add the results of steps 1 through 5.	113
Step 7	Divide the sum in step 6 by 7. Write the remainder.	1
Step 8	Find the day that has this remainder as the code number. (See table below)	Sunday

Neil Armstrong first walked on the moon on a Sunday.

Month	Code number
June	0
Sept., Dec.	1
Apr., July	2
Jan.*, Oct.	3
May	4
Aug.	5
Mar., Feb.**, Nov.	6

*2 in leap years
**5 in leap years

Number of hundreds in the year	Code number
16	4
17	2
18	0
19	5

Day	Code number
Sunday	1
Monday	2
Tuesday	3
Wednesday	4
Thursday	5
Friday	6
Saturday	0

Note: Leap years are multiples
of 4 except for 1700, 1800 and 1900.
The year 2000 is a leap year.

Find the day of the week for each of these.

1. Your birthday
2. July 4, 1776
3. New Year's Day, 2000

Using Your Skills

Appliance service persons repair a variety of home appliances. They make estimates for customers for the cost of new parts and the time needed to repair the appliance. Appliance service persons need to be able to interpret numbers on instruments as well as make accurate measurements.

When repair persons estimate the cost of a certain job, they must make sure their estimates make sense. The final bill to the customer should be close to the estimated cost.

Read each cost list carefully. Decide if the given estimate is about right. Then find the exact cost.

1. Washer repair—
   Labor: 2 hours
     at $12.50 per hour
   Parts: New belt and bearings $8.95
   Overhead expense: Truck, tools, etc. $10.00
   Given estimate: $30

2. Vacuum repair—
   Labor: 1 hour and 15 minutes
     at $9.50 an hour
   Parts: New motor $9.75
   Overhead expense: $5.00
   Given estimate: $25

3. TV repair—
   Labor: 1 hour and 30 minutes
     at $14 per hour
   Parts: Picture tube $69.50
   Overhead expense: Pick up and delivery, shop rental, etc. $7.00
   Given estimate: $75

4. Oven repair—
   Labor: 1 hour at $12.50 per hour
   Parts: New timer $19.75
   Overhead expense: $12.50
   Given estimate: $30

Making repairs

Estimate each answer.
Then find the exact answer.

Desk repair

1. Preparation for painting—
   Sandpaper: $0.96
   Steel wool: $0.72
   Paint remover: $2.56
   Tax: $0.17
   How much in all?

2. New paint job—
   Brush: $2.42
   3 ℓ of paint at $3.79 per liter.
   Tax: $0.45
   How much in all?

3. New handles—
   4 handles at $0.89 each
   Tax: $0.18
   How much in all?

4. What was the total amount for
   repairing and repainting the desk?

Bicycle repair

5. Flat tire—
   Repair kit (tax incl.): $1.78
   The kit fixes 6 flats.
   What is the cost of fixing each one?

6. Replace tire—
   Old tire: 1875 km
   New tire: same distance
   How many kilometers for both tires?

7. Spare part replacement—
   8 spokes at $0.29 each
   1 pedal at $3.59
   Tax: $0.35
   How much in all?

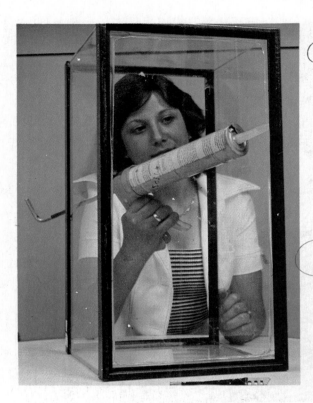

Aquarium repair

8. Replace broken glass—
length: 78 cm
width: 35 cm
What is the area of the glass
in square centimeters?

9. New piece of glass—
length: 100 cm
width: 50 cm
Cut off how much length?
Cut off how much width?

10. What is the total area of the
glass that is not used?

11. Cost of materials—
Glass: $14.95
Tube of sealer: $2.49
Tax: $0.87
How much in all?

Battery-operated game

12. Needs new batteries—
3 batteries at 1.5 volts each
How many volts all together?

13. Regular batteries—
3 batteries at $0.59 each
Tax: $0.09
How much in all?

14. Long-life batteries—
3 batteries at $0.98 each
Tax: $0.15
How much in all?

15. If the long-life batteries last for
9 hours of play and the regular
batteries last for 5 hours, which
is the better buy?

Averages

What is the average height of the students listed in the chart?

NAME	HEIGHT (centimeters)
KAYE	165
REED	154
TOM	160
DOTTY	157
JEFF	148
LIZ	162

Finding the answer

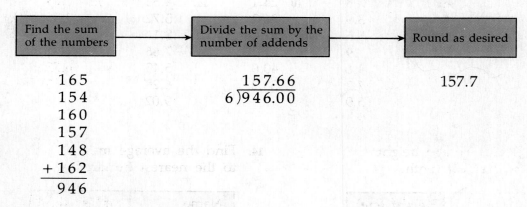

Find the sum of the numbers	Divide the sum by the number of addends	Round as desired

```
  165
  154
  160
  157
  148
+ 162
  946
```

```
   157.66
6)946.00
```

157.7

The average height of the six students is 157.7 cm when rounded to the nearest tenth of a centimeter.

Other example

Find the average to the nearest hundredth:

7.2, 4.3, 5.9, 6.1, 3.7, 6.9, 5.4

```
   7.2
   4.3
   5.9
   6.1
   3.7
   6.9
 + 5.4
  39.5
```

```
    5.642
7)39.500
```

Average: 5.64

Find the average of each list of numbers to the nearest tenth.

1. 418, 379, 527   2. 6, 9, 7, 5, 8, 4   3. 326.7, 430.5, 392.6, 543.1

Find the average of each column of numbers to the nearest tenth.

	1.	2.	3.	4.	5.	6.
	34	247	7	38.2	249.1	7.3
	46	356	12	43.6	356.4	2.9
	38	421	16	39.7	218.7	5.4
	42	392	12	40.6	324.2	6.8
	36	418	8	41.1	654.3	7.2
	39	307	13	37.8		4.7
	43	254		42.4		

Find the averages of each column of numbers to the nearest hundredth.

	7.	8.	9.	10.	11.	12.
	32	3467	7.8	24.1	4.36	0.78
	56	2856	3.9	36.3	5.72	0.56
	29	3114	5.6	51.0	8.12	0.84
	42	3891	2.9	47.2	7.66	0.67
	37	4250	4.6	40.0	5.43	0.75
	51		7.2	38.2	6.28	0.80
	48		5.9		9.02	

13. Find the average height to the nearest tenth.

Name	Height (cm)
Carla	151
Robert	146
Ross	162
Lynn	159
Mark	156
Jan	150
Ken	149

14. Find the average mass to the nearest hundredth.

Name	Mass (kg)
Mike	52
Nancy	42
Polly	54
Steve	44
Bev	43
Dave	49
Kathy	46

☆ 15. Find the person in your class whose height is closest to the average height for your class.

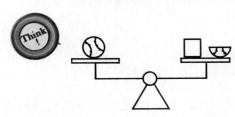

A baseball will balance a 75 g mass and half of a baseball. How many grams are in a baseball and a half?

Averages in sports

Some of the many ways averages are used in sports are:

Bowling average
Average team score per game
Average attendance per game
Scoring average for a player
Average winning or losing margin

1. Carol had these scores for the 6 games she bowled one week.
   132, 103, 114, 141, 124, 96
   What was Carol's average score (to the nearest whole number)?

2. Tom had these bowling scores: 120, 136, 104, 128, 115, 101.
   Was his average higher or lower than Carol's?

3. Rick was the high scorer for the school basketball team. His scores for the first 8 games were 18, 12, 16, 21, 15, 20, 12, and 24. In the ninth game he scored 19 points. How much was this above his average for the first 8 games?

4. Linda's volleyball team practiced 7 times in two weeks.
   The practice periods lasted 90 minutes, 60 minutes, 80 minutes, 45 minutes, 75 minutes, 105 minutes, and 75 minutes.
   What was the average practice time to the nearest minute?

5. The school baseball team had the following attendance at the first 3 games:

125, 136, 144

At the next game, their attendance was up 52 from the average of the first 3 games. How many attended the fourth game?

6. The chart shows the scores for Jefferson's 6 wins in basketball. What was Jefferson's average score per game (to the nearest whole number?)

Jefferson	Visitors
76	75
83	48
56	50
71	68
90	56
72	64

7. What was Jefferson's average winning margin (the difference between Jefferson's average and the visitor's average)?

8. What was the average winning margin, to the nearest tenth, for Willow Creek's first four games?

Willow Creek	Visitors
72	54
48	47
59	50
83	46
64	75
68	69
61	80

9. Willow Creek lost their eighth game by 9 points. Their score was 12 points below the average of their first seven games. What was the score for each team in the eighth game?

☆ 10. Johnson and Smith were the leading scorers for Rocky River. Johnson's average for nine games was 23.8. Smith won the scoring race with an average of 24.1. How many points did Smith score in the 9th game if his first 8 scores were 20, 18, 32, 24, 21, 13, 41, and 26?

✪ Electricity

Although electrical equipment is complicated, many electrical circuits or paths are very simple. You can think of electrical energy flowing through a wire in the same way that you think of water flowing through a pipe.

Units for Measuring Electricity	
Ampere	**rate** of flow of electricity
Volt	**pressure** behind the flow
Ohm	**resistance** to the flow
Watt	**power**

The following relationships between the units might help you to solve the problems.

A amperes = watts ÷ volts

B volts = amperes × ohms

C ohms = watts ÷ amperes²

D watts = volts × amperes

Find all answers to the nearest tenth.

1. Suppose a toaster uses 1000 watts on a house voltage of 115 volts. How many amperes does the toaster take? (Hint: use **A**.)

2. A model train has a 35-ohm motor. When it uses 0.3 amperes of current, what is the number of volts? (Hint: use **B**.)

3. Suppose 0.83 amperes flows through a 100-watt light bulb. What is the number of ohms for the light bulb? (Hint: use **C**.)

4. Suppose an electric oven uses 37.5 amperes on house voltage of 120 volts. How many watts is the oven using? (Hint: use **D**.)

5. Suppose a 150-ohm transistor radio uses 0.06 amperes of current. What size battery (volts) does it use?

6. How many amperes does a 200 watt record player use on a house circuit of 120 volts?

7. Suppose the starter of a car draws 95 amperes from the 12-volt battery. How many watts is this?

8. How many amperes of current does a 3500-watt elevator motor use if it is on a 440-volt circuit?

9. Suppose each headlamp of a car draws 7.5 amperes from the 12-volt battery. How many watts are being used?

10. How many amperes does a 200-watt furnace motor use on a 120-volt circuit?

☆ 11. Look at the back of an electrical appliance such as a clock or radio to find the listing of the watts and volts for the appliance. Then find the number of amperes for the appliance.

Self-check

Estimate first. Then find the exact answers.

1. Clock repair—
   Labor: 2 h at $9.00 an hour
   Parts: $5.75
   What is the total cost?

2. Supplies—
   Binder: $2.50
   Two packs of paper at $0.72 each
   Tax: $0.18
   How much in all?

3. Tom bowled 113, 94, 105, 137, 124, and 140. What was his average, to the nearest whole number?

4. Find the average temperature to the nearest tenth of a degree.

   22°C, 20°C, 21°C, 23°C, 18°C, 19°C

5. Find the average to the nearest tenth.

   24.3, 56.8, 42.4, 37.9

☆ 6. How many amperes, to the nearest tenth, does a 200-watt bulb draw on a 120-volt house circuit?
   (amperes = watts ÷ volts)

Answers for Self-check—page 173

Test

1. Stereo repair—
   Labor: 3 h at $7.25 an hour
   Parts: $8.95
   What is the total cost?

2. Materials—
   12 shelf boards at $3.85 each
   Nails: $1.49
   Tax: $1.91
   How much in all?

3. Charlene bowled 118, 127, 85, 106, 129, and 115. What was her average, to the nearest whole number?

4. Find the average to the nearest tenth.

   54, 42, 39, 46, 51, 67

5. Find the average to the nearest tenth.

   19.3, 14.8, 16.9, 15.1

☆ 6. How many watts of power does a motor use that draws 3.6 amperes on a 220-volt circuit?
   (watts = volts × amperes)

The Four-Color Map Problem

Any map can be colored with **four** or fewer colors
so that bordering regions have different colors.

For many years mathematicians thought the statement above was true, but they
couldn't prove it. Only in recent years has a satisfactory proof been offered.

Some maps are "easy" and can be colored with two or three colors. Others need
four. None have been found to need five.

Four colors needed.   Only three colors needed.

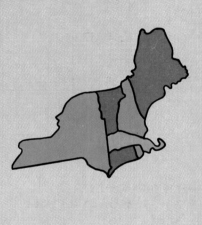

Trace and color these "maps" using the given number of colors.
(Like colors can touch at a point)

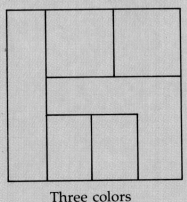
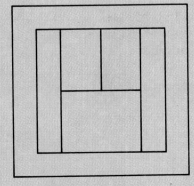
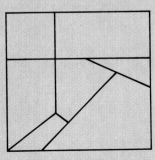

Three colors   Four colors   Four colors

Number Theory

The Greek mathematician Eratosthenes, who lived over 2000 years ago, invented a special way of finding a subset of whole numbers called **prime numbers**. His method is called the Sieve of Eratosthenes.

To make your own Sieve, start with a table of whole numbers, omitting 0 and 1. Make your table as large as you like. Follow the steps on the next page.

2	3	4	5	6	7	8	9	10
11	12	13	14	15	16	17	18	19	20
21	22	23	24	25	26	27	28	29	30
31	32	33	34	35	36	37	38	39	40
41	42	43	44	45	46	47	48	49	50
51	52	53	54	55	56	57	58	59	60
61	62	63	64	65	66	67	68	69	70
71	72	73	74	75	76	77	78	79	80
81	82	83	84	85	86	87	88	89	90
91	92	93	94	95	96	97	98	99	100

Step 1
Ring the first number (2). Mark out all the multiples of 2.

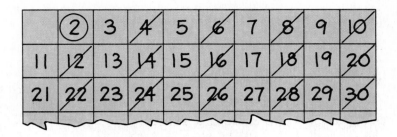

Step 2
Ring the next number not marked out (3). Mark out all the multiples of 3 that are not already marked.

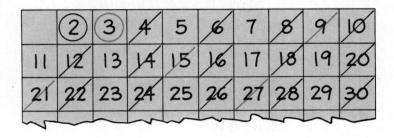

Step 3
Ring the next number not marked out (5). Mark out all multiples of 5 that are not already marked.

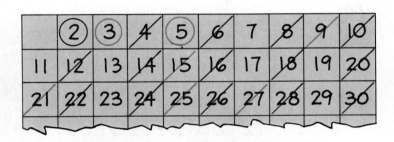

Step 4
Ring the next number not marked out. Mark out its unmarked multiples.

Step 5
Continue this process until all the numbers on the table have a ring or have been marked out.

1. The numbers with a ring are **prime numbers**.
   Make a list of the prime numbers you have found.

2. The numbers crossed out are **composite numbers**.
   Make a list of the composite numbers you have found.

Finding factors of numbers

What are the factors of 20?

Finding the answer

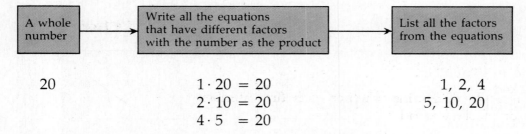

20

$$1 \cdot 20 = 20$$
$$2 \cdot 10 = 20$$
$$4 \cdot 5 \ = 20$$

1, 2, 4
5, 10, 20

Other examples

Number	Equations	Factors
16	$1 \cdot 16 = 16$ $2 \cdot 8 \ = 16$ $4 \cdot 4 \ = 16$	1, 2, 4 8, 16

Copy the table and give the missing numbers.

	Number	Equations		Factors
	12	$1 \cdot 12 = 12$ $2 \cdot 6 \ = 12$	$3 \cdot 4 = 12$	1, 2, 3, 4, 6, 12
1.	18	$1 \cdot 18 = 18$ $2 \cdot 9 \ = 18$	$3 \cdot 6 = 18$	
2.	15	$1 \cdot 15 = 15$	$3 \cdot 5 = 15$	
3.	24	$1 \cdot 24 = 24$ $2 \cdot 12 = 24$	$3 \cdot 8 = 24$ $4 \cdot 6 = 24$	
4.	13	$1 \cdot 13$		
5.	30	$1 \cdot 30 = 30$ $2 \cdot 15 = 30$	$3 \cdot 10 = 30$ $5 \cdot 6 \ = 30$	

Division can be used to determine whether one number
is a factor of another.

Example 1: Is 7 a factor of 105?

```
   15
7)105      The remainder is 0.
   7
  35       7·15 = 105
  35
   0       7 is a factor of 105
```

Example 2: Is 13 a factor of 223?

```
    17
13)223      The remainder is not 0.
   13
   93       13 is not a factor of 223.
   91
    2
```

Use division to determine whether each first number
is a factor of the second.

1. 9 and 216
2. 7 and 213
3. 17 and 649
4. 8 and 354

5. 13 and 741
6. 18 and 666
7. 29 and 1769
8. 25 and 625

9. 14 and 520
10. 31 and 967
11. 23 and 1541
12. 42 and 2142

List all the factors of each number.

13. 10
14. 20
15. 17
16. 25
17. 42

18. 36
19. 35
20. 45
21. 40
22. 90

23. 48
24. 32
25. 60
26. 96
27. 72

Calculator problems

Decide whether each first number is a
factor of the second.

28. 2769 and 994 071

29. 3427 and 23 396 129

30. 9683 and 33 803 357

31. 47 287 and 13 902 378

32. 64 543 and 13 560 885

33. 15 625 and 1 000 000

The factors of 6 (less than 6)
are {1, 2, 3}.

The sum of these factors is 6

$$1 + 2 + 3 = 6$$

For this reason, 6 is called a
perfect number. Which number
below is a perfect number?

A 24   B 30   C 28   D 42

Prime and composite numbers

A prime number has exactly
2 different factors, itself and 1.

A composite number is greater than 0,
and has more than 2 factors.

The numbers 0 and 1 are neither prime nor composite.

Every number is a factor of 0.
$0 \cdot 0 = 0$, $0 \cdot 1 = 0$, $0 \cdot 2 = 0$, $0 \cdot 3 = 0$, . . .

1 is the only factor of 1.
$1 \cdot 1 = 1$

Which of these numbers is prime, 39 or 41?

Finding the answer

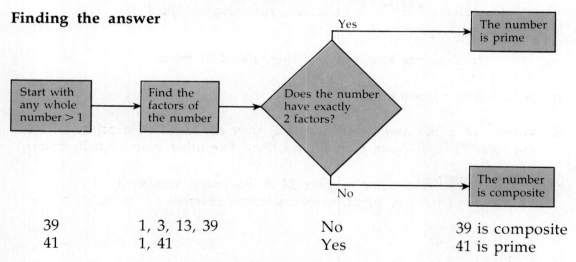

| 39 | 1, 3, 13, 39 | No | 39 is composite |
| 41 | 1, 41 | Yes | 41 is prime |

Give the missing word, **prime** or **composite**.

	Number	Factors	Only 2 factors?	Prime or Composite
1.	2	1, 2	Yes	2 is ____?____
2.	3	1, 3	Yes	3 is ____?____
3.	4	1, 2, 4	No	4 is ____?____
4.	5	1, 5	Yes	5 is ____?____
5.	6	1, 2, 3, 6	No	6 is ____?____

Find the missing numbers and words.

Number	Factors	Prime or Composite
7	1, 7	Prime
8	1, 2, 4, 8	Composite
9	1, 3, 9	Composite
10	1, 2, 5, 10	Composite
11	1, 11	Prime
1. 12		?
2. 13		?
3. 14		?
4. 15		?
5. 16		?
6. 17		?
7. 18		?
8. 19		?
9. 20		?

10. There are 25 prime numbers less than 100. List them.

11. How many prime numbers are even?

12. When two prime numbers differ by 2, they are called **twin primes**. For example, 71 and 73 are twin primes. Find five other pairs of twin primes.

13. The reverse of the prime number 13 is the prime number 31. Find 3 other pairs of prime numbers whose reverses are prime numbers.

An eighteenth-century mathematician, Christian Goldbach, suggested that every even number greater than 2 is the sum of two prime numbers. No one has ever been able to prove that this is true, or that it is not true.

See if you can check it for the even numbers to 100.

$$4 = 2 + 2$$
$$6 = 3 + 3$$
$$8 = 3 + 5$$
$$10 = 3 + 7$$
$$12 = 5 + 7$$

$$14 = 3 + 11$$
$$16 = 5 + 11$$
$$18 = 7 + 11$$
$$20 = 7 + 13$$
$$\vdots \quad \vdots$$

Prime factorization

> Each composite number can be expressed as a product of prime numbers in exactly one way, except for the order of the factors.

A composite number may be written as the product of prime numbers, called the **prime factorization** of the number.
A **factor tree** shows the factorization of a number. The top, or last, row of factors is the prime factorization of the number.

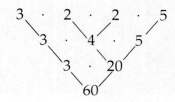

$$60 = 3 \cdot 2 \cdot 2 \cdot 5$$

Prime factorization of 60

The prime numbers in the top row are the same, even though their order may be different.

$$30 = 2 \cdot 3 \cdot 5$$

Prime factorization of 30

Copy and complete each factor tree. Then give the prime factorization.

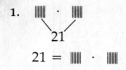

1. ▦ · ▦
   21
   21 = ▦ · ▦

2. ▦ · ▦ · ▦
   6 · 7
   42
   42 = ▦ · ▦ · ▦

3.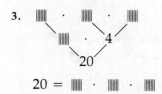
   ▦ · ▦ · ▦
   ▦ · 4
   20
   20 = ▦ · ▦ · ▦

Copy and complete each factor tree. Then give the prime factorization of the given composite number.

1.

2.

3.

4.

5.

6.

7.

8.

9.

Complete a factor tree for each number. Then give the prime factorization.

10. 54

11. 35

12. 16

13. 48

14. 81

☆ 15. 126

☆ 16. 66

☆ 17. 231

☆ 18. 442

☆ 19. 525

Calculator problems

The table gives some prime numbers.

2	3	5	7
101	103	107	109
113	127	131	137

Each number below is the product of three of these primes, one from each row. Give the prime factorizations.

20. 27 178

21. 66 155

22. 42 051

23. 86 219

More practice, page 386, Set A

s and exponents

... be used to give the prime factorization of a number.

... of 32:

$$\ldots = 2 \cdot 2 \cdot 2 \cdot 2 \cdot 2$$

Using an exponent:

$$32 = 2^5$$

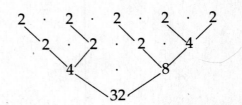

Other examples

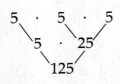

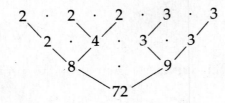

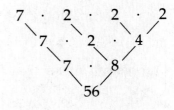

$125 = 5 \cdot 5 \cdot 5$

$125 = 5^3$

$72 = 2 \cdot 2 \cdot 2 \cdot 3 \cdot 3$

$72 = 2^3 \cdot 3^2$

$56 = 7 \cdot 2 \cdot 2 \cdot 2$

$56 = 7 \cdot 2^3$

Copy and complete each factor tree. Then give the prime factorization using exponents.

1.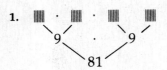

2.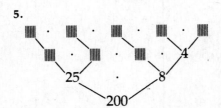

3.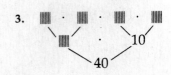

4.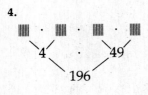

5.

6.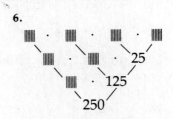

Give each prime factorization using exponents.

1. $81 = 3 \cdot 3 \cdot 3 \cdot 3$
2. $24 = 2 \cdot 2 \cdot 2 \cdot 3$
3. $1125 = 3 \cdot 3 \cdot 5 \cdot 5 \cdot 5$
4. $968 = 2 \cdot 2 \cdot 2 \cdot 11 \cdot 11$
5. $1372 = 2 \cdot 2 \cdot 7 \cdot 7 \cdot 7$
6. $162 = 2 \cdot 3 \cdot 3 \cdot 3 \cdot 3$
7. $396 = 2 \cdot 2 \cdot 3 \cdot 3 \cdot 11$
8. $18\ 865 = 5 \cdot 7 \cdot 7 \cdot 7 \cdot 11$
9. $300 = 2 \cdot 2 \cdot 3 \cdot 5 \cdot 5$
10. $900 = 2 \cdot 2 \cdot 3 \cdot 3 \cdot 5 \cdot 5$

Give the prime factorization of each number. Use exponents.

11. 8   12. 63   13. 90   14. 50   15. 16

16. 64   17. 108   18. 75   19. 98   20. 100

Find the missing numbers.

21. $\text{▥} = 3^2 \cdot 5^2$
22. $\text{▥} = 2 \cdot 3^2 \cdot 5$
23. $\text{▥} = 2^2 \cdot 3^2$

24. $\text{▥} = 3^3 \cdot 5$
25. $\text{▥} = 2^4 \cdot 7$
26. $\text{▥} = 2^2 \cdot 3 \cdot 5^2$

27. $\text{▥} = 2^4 \cdot 3^2$
28. $\text{▥} = 2^3 \cdot 7^2$
29. $\text{▥} = 5^2 \cdot 7^2$

30. $\text{▥} = 2^5 \cdot 7$
31. $\text{▥} = 3^4 \cdot 5^2$
32. $\text{▥} = 2^2 \cdot 3^2 \cdot 5^2$

Calculator problems

Find the missing numbers.

33. $\text{▥} = 13^3 \cdot 23^2$

34. $\text{▥} = 11^1 \cdot 17^2 \cdot 19^2$

35. $\text{▥} = 17^3 \cdot 23^2$

36. $\text{▥} = 7 \cdot 29^3 \cdot 31$

37. $\text{▥} = 37^2 \cdot 41^3$

38. $\text{▥} = 31^3 \cdot 41^2 \cdot$

Using the table, solve the equations mentally.
No pencil and paper.
No calculator.

1. $a = 2^3 \cdot 5^3 \cdot 139$
2. $b = 2^4 \cdot 5^4 \cdot 1103$
3. $c = 2^2 \cdot 1123 \cdot 5^2$
4. $d = 2^5 \cdot 5^6 \cdot 7$
5. $e = 2^6 \cdot 5^7 \cdot 11$

$$2 \cdot 5 = 10$$
$$2^2 \cdot 5^2 = 100$$
$$2^3 \cdot 5^3 = 1000$$
$$2^4 \cdot 5^4 = 10\ 000$$
$$2^5 \cdot 5^5 = 100\ 000$$
$$2^6 \cdot 5^6 = 1\ 000\ 000$$

Greatest common factor (GCF)

> The greatest common factor (GCF) of two numbers is the greatest number that is a factor of both numbers.

The flow chart shows how you can use factors to find the GCF of two numbers.

What is the GCF of 12 and 18?

Finding the answer

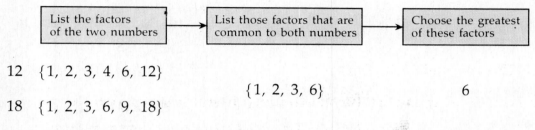

12 {1, 2, 3, 4, 6, 12}

18 {1, 2, 3, 6, 9, 18}   {1, 2, 3, 6}   6

The GCF of 12 and 18 is 6.

Other example

What is the GCF of 30 and 45?

30   {1, 2, 3, 5, 6, 10, 15, 30}

45   {1, 3, 5, 9, 15, 45}   Common factors: {1, 3, 5, 15}

The GCF of 30 and 45 is 15.

Find the GCF of each pair of numbers. The factors are given.

1. 28   {1, 2, 4, 7, 14, 28}   2. 30   {1, 2, 3, 5, 6, 10, 15, 30}
   35   {1, 5, 7, 35}   24   {1, 2, 3, 4, 6, 8, 12, 24}

3. 18   {1, 2, 3, 6, 9, 18}   4. 20   {1, 2, 4, 5, 10, 20}
   45   {1, 3, 5, 9, 15, 45}   30   {1, 2, 3, 5, 6, 10, 15, 30}

5. 24   {1, 2, 3, 4, 6, 8, 12, 24}   6. 35   {1, 5, 7, 35}
   32   {1, 2, 4, 8, 16, 32}   18   {1, 2, 3, 6, 9, 18}

This flow chart shows how you can use prime factorization to find the GCF of two numbers.

What is the GCF of 60 and 75?

Finding the answer

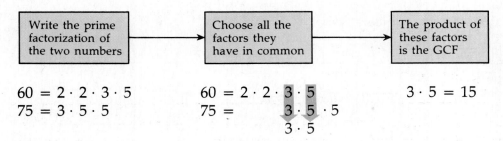

Write the prime factorization of the two numbers	Choose all the factors they have in common	The product of these factors is the GCF

$60 = 2 \cdot 2 \cdot 3 \cdot 5$
$75 = 3 \cdot 5 \cdot 5$

$60 = 2 \cdot 2 \cdot 3 \cdot 5$
$75 = \qquad 3 \cdot 5 \cdot 5$
$\qquad 3 \cdot 5$

$3 \cdot 5 = 15$

The GCF of 60 and 75 is 15.

Find the GCF of each pair of numbers. Use whatever method you choose.

1. $18 = 2 \cdot 3 \cdot 3$
   $45 = 3 \cdot 3 \cdot 5$

2. $42 = 2 \cdot 3 \cdot 7$
   $105 = 3 \cdot 5 \cdot 7$

3. $90 = 2 \cdot 3 \cdot 3 \cdot 5$
   $105 = 3 \cdot 5 \cdot 7$

4. $12 = 2 \cdot 2 \cdot 3$
   $60 = 2 \cdot 2 \cdot 3 \cdot 5$

5. $150 = 2 \cdot 3 \cdot 5 \cdot 5$
   $105 = 3 \cdot 5 \cdot 7$

6. $108 = 2 \cdot 2 \cdot 3 \cdot 3 \cdot 3$
   $90 = 2 \cdot 3 \cdot 3 \cdot 5$

Find the GCF of each pair of numbers. Use whatever method you choose. For some pairs the GCF is 1.

7. 36, 42

8. 27, 36

9. 20, 45

10. 18, 24

11. 42, 90

12. 60, 18

13. 36, 24

14. 30, 105

15. 18, 42

16. 40, 36

17. 8, 15

18. 14, 90

19. 63, 56

20. 24, 25

21. 100, 350

22. 39, 65

 Find the missing numbers.

$2\ 803\ 979 = 97 \cdot \text{▥} \cdot 211$
$3\ 150\ 863 = 109 \cdot 137 \cdot \text{▥}$

What is the GCF of 2 803 979 and 3 150 863?

More practice, page 386, Set B

Least common multiple (LCM)

> The least common multiple (LCM) of two numbers is the smallest non-zero number that is a multiple of both numbers.

The flow chart shows how you can use multiples to find the LCM of two numbers. What is the LCM of 6 and 8?

Finding the answer

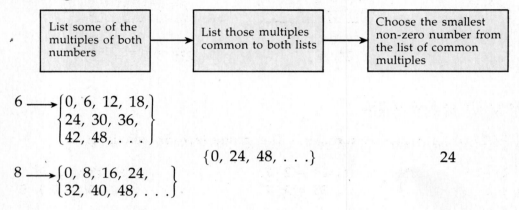

The LCM of 6 and 8 is 24.

Other example

What is the LCM of 4 and 6?

$$4 \longrightarrow \begin{Bmatrix} 0, 4, 8, 12, \\ 16, 20, 24, \ldots \end{Bmatrix}$$

$$\{0, 12, 24, \ldots\} \qquad 12$$

$$6 \longrightarrow \begin{Bmatrix} 0, 6, 12, 18, \\ 24, 30, \ldots \end{Bmatrix}$$

The LCM of 4 and 6 is 12.

Find the LCM of each pair of numbers. Sets of multiples are given.

1. 2   {0, 2, 4, 6, 8, 10, 12, . . .}
   3   {0, 3, 6, 9, 12, 15, 18, . . .}

2. 3   {0, 3, 6, 9, 12, 15, 18, . . .}
   4   {0, 4, 8, 12, 16, 20, 24, . . .}

3. 6   {0, 6, 12, 18, 24, 30, 36, . . .}
   10   {0, 10, 20, 30, 40, 50, 60, . . .}

4. 8   {0, 8, 16, 24, 32, 40, 48, . . .}
   10   {0, 10, 20, 30, 40, 50, 60, . . .}

The flow chart shows how you can use prime factorization to find the LCM of two numbers.

What is the LCM of 12 and 63?

Finding the answer

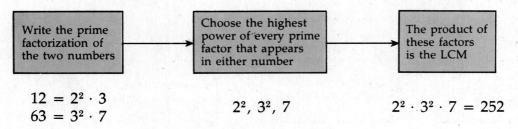

| Write the prime factorization of the two numbers | Choose the highest power of every prime factor that appears in either number | The product of these factors is the LCM |

$$12 = 2^2 \cdot 3$$
$$63 = 3^2 \cdot 7$$

$$2^2, 3^2, 7$$

$$2^2 \cdot 3^2 \cdot 7 = 252$$

The LCM of 12 and 63 is 252.

Find the LCM of each pair of numbers. The prime factorization is given.

1. $12 = 2^2 \cdot 3$
   $10 = 2 \cdot 5$

2. $14 = 2 \cdot 7$
   $35 = 5 \cdot 7$

3. $18 = 2 \cdot 3^2$
   $30 = 2 \cdot 3 \cdot 5$

4. $75 = 3 \cdot 5^2$
   $35 = 5 \cdot 7$

5. $8 = 2^3$
   $12 = 2^2 \cdot 3$

6. $36 = 2^2 \cdot 3^2$
   $42 = 2 \cdot 3 \cdot 7$

Find the LCM of each pair of numbers. Use whatever method you choose.

7. 10, 12

8. 6, 5

9. 21, 6

10. 4, 6

11. 6, 14

12. 21, 12

13. 20, 24

14. 24, 42

Calculator problems

Find the LCM of each pair of numbers.

15. $133\,518 = 2 \cdot 3 \cdot 7 \cdot 11 \cdot 17^2$
    $20\,349 = 3^2 \cdot 7 \cdot 17 \cdot 19$

16. $8993 = 17 \cdot 23^2$
    $154\,037 = 13 \cdot 17^2 \cdot 41$

Self-check

1. List the factors of 6.

2. Is 17 a factor of 1055?

3. List the prime numbers between 30 and 40.

4. Copy and complete.

Give the prime factorization of each number.

5. 45

6. 28

Give the prime factorization of each number using exponents.

7. 18

8. 100

Give the greatest common factor of each pair.

9. 18 and 24

10. 16 and 28

Give the least common multiple of each pair.

11. 5 and 6

12. 12 and 10

Answers for Self-check—page 189

Test

1. List the factors of 10.

2. Is 19 a factor of 1596?

3. List the prime numbers between 50 and 60.

4. Copy and complete.

Give the prime factorization of each number.

5. 42

6. 18

Give the prime factorization of each number using exponents.

7. 36

8. 54

Give the greatest common factor of each pair.

9. 20 and 45

10. 24 and 30

Give the least common multiple of each pair.

11. 3 and 5

12. 6 and 14

Math lab

Clock Arithmetic

To work the problems on this page, you will
need to think about a one-handed "eight-clock."

The examples below show how you can use one
direction for adding and the other direction
for subtracting.

Adding

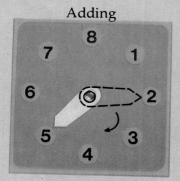

$$2 + 3 = 5$$

Subtracting

$$1 - 5 = 4$$

Find the sums and differences. Remember you have only **eight numbers**.
Think about the eight-clock.

1. $4 + 2 = g$
2. $4 + 3 = x$
3. $4 + 4 = b$

4. $4 + 5 = c$
5. $4 + 6 = l$
6. $4 + 7 = s$

7. $4 + 8 = m$
8. $5 + 8 = a$
9. $6 + 8 = i$

10. $5 - 2 = q$
11. $5 - 3 = p$
12. $5 - 4 = k$

13. $5 - 5 = w$
14. $5 - 6 = e$
15. $5 - 7 = t$

16. $5 - 8 = f$
17. $6 - 8 = r$
18. $7 - 8 = h$

19. $8 - 8 = n$
20. $1 - 8 = j$
21. $3 - 8 = y$

What number acts like zero in clock arithmetic?
Decide how you would multiply in clock arithmetic.
Then make up and solve some multiplication problems.

Unit 3 review

Solve.

1. $630 \div 90 = r$ 2. $240 \div 6 = s$ 3. $3200 \div 40 = t$

4. $7200 \div 80 = a$ 5. $5600 \div 70 = f$ 6. $2100 \div 30 = j$

7. $2000 \div 40 = b$ 8. $3500 \div 500 = c$ 9. $6400 \div 80 = d$

Find the quotients and remainders.

10. $42\overline{)5623}$ 11. $48\overline{)9581}$ 12. $62\overline{)4126}$ 13. $23\overline{)1872}$

14. $74\overline{)60\ 238}$ 15. $93\overline{)81\ 429}$ 16. $27\overline{)14\ 607}$ 17. $52\overline{)32\ 138}$

Find the quotients to the nearest hundredth.

18. $3.2\overline{)20.32}$ 19. $0.56\overline{)44.968}$ 20. $2.8\overline{)3.892}$ 21. $0.84\overline{)52.17}$

22. $45\overline{)40}$ 23. $37\overline{)52}$ 24. $30\overline{)15}$ 25. $48\overline{)64}$

Copy and complete each factor tree.

26. 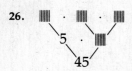   27. 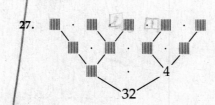   28.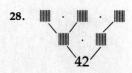

Give the prime factorization of each number, using exponents.

29. 27   30. 64   31. 35   32. 81   33. 28   34. 112

Give the greatest common factor of each pair.

35. 48 and 32   36. 12 and 30   37. 18 and 24

Give the least common multiple of each pair.

38. 4 and 3   39. 2 and 5   40. 8 and 12

Unit **4**

Fractional Numbers
Adding and Subtracting Fractional Numbers
Multiplying and Dividing Fractional Numbers
Ratio and Proportion
Geometric Relationships

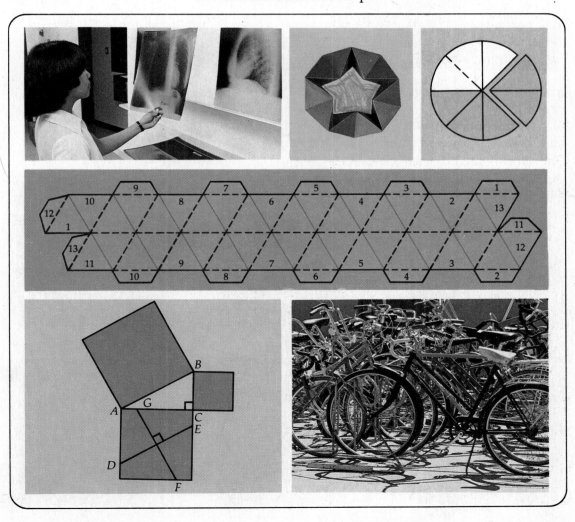

Fractional Numbers

Students shared large cork boards to show
their pictures at the Art Fair.

1 board was shared by 3 students.
1 board was divided into 3 equal parts.
Each student used $\frac{1}{3}$ of the board.

Give a fraction that tells what part of each
cork board is covered by the colored paper.

1. 2. 3.

4. 5. 6.

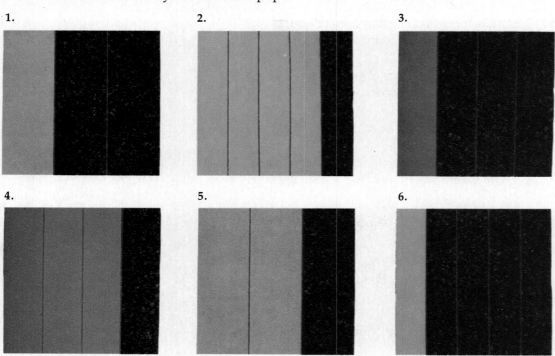

Some students shared more than one cork board.

2 boards were divided among 3 students.
2 boards were divided into 3 equal parts.
Each student used $\frac{1}{3}$ of 2 boards or $\frac{2}{3}$ of one board.

Give the missing fractions.

1. 3 boards are divided into 4 equal parts.
   Each part is ▦ of a board.

2. 2 boards are divided into 5 equal parts.
   Each part is ▦ of a board.

3. 1 board is divided into 2 equal parts.
   Each part is ▦ of a board.

4. 6 boards are divided into 5 equal parts.
   Each part is ▦ of a board.

Complete.

5. The fraction $\frac{2}{5}$ can be thought of as
   2 divided by ▦.

6. The fraction $\frac{3}{4}$ can be thought of as
   ▦ divided by 4.

7. The fraction $\frac{7}{10}$ can be thought of as
   ▦ divided by ▦.

A relation between fractions and decimals

Diana used $\frac{5}{8}$ of a sheet of matt board to make a frame for a water color picture. What is the decimal for $\frac{5}{8}$?

Finding the answer

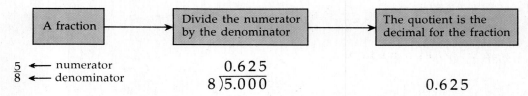

| A fraction | → | Divide the numerator by the denominator | → | The quotient is the decimal for the fraction |

$\frac{5}{8}$ ← numerator
   ← denominator

$$\begin{array}{r} 0.625 \\ 8\overline{)5.000} \end{array}$$

0.625

The decimal for $\frac{5}{8}$ is 0.625.
The decimal and the fraction name the same number. $\frac{5}{8} = 0.625$

Other examples

$\frac{3}{5} \longrightarrow \begin{array}{r} 0.6 \\ 5\overline{)3.0} \end{array}$ $\frac{13}{8} \longrightarrow \begin{array}{r} 1.625 \\ 8\overline{)13.000} \end{array}$

$\frac{3}{5} = 0.6$ $\frac{13}{8} = 1.625$

Write a decimal for each fraction.

1. $\frac{1}{2}$ 2. $\frac{1}{4}$ 3. $\frac{7}{8}$ 4. $\frac{7}{5}$ 5. $\frac{1}{8}$ 6. $\frac{5}{4}$

7. $\frac{7}{10}$ 8. $\frac{3}{16}$ 9. $\frac{9}{20}$ 10. $\frac{7}{2}$ 11. $\frac{13}{16}$ 12. $\frac{17}{20}$

13. $\frac{9}{4}$ 14. $\frac{3}{25}$ 15. $\frac{17}{50}$ 16. $\frac{4}{5}$ 17. $\frac{9}{12}$ 18. $\frac{3}{8}$

The decimals for some fractions are **repeating decimals**. These decimals have one digit or a set of digits that repeats over and over without end.

Find a decimal for $\frac{2}{3}$.

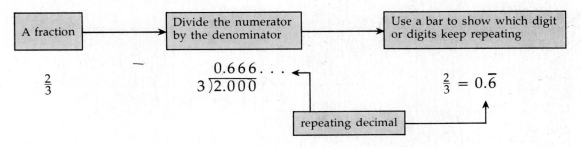

$\frac{2}{3}$

$$3\overline{)2.000} \quad 0.666\ldots$$

$\frac{2}{3} = 0.\overline{6}$

repeating decimal

Other examples

$\frac{4}{11} \longrightarrow 11\overline{)4.0000} \quad 0.3636\ldots$

$\frac{4}{11} = 0.\overline{36}$

$\frac{5}{6} \longrightarrow 6\overline{)5.000} \quad 0.833\ldots$

$\frac{5}{6} = 0.8\overline{3}$

Write a decimal for each fraction.

1. $\frac{1}{3}$
2. $\frac{1}{6}$
3. $\frac{5}{3}$
4. $\frac{9}{6}$
5. $\frac{10}{6}$

6. $\frac{7}{11}$
7. $\frac{35}{99}$
8. $\frac{11}{6}$
9. $\frac{15}{16}$
10. $\frac{24}{99}$

11. $\frac{3}{11}$
12. $\frac{16}{12}$
13. $\frac{12}{18}$
14. $\frac{8}{12}$
15. $\frac{1}{7}$

Calculator problems

16. $\frac{27}{37}$
17. $\frac{825}{909}$
18. $\frac{399}{495}$

19. $\frac{1158}{3088}$
20. $\frac{3715}{11\,888}$
21. $\frac{18\,502}{999\,108}$

Find two numbers whose product is one million, although neither number has a 0 in it.

Hint: $1\,000\,000 = 10^6$
$= (2 \cdot 5)^6$

More practice, page 387, Set A

Equivalent fractions

0.6 of each region is shaded.

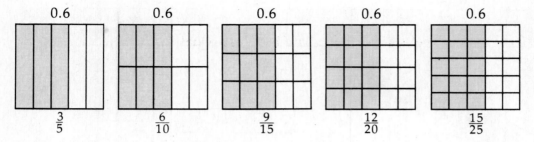

| 0.6 | 0.6 | 0.6 | 0.6 | 0.6 |

$\frac{3}{5}$ $\frac{6}{10}$ $\frac{9}{15}$ $\frac{12}{20}$ $\frac{15}{25}$

The fractions $\frac{3}{5}$, $\frac{6}{10}$, $\frac{9}{15}$, $\frac{12}{20}$, and $\frac{15}{25}$ are equivalent.
They name the same number, 0.6.

$$0.6 = \frac{3}{5} = \frac{6}{10} = \frac{9}{15} = \frac{12}{20} = \frac{15}{25} \quad \cdots$$

> Different fractions that are equal to the same decimal are equivalent to each other.

Equivalent fractions can be formed by multiplying both the numerator and denominator of a fraction by the same nonzero number.

$$\frac{1 \cdot 1}{2 \cdot 1} = \frac{1 \cdot 2}{2 \cdot 2} = \frac{1 \cdot 3}{2 \cdot 3} = \frac{1 \cdot 4}{2 \cdot 4} = \frac{1 \cdot 5}{2 \cdot 5} \cdots$$

$$0.5 = \frac{1}{2} = \frac{2}{4} = \frac{3}{6} = \frac{4}{8} = \frac{5}{10} \cdots$$

Give the missing fractions.

1.

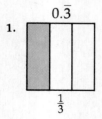 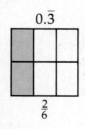 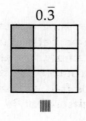 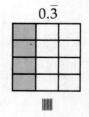 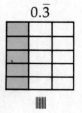

| $0.\overline{3}$ | $0.\overline{3}$ | $0.\overline{3}$ | $0.\overline{3}$ | $0.\overline{3}$ |

$\frac{1}{3}$ $\frac{2}{6}$

2.

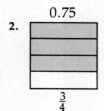 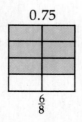 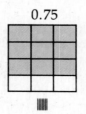 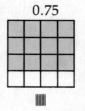

| 0.75 | 0.75 | 0.75 | 0.75 | 0.75 |

$\frac{3}{4}$ $\frac{6}{8}$

1. $\frac{3}{8} = 0.375$ Give the missing fractions which also equal 0.375.

$$\frac{3 \cdot 1}{8 \cdot 1}$$ $$\frac{3 \cdot 2}{8 \cdot 2}$$ $$\frac{3 \cdot 3}{8 \cdot 3}$$ $$\frac{3 \cdot 4}{8 \cdot 4}$$ $$\frac{3 \cdot 5}{8 \cdot 5}$$ $$\frac{3 \cdot 6}{8 \cdot 6}$$

$$\frac{3}{8}$$ $$\frac{6}{16}$$ $$\frac{9}{24}$$ ▦   ▦   ▦

2. $\frac{2}{3} = 0.\overline{6}$ Give the missing fractions which also equal $0.\overline{6}$.

$$\frac{2 \cdot 1}{3 \cdot 1}$$ $$\frac{2 \cdot 2}{3 \cdot 2}$$ $$\frac{2 \cdot 3}{3 \cdot 3}$$ $$\frac{2 \cdot 4}{3 \cdot 4}$$ $$\frac{2 \cdot 5}{3 \cdot 5}$$ $$\frac{2 \cdot 6}{3 \cdot 6}$$

$$\frac{2}{3}$$ $$\frac{4}{6}$$ $$\frac{6}{9}$$ ▦   ▦   ▦

3. $\frac{1}{4} = 0.25$ Give the missing fractions which also equal 0.25.

$$\frac{1 \cdot 1}{4 \cdot 1}$$ $$\frac{1 \cdot 2}{4 \cdot 2}$$ $$\frac{1 \cdot 3}{4 \cdot 3}$$ $$\frac{1 \cdot 4}{4 \cdot 4}$$ $$\frac{1 \cdot 5}{4 \cdot 5}$$ $$\frac{1 \cdot 6}{4 \cdot 6}$$

$$\frac{1}{4}$$ $$\frac{2}{8}$$ ▦   ▦   ▦   ▦

Find four more fractions in each set.
Give the decimal for each set.

4. $\left\{ \frac{4}{5}, \text{▦}, \text{▦}, \text{▦}, \text{▦}, \ldots \right\}$

5. $\left\{ \frac{3}{16}, \text{▦}, \text{▦}, \text{▦}, \text{▦}, \ldots \right\}$

6. $\left\{ \frac{1}{8}, \text{▦}, \text{▦}, \text{▦}, \text{▦}, \ldots \right\}$

7. $\left\{ \frac{7}{12}, \text{▦}, \text{▦}, \text{▦}, \text{▦}, \ldots \right\}$

8. $\left\{ \frac{5}{6}, \text{▦}, \text{▦}, \text{▦}, \text{▦}, \ldots \right\}$

9. $\left\{ \frac{9}{10}, \text{▦}, \text{▦}, \text{▦}, \text{▦}, \ldots \right\}$

Find the missing numerator or denominator that will make each incomplete fraction equivalent to the first fraction in the set. Each of the fractions contains all the digits except 0.

$$\left\{ \frac{1}{2}, \frac{2}{4}, \frac{3}{6}, \ldots \ldots, \frac{6729}{\blacksquare}, \ldots \right\}$$

$$\left\{ \frac{1}{3}, \frac{2}{6}, \frac{3}{9}, \ldots \ldots, \frac{\blacksquare}{17\,469}, \ldots \right\}$$

$$\left\{ \frac{1}{6}, \frac{2}{12}, \frac{3}{18}, \ldots \ldots, \frac{2943}{\blacksquare}, \ldots \right\}$$

$$\left\{ \frac{1}{9}, \frac{2}{18}, \frac{3}{27}, \ldots \ldots, \frac{\blacksquare}{57\,429}, \ldots \right\}$$

Lowest-terms fractions

> A fraction is in lowest terms if the greatest common factor (GCF) of the numerator and denominator is 1.

What is the lowest-terms fraction for $\frac{18}{24}$?

Finding the answer

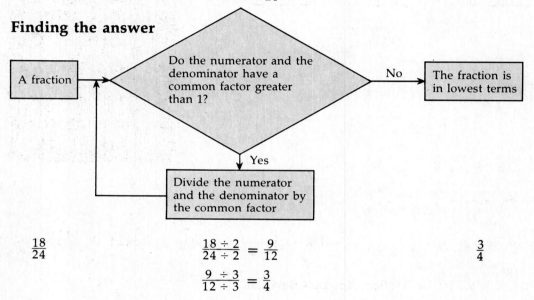

$$\frac{18}{24} \qquad \frac{18 \div 2}{24 \div 2} = \frac{9}{12} \qquad \frac{3}{4}$$

$$\frac{9 \div 3}{12 \div 3} = \frac{3}{4}$$

Dividing by the greatest common factor first can save some steps.

$$\frac{18}{24} \longrightarrow \frac{18 \div 6}{24 \div 6} = \frac{3}{4}$$

The lowest-terms fraction for $\frac{18}{24}$ is $\frac{3}{4}$.

Other examples

$$\frac{15}{18} = \frac{5}{6} \qquad \frac{12}{24} = \frac{1}{2} \qquad \frac{24}{32} = \frac{6}{8} = \frac{3}{4} \qquad \frac{32}{36} = \frac{8}{9} \qquad \frac{50}{100} = \frac{1}{2}$$

Simplify each fraction by writing it in lowest terms.

1. $\frac{9}{15}$ 2. $\frac{4}{8}$ 3. $\frac{8}{12}$ 4. $\frac{2}{14}$ 5. $\frac{8}{10}$ 6. $\frac{3}{24}$

7. $\frac{4}{10}$ 8. $\frac{21}{24}$ 9. $\frac{3}{12}$ 10. $\frac{4}{24}$ 11. $\frac{20}{32}$ 12. $\frac{10}{100}$

13. $\frac{6}{15}$ 14. $\frac{4}{12}$ 15. $\frac{3}{15}$ 16. $\frac{10}{16}$ 17. $\frac{12}{32}$ 18. $\frac{25}{100}$

Jim got this answer to a problem that he worked on his calculator. He wanted to give the answer as a lowest-terms fraction.

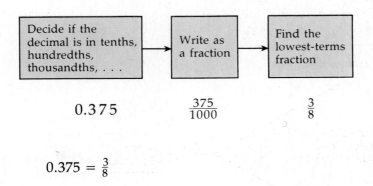

| Decide if the decimal is in tenths, hundredths, thousandths, . . . | → | Write as a fraction | → | Find the lowest-terms fraction |

$$0.375 \qquad \frac{375}{1000} \qquad \frac{3}{8}$$

$$0.375 = \frac{3}{8}$$

Other examples

$$0.75 = \frac{75}{100} = \frac{3}{4} \qquad 0.4 = \frac{4}{10} = \frac{2}{5} \qquad 0.3125 = \frac{3125}{10\,000} = \frac{5}{16}$$

Find the lowest-terms fraction for each decimal.

1. 0.25	2. 0.2	3. 0.5	4. 0.60	5. 0.8	6. 0.250
7. 0.125	8. 0.1	9. 0.750	10. 0.4	11. 0.875	12. 0.6
13. 0.20	14. 0.625	15. 0.7	16. 0.50	17. 0.06	18. 0.30
19. 0.04	20. 0.075	21. 0.800	22. 0.08	23. 0.016	24. 0.15

Calculator problems

Use trial and error to find the lowest-terms fraction for each repeating decimal below. Hint: Each fraction has a denominator of 3, 6, 9, 11, or 12.

25. $0.333\overline{3}$	26. $0.666\overline{6}$	27. $0.444\overline{4}$	28. $0.90909\overline{0}$
29. $0.555\overline{5}$	30. $0.2727\overline{27}$	31. $0.7272\overline{72}$	32. $0.4166\overline{6}$
33. $0.8333\overline{3}$	34. $0.777\overline{7}$	35. $0.818\overline{1}$	36. $0.636\overline{3}$

More practice, page 387, Set B

Comparing fractional numbers

Fractional numbers which have the same denominators can be compared by comparing their numerators.

Compare $\frac{9}{10}$ and $\frac{7}{10}$. $9 > 7$ so $\frac{9}{10} > \frac{7}{10}$

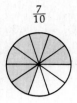 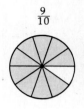

$\frac{9}{10}$ $\frac{7}{10}$

Compare $\frac{1}{2}$ and $\frac{5}{8}$. $\frac{1}{2} = \frac{4}{8}$ $\frac{4}{8} < \frac{5}{8}$ so $\frac{1}{2} < \frac{5}{8}$

$\frac{1}{2}$ $\frac{5}{8}$

To compare some fractional numbers, it is easier to compare their decimals.

Compare $\frac{7}{12}$ and $\frac{8}{15}$.

$\frac{7}{12} = 0.58\overline{3}$ $\frac{8}{15} = 0.5\overline{3}$ $0.58\overline{3} > 0.5\overline{3}$ so $\frac{7}{12} > \frac{8}{15}$

Other examples

Compare $\frac{5}{9}$ and $\frac{7}{15}$.

$\left. \begin{array}{l} \frac{5}{9} = 0.\overline{5} \\[2mm] \frac{7}{15} = 0.4\overline{6} \end{array} \right\}$ $\frac{5}{9} > \frac{7}{15}$

Compare $\frac{3}{8}$ and $\frac{9}{20}$.

$\left. \begin{array}{l} \frac{3}{8} = 0.375 \\[2mm] \frac{9}{20} = 0.45 \end{array} \right\}$ $\frac{3}{8} < \frac{9}{20}$

Compare the fractions. Find common denominators if necessary.

1. $\frac{7}{8}$ and $\frac{5}{8}$ 2. $\frac{1}{2}$ and $\frac{3}{4}$ 3. $\frac{1}{3}$ and $\frac{2}{3}$ 4. $\frac{1}{2}$ and $\frac{1}{3}$

5. $\frac{9}{10}$ and $\frac{4}{5}$ 6. $\frac{1}{8}$ and $\frac{1}{4}$ 7. $\frac{3}{10}$ and $\frac{1}{2}$ 8. $\frac{1}{3}$ and $\frac{1}{4}$

Use the decimals to compare the fractions.

9. $\frac{3}{16} = 0.1875$ 10. $\frac{5}{6} = 0.8\overline{3}$ 11. $\frac{7}{18} = 0.38\overline{8}$ 12. $\frac{4}{9} = 0.\overline{4}$

$\frac{2}{11} = 0.\overline{18}$ $\frac{7}{8} = 0.875$ $\frac{3}{8} = 0.375$ $\frac{5}{12} = 0.41\overline{6}$

Give the correct symbol, $>$ or $<$, for each ●.

1. $\frac{4}{9}$ ● $\frac{3}{8}$ 2. $\frac{3}{7}$ ● $\frac{7}{15}$ 3. $\frac{5}{6}$ ● $\frac{7}{9}$ 4. $\frac{13}{20}$ ● $\frac{11}{16}$

5. $\frac{11}{12}$ ● $\frac{9}{10}$ 6. $\frac{9}{14}$ ● $\frac{2}{3}$ 7. $\frac{13}{24}$ ● $\frac{7}{18}$ 8. $\frac{3}{32}$ ● $\frac{2}{21}$

To answer the questions, compare the decimals for the fractions.

Baseball

9. Who has the better hitting record?

Peter: hits ⟶ 11
    times at bat ⟶ 18
Fred: hits ⟶ 9
    times at bat ⟶ 16

10. Who has the better pitching record?

Jane: won ⟶ 8
    total decisions ⟶ 14
Terry: won ⟶ 6
    total decisions ⟶ 9

Football

11. Who has the better kicking record as an extra-point kicker?

Wilcox: made ⟶ 16
    total tries ⟶ 20
Yates: made ⟶ 12
    total tries ⟶ 18

12. Who has the better pass completion record?

Morris: completed passes ⟶ 15
    passes attempted ⟶ 24
Dolan: completed passes ⟶ 14
    passes attempted ⟶ 21

When you read about a batting average of 0.333, this is a decimal, rounded to 3 places, for the fraction:

$$\frac{\text{number of hits}}{\text{number of times at bat}}$$

Example:
hits (H) ⟶ $\frac{173}{519}$ = 0.333
times at bat (AB) ⟶

Find the batting averages that are missing from the table.

American League			
Player	AB	H	AVG.
McRae	519	173	0.333
G. Brett	638	209	0.328
Carew	593	193	0.325
Bostock	471	153	▦
LeFlore	544	172	▦
Rivers	590	184	▦
Lynn	508	158	▦
Carty	542	166	▦
Munson	611	184	▦
Staub	575	173	▦

Improper fractions and mixed numerals

$\frac{94}{6}$ is between two consecutive whole numbers x and y.

We write: $x < \frac{94}{6} < y$

What are the whole numbers for x and y?

You can find x and y by writing $\frac{94}{6}$ as a mixed numeral.

Finding the answer

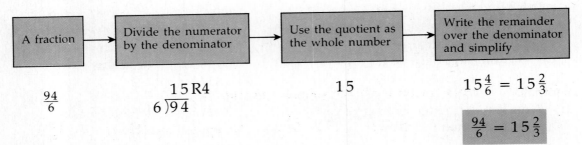

A fraction	Divide the numerator by the denominator	Use the quotient as the whole number	Write the remainder over the denominator and simplify

$$\frac{94}{6}$$

$$\begin{array}{r} 15\,\text{R}4 \\ 6\,\overline{)94} \end{array}$$

$$15$$

$$15\frac{4}{6} = 15\frac{2}{3}$$

$$\frac{94}{6} = 15\frac{2}{3}$$

$\frac{94}{6}$ is between 15 and 16.
$x = 15$ and $y = 16$

Other examples

$$\frac{19}{3} = 6\frac{1}{3} \qquad\qquad \frac{20}{5} = 4 \qquad\qquad \frac{28}{8} = 3\frac{4}{8} = 3\frac{1}{2}$$

$$\begin{array}{r} 6 \\ 3\,\overline{)19} \\ 18 \\ \hline 1 \end{array} \qquad\qquad \begin{array}{r} 4 \\ 5\,\overline{)20} \\ 20 \\ \hline 0 \end{array} \qquad\qquad \begin{array}{r} 3 \\ 8\,\overline{)28} \\ 24 \\ \hline 4 \end{array}$$

Write the mixed numeral or whole number for each improper fraction.

1. $\frac{17}{3}$ 2. $\frac{18}{5}$ 3. $\frac{23}{6}$ 4. $\frac{13}{4}$ 5. $\frac{22}{3}$ 6. $\frac{11}{8}$ 7. $\frac{21}{4}$

8. $\frac{4}{1}$ 9. $\frac{10}{8}$ 10. $\frac{22}{4}$ 11. $\frac{14}{6}$ 12. $\frac{14}{3}$ 13. $\frac{31}{5}$ 14. $\frac{44}{8}$

Find consecutive whole numbers x and y.

15. $x < \frac{75}{4} < y$ 16. $x < \frac{86}{5} < y$ 17. $x < \frac{91}{3} < y$

18. $x < \frac{55}{2} < y$ 19. $x < \frac{67}{3} < y$ 20. $x < \frac{98}{5} < y$

What is the improper fraction for $3\frac{4}{5}$?

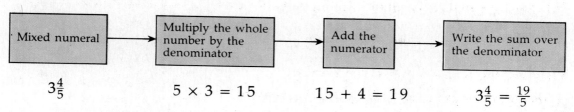

3          $3\frac{4}{5}$ 4

Finding the answer

Mixed numeral	Multiply the whole number by the denominator	Add the numerator	Write the sum over the denominator

$3\frac{4}{5}$ $5 \times 3 = 15$ $15 + 4 = 19$ $3\frac{4}{5} = \frac{19}{5}$

The improper fraction for $3\frac{4}{5}$ is $\frac{19}{5}$.

Other examples

$2\frac{3}{4} = \frac{11}{4}$ $5\frac{1}{8} = \frac{41}{8}$ $6\frac{2}{3} = \frac{20}{3}$

Write an improper fraction for each mixed numeral.

1. $3\frac{1}{6}$ 2. $2\frac{3}{5}$ 3. $1\frac{3}{8}$ 4. $5\frac{5}{6}$ 5. $4\frac{1}{2}$ 6. $2\frac{1}{4}$ 7. $4\frac{1}{8}$

8. $2\frac{7}{8}$ 9. $3\frac{1}{2}$ 10. $1\frac{9}{10}$ 11. $3\frac{7}{8}$ 12. $5\frac{1}{3}$ 13. $1\frac{3}{4}$ 14. $6\frac{1}{4}$

15. $7\frac{1}{3}$ 16. $3\frac{3}{4}$ 17. $8\frac{2}{3}$ 18. $2\frac{5}{6}$ 19. $9\frac{1}{2}$ 20. $1\frac{7}{8}$ 21. $7\frac{1}{4}$

Find the improper fraction for point A.

22.
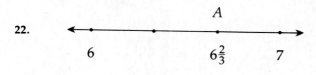
6          $6\frac{2}{3}$ 7

23.
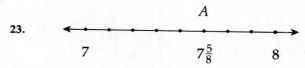
7          $7\frac{5}{8}$ 8

24.
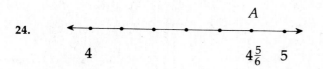
4          $4\frac{5}{6}$ 5

25.
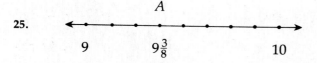
9          $9\frac{3}{8}$ 10

Suppose a tire is guaranteed for 65 000 km. The circumference of the tire is 2.23 m.

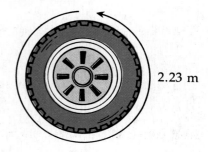

2.23 m

About how many times will the tire go around before the guarantee runs out?

More practice, page 387, Set C

Fractions and mixed decimals

Instead of writing a repeating decimal for $\frac{2}{3}$, we often write a mixed decimal numeral.

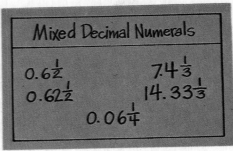

$$\frac{2}{3} = 0.666\ldots = 0.66\frac{2}{3}$$

We read: sixty-six and two-thirds hundredths

What is the mixed decimal, in hundredths, for $\frac{3}{8}$?

Finding the answer

A fraction	Divide the numerator by the denominator (to hundredths)	Write a fraction using the remainder and the divisor

$$\frac{3}{8}$$

$$\begin{array}{r} 0.37 \\ 8\overline{)3.00} \\ 2\,4 \\ \hline 6\,0 \\ 5\,6 \\ \hline 4 \end{array}$$

$0.37\frac{4}{8}$ or $0.37\frac{1}{2}$

The mixed decimal for $\frac{3}{8}$ is $0.37\frac{1}{2}$.

Other examples

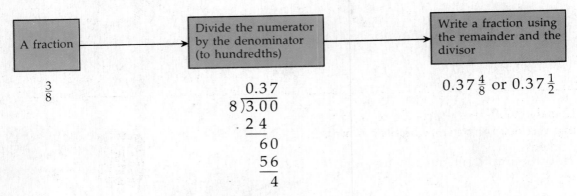

$\frac{2}{3} \longrightarrow \begin{array}{r} 0.66 \\ 3\overline{)2.00} \\ 1\,8 \\ \hline 20 \\ 18 \\ \hline 2 \end{array} \longrightarrow 0.66\frac{2}{3}$

$\frac{21}{8} \longrightarrow \begin{array}{r} 2.62 \\ 8\overline{)21.00} \\ 16 \\ \hline 5\,0 \\ 4\,8 \\ \hline 20 \\ 16 \\ \hline 4 \end{array} \longrightarrow 2.62\frac{1}{2}$

Write a mixed decimal, in hundredths, for each fraction.

1. $\frac{5}{8}$ 2. $\frac{1}{3}$ 3. $\frac{11}{8}$ 4. $\frac{5}{6}$ 5. $\frac{5}{12}$ 6. $\frac{15}{8}$

Write a mixed decimal, in hundredths, for each fraction.

1. $\frac{7}{6}$
2. $\frac{4}{9}$
3. $\frac{5}{16}$
4. $\frac{5}{3}$
5. $\frac{7}{12}$

6. $\frac{7}{3}$
7. $\frac{9}{16}$
8. $\frac{17}{12}$
9. $\frac{27}{8}$
10. $\frac{15}{16}$

11. $\frac{17}{6}$
12. $\frac{9}{8}$
13. $\frac{31}{12}$
14. $\frac{21}{16}$
15. $\frac{11}{6}$

16. Copy this table and give the missing decimals in hundredths.

Common Fractions and Their Decimals				
Halves	*Fourths*	*Fifths*	*Sixths*	*Eighths*
$\frac{1}{2} = $ ▓	$\frac{1}{4} = $ ▓	$\frac{1}{5} = $ ▓	$\frac{1}{6} = $ ▓	$\frac{1}{8} = $ ▓
Thirds	$\frac{3}{4} = $ ▓	$\frac{2}{5} = $ ▓	$\frac{5}{6} = $ ▓	$\frac{3}{8} = $ ▓
$\frac{1}{3} = $ ▓		$\frac{3}{5} = $ ▓		$\frac{5}{8} = $ ▓
$\frac{2}{3} = $ ▓		$\frac{4}{5} = $ ▓		$\frac{7}{8} = $ ▓

Use the table in exercise 16 to help you express each mixed decimal as a mixed numeral.

17. $8.66\frac{2}{3}$
18. $3.87\frac{1}{2}$
19. $15.37\frac{1}{2}$
20. $9.83\frac{1}{3}$
21. $38.12\frac{1}{2}$
22. $47.33\frac{1}{3}$
23. $56.16\frac{2}{3}$
24. $30.37\frac{1}{2}$
25. $49.62\frac{1}{2}$
26. $87.12\frac{1}{2}$

The Sears Tower in Chicago is one of the world's tallest buildings, with a height of about 443.1 m.

Suppose a stairway to the top of the tower had steps each 0.175 m high. How many steps would there be in the stairway?

Answers for Self-check 1. 0.25 2. 0.2 3. 0.125 4. $0.\overline{6}$ 5. $0.1\overline{6}$ 6. yes, $\frac{3}{4} = \frac{9}{12}$ 7. no, $\frac{2}{3} \neq \frac{12}{16}$ 8. yes, $\frac{5}{6} = \frac{10}{12}$ 9. $\frac{2}{3}$ 10. $\frac{5}{6}$ 11. $\frac{3}{4}$ 12. $\frac{1}{5}$ 13. $\frac{3}{4}$ 14. < 15. < 16. > 17. < 18. $\frac{7}{2}$ 19. $\frac{17}{3}$ 20. $2.66\frac{2}{3}$ 21. $1.83\frac{1}{3}$

Self-check

Write a decimal or repeating decimal for each fraction.

1. $\frac{1}{4}$ 2. $\frac{1}{5}$ 3. $\frac{1}{8}$ 4. $\frac{2}{3}$ 5. $\frac{1}{6}$

Tell whether or not the two fractions are equivalent.

6. $\frac{3}{4}, \frac{9}{12}$ 7. $\frac{2}{3}, \frac{12}{16}$ 8. $\frac{5}{6}, \frac{10}{12}$

Find the lowest-terms fraction for each fraction or decimal.

9. $\frac{8}{12}$ 10. $\frac{25}{30}$ 11. $\frac{6}{8}$ 12. 0.2   13. 0.75

Give the correct symbol, < or >, for each ●.

14. $\frac{2}{5}$ ● $\frac{2}{3}$ 15. $\frac{1}{8}$ ● $\frac{1}{6}$ 16. $\frac{4}{5}$ ● $\frac{3}{4}$ 17. $\frac{7}{10}$ ● $\frac{3}{4}$

Write an improper fraction for each mixed numeral. 18. $3\frac{1}{2}$ 19. $5\frac{2}{3}$ Write the mixed decimal, in hundredths, for each fraction. ☆ 20. $\frac{8}{3}$ ☆ 21. $\frac{11}{6}$

Answers for Self-check—page 207

Test

Write a decimal or repeating decimal for each fraction.

1. $\frac{1}{2}$ 2. $\frac{3}{4}$ 3. $\frac{3}{5}$ 4. $\frac{1}{3}$ 5. $\frac{7}{9}$

Tell whether or not the two fractions are equivalent.

6. $\frac{2}{3}, \frac{6}{9}$ 7. $\frac{3}{4}, \frac{8}{12}$ 8. $\frac{3}{8}, \frac{6}{16}$

Find the lowest-terms fraction for each fraction or decimal.

9. $\frac{9}{12}$ 10. $\frac{15}{40}$ 11. $\frac{4}{6}$ 12. 0.4   13. 0.25

Give the correct symbol, < or >, for each ●.

14. $\frac{3}{4}$ ● $\frac{3}{5}$ 15. $\frac{1}{6}$ ● $\frac{1}{5}$ 16. $\frac{3}{8}$ ● $\frac{2}{5}$ 17. $\frac{1}{3}$ ● $\frac{3}{10}$

Write an improper fraction for each mixed numeral. 18. $2\frac{1}{3}$ 19. $6\frac{3}{4}$ Write the mixed decimal, in hundredths, for each fraction. ☆ 20. $\frac{5}{3}$ ☆ 21. $\frac{15}{4}$

The Rule of Pythagoras

Pythagoras was a Greek mathematician
and philosopher who lived in the 6th
century B.C. He was the leader of a
secret group called the Pythagoreans.
The Pythagoreans believed that the
natural numbers 1, 2, 3, 4, 5, . . . were
the most basic elements of nature.

The Pythagoreans discovered an
important rule about any right triangle.

Symbol of the Pythagoreans

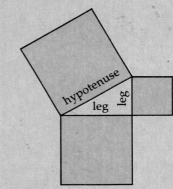

The Rule of Pythagoras

In any right triangle, the area of the
square on the hypotenuse is equal to
the sum of the areas of the squares on
the legs.

There are many different ways to show
that the Rule of Pythagoras is true. Try
the method suggested below.

1. Construct a right △*ABC* with
   squares on the sides, as in the
   figure.

2. Find point *O*, the center of the
   middle-sized square.

3. Draw $\overline{DE}$ through *O* parallel to $\overline{AB}$.
   Draw $\overline{GF}$ through *O* perpendicular
   to $\overline{DE}$.

4. Cut out the small square and the
   four regions formed in the middle-
   sized square.

5. Fit the five pieces together so they
   exactly cover the large square on
   the hypotenuse of the right triangle.

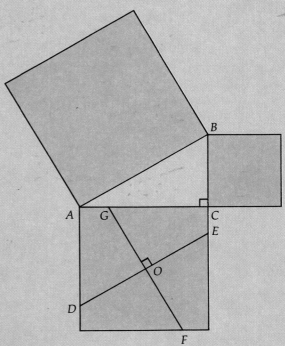

Adding and Subtracting Fractional Numbers

The examples below compare addition of
decimals and addition of fractions.

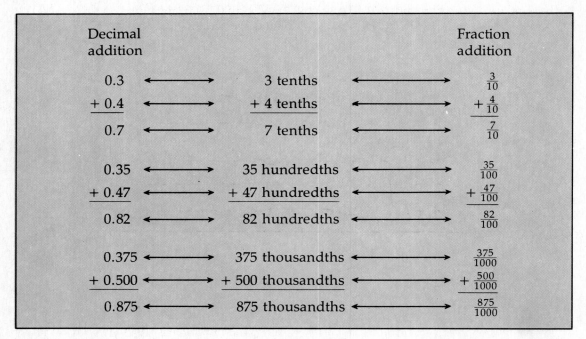

Decimal addition		Fraction addition
0.3 ⟷	3 tenths ⟷	$\frac{3}{10}$
+ 0.4 ⟷	+ 4 tenths ⟷	$+ \frac{4}{10}$
0.7 ⟷	7 tenths ⟷	$\frac{7}{10}$
0.35 ⟷	35 hundredths ⟷	$\frac{35}{100}$
+ 0.47 ⟷	+ 47 hundredths ⟷	$+ \frac{47}{100}$
0.82 ⟷	82 hundredths ⟷	$\frac{82}{100}$
0.375 ⟷	375 thousandths ⟷	$\frac{375}{1000}$
+ 0.500 ⟷	+ 500 thousandths ⟷	$+ \frac{500}{1000}$
0.875 ⟷	875 thousandths ⟷	$\frac{875}{1000}$

Find the sums.
Then write each decimal addition problem as
a fraction addition problem.

1. 0.2
   + 0.5

2. 0.17
   + 0.09

3. 0.53
   + 0.28

4. 0.125
   + 0.221

5. 0.9
   + 0.4

6. 0.16
   + 0.57

7. 0.638
   + 0.362

8. 0.8
   + 0.7

Add.

9. $\frac{7}{10}$
   $+ \frac{1}{10}$

10. $\frac{33}{100}$
   $+ \frac{52}{100}$

11. $\frac{3}{10}$
   $+ \frac{4}{10}$

12. $\frac{410}{1000}$
   $+ \frac{231}{1000}$

These examples compare subtraction of decimals
and subtraction of fractions.

Decimal subtraction			Fraction subtraction
0.8	⟷ 8 tenths ⟷		$\frac{8}{10}$
− 0.5	⟷ − 5 tenths ⟷		− $\frac{5}{10}$
0.3	⟷ 3 tenths ⟷		$\frac{3}{10}$
0.74	⟷ 74 hundredths ⟷		$\frac{74}{100}$
− 0.43	⟷ − 43 hundredths ⟷		− $\frac{43}{100}$
0.31	⟷ 31 hundredths ⟷		$\frac{31}{100}$
0.604	⟷ 604 thousandths ⟷		$\frac{604}{1000}$
− 0.391	⟷ − 391 thousandths ⟷		− $\frac{391}{1000}$
0.213	⟷ 213 thousandths ⟷		$\frac{213}{1000}$

Find the differences.
Then write each decimal subtraction problem as
a fraction subtraction problem.

1. $\begin{array}{r} 0.9 \\ -\ 0.6 \\ \hline \end{array}$
2. $\begin{array}{r} 0.52 \\ -\ 0.18 \\ \hline \end{array}$
3. $\begin{array}{r} 0.85 \\ -\ 0.24 \\ \hline \end{array}$
4. $\begin{array}{r} 0.649 \\ -\ 0.328 \\ \hline \end{array}$

5. $\begin{array}{r} 0.81 \\ -\ 0.46 \\ \hline \end{array}$
6. $\begin{array}{r} 0.941 \\ -\ 0.762 \\ \hline \end{array}$
7. $\begin{array}{r} 0.8 \\ -\ 0.3 \\ \hline \end{array}$
8. $\begin{array}{r} 0.485 \\ -\ 0.193 \\ \hline \end{array}$

Subtract.

9. $\begin{array}{r} \frac{4}{10} \\ -\ \frac{1}{10} \\ \hline \end{array}$
10. $\begin{array}{r} \frac{34}{100} \\ -\ \frac{21}{100} \\ \hline \end{array}$
11. $\begin{array}{r} \frac{92}{100} \\ -\ \frac{75}{100} \\ \hline \end{array}$
12. $\begin{array}{r} \frac{586}{1000} \\ -\ \frac{327}{1000} \\ \hline \end{array}$

Choosing common denominators

To add or subtract two fractional numbers, you could add or subtract their decimals.

Fractions	Decimals	Fractions	Decimals

$$\begin{array}{r}\frac{3}{8}\\+\frac{2}{8}\\\hline ?\end{array}$$

$$\begin{array}{r}0.375\\+0.250\\\hline 0.625\end{array}$$

$$\begin{array}{r}\frac{3}{8}\\-\frac{2}{8}\\\hline ?\end{array}$$

$$\begin{array}{r}0.375\\-0.250\\\hline 0.125\end{array}$$

When the denominators are the same, it is easy to use fractions.

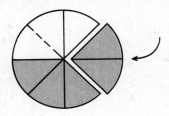

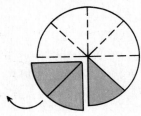

$$\frac{3}{8} + \frac{2}{8} = \frac{5}{8}$$

$$\frac{3}{8} - \frac{2}{8} = \frac{1}{8}$$

Other examples

$$\begin{array}{r}\frac{7}{8}\\+\frac{3}{8}\\\hline \frac{10}{8}=1\frac{1}{4}\end{array}$$

$$\begin{array}{r}\frac{5}{6}\\-\frac{1}{6}\\\hline \frac{4}{6}=\frac{2}{3}\end{array}$$

$$\begin{array}{r}\frac{3}{2}\\+\frac{1}{2}\\\hline \frac{4}{2}=2\end{array}$$

$$\begin{array}{r}\frac{4}{5}\\-\frac{1}{5}\\\hline \frac{3}{5}\end{array}$$

Find the sums and differences.

1. $\frac{3}{4} + \frac{3}{4}$ 2. $\frac{7}{10} + \frac{8}{10}$ 3. $\frac{5}{6} - \frac{1}{6}$ 4. $\frac{4}{3} - \frac{1}{3}$

5. $\begin{array}{r}\frac{2}{5}\\+\frac{1}{5}\\\hline\end{array}$ 6. $\begin{array}{r}\frac{1}{3}\\+\frac{1}{3}\\\hline\end{array}$ 7. $\begin{array}{r}\frac{9}{10}\\-\frac{1}{10}\\\hline\end{array}$ 8. $\begin{array}{r}\frac{3}{4}\\-\frac{1}{4}\\\hline\end{array}$

9. Give a rule for adding or subtracting fractions that have common denominators.

To add or subtract two fractional numbers which do not have common denominators, you could add or subtract their decimals.

Fractions	Decimals	Fractions	Decimals

$$\frac{1}{2} \longleftrightarrow \quad 0.50$$
$$+\frac{1}{4} \longleftrightarrow \quad +0.25$$
$$\overline{\quad ? \quad} \longleftrightarrow \quad \overline{0.75}$$

$$\frac{3}{8} \longleftrightarrow \quad 0.375$$
$$-\frac{1}{4} \longleftrightarrow \quad -0.250$$
$$\overline{\quad ? \quad} \longleftrightarrow \quad \overline{0.125}$$

You can add or subtract with fractions if you choose fractions that have a common denominator.

$$\frac{1}{2} \rightarrow \frac{2}{4} \rightarrow \frac{4}{8} \rightarrow \frac{6}{12} \cdots$$
$$+\frac{1}{4} \rightarrow +\frac{1}{4} \rightarrow +\frac{2}{8} \rightarrow +\frac{3}{12} \cdots$$
$$\overline{\quad} \quad \overline{\frac{3}{4}} \quad \overline{\frac{6}{8}} \quad \overline{\frac{9}{12}} \cdots$$

$$\frac{3}{8} \rightarrow \frac{3}{8} \rightarrow \frac{6}{16} \rightarrow \frac{9}{24} \cdots$$
$$-\frac{1}{4} \rightarrow -\frac{2}{8} \rightarrow -\frac{4}{16} \rightarrow -\frac{6}{24} \cdots$$
$$\overline{\quad} \quad \overline{\frac{1}{8}} \quad \overline{\frac{2}{16}} \quad \overline{\frac{3}{24}} \cdots$$

The work is usually easier if the **least common denominator** is chosen. The least common denominator is the **least common multiple** of the denominators.

Choose the least common denominator for each pair of fractions.

1. $\frac{3}{4}$ and $\frac{1}{8}$ 2. $\frac{1}{3}$ and $\frac{1}{2}$ 3. $\frac{1}{5}$ and $\frac{1}{2}$ 4. $\frac{5}{6}$ and $\frac{2}{3}$

5. $\frac{1}{3}$ and $\frac{3}{4}$ 6. $\frac{1}{3}$ and $\frac{4}{5}$ 7. $\frac{1}{2}$ and $\frac{3}{10}$ 8. $\frac{3}{4}$ and $\frac{3}{5}$

Give the missing numerators and then give the sum or difference.

9. $\frac{1}{2} = \frac{\blacksquare}{6}$
   $+\frac{1}{3} = \frac{\blacksquare}{6}$

10. $\frac{7}{8} = \frac{\blacksquare}{24}$
    $-\frac{2}{3} = \frac{\blacksquare}{24}$

11. $\frac{9}{10} = \frac{\blacksquare}{20}$
    $-\frac{3}{4} = \frac{\blacksquare}{20}$

12. $\frac{2}{3} = \frac{\blacksquare}{12}$
    $+\frac{1}{4} = \frac{\blacksquare}{12}$

13. $\frac{4}{5} = \frac{\blacksquare}{10}$
    $-\frac{3}{10} = \frac{\blacksquare}{10}$

14. $\frac{1}{4} = \frac{\blacksquare}{20}$
    $+\frac{3}{5} = \frac{\blacksquare}{20}$

15. $\frac{5}{8} = \frac{\blacksquare}{8}$
    $-\frac{1}{4} = \frac{\blacksquare}{8}$

16. $\frac{3}{4} = \frac{\blacksquare}{12}$
    $+\frac{1}{3} = \frac{\blacksquare}{12}$

Adding and subtracting fractional numbers

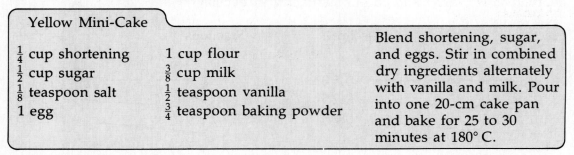

Yellow Mini-Cake

$\frac{1}{4}$ cup shortening
$\frac{1}{2}$ cup sugar
$\frac{1}{8}$ teaspoon salt
1 egg

1 cup flour
$\frac{3}{8}$ cup milk
$\frac{1}{2}$ teaspoon vanilla
$\frac{3}{4}$ teaspoon baking powder

Blend shortening, sugar, and eggs. Stir in combined dry ingredients alternately with vanilla and milk. Pour into one 20-cm cake pan and bake for 25 to 30 minutes at 180° C.

The salt and baking powder combined will fill how much of a teaspoon?

Finding the answer

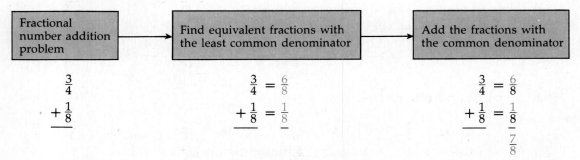

| Fractional number addition problem | Find equivalent fractions with the least common denominator | Add the fractions with the common denominator |

$$\begin{array}{r} \frac{3}{4} \\ +\frac{1}{8} \\ \hline \end{array}$$

$$\begin{array}{r} \frac{3}{4} = \frac{6}{8} \\ +\frac{1}{8} = \frac{1}{8} \\ \hline \end{array}$$

$$\begin{array}{r} \frac{3}{4} = \frac{6}{8} \\ +\frac{1}{8} = \frac{1}{8} \\ \hline \frac{7}{8} \end{array}$$

The combined salt and baking powder will fill $\frac{7}{8}$ of a teaspoon.

Other examples

$$\begin{array}{r} \frac{3}{4} = \frac{15}{20} \\ +\frac{2}{5} = \frac{8}{20} \\ \hline \frac{23}{20} = 1\frac{3}{20} \end{array}$$

$$\begin{array}{r} \frac{1}{6} = \frac{2}{12} \\ +\frac{7}{12} = \frac{7}{12} \\ \hline \frac{9}{12} = \frac{3}{4} \end{array}$$

$$\begin{array}{r} \frac{7}{12} = \frac{7}{12} \\ +\frac{3}{4} = \frac{9}{12} \\ \hline \frac{16}{12} = 1\frac{4}{12} = 1\frac{1}{3} \end{array}$$

Find the sums.

1. $\begin{array}{r} \frac{1}{2} \\ +\frac{3}{10} \\ \hline \end{array}$

2. $\begin{array}{r} \frac{2}{5} \\ +\frac{1}{3} \\ \hline \end{array}$

3. $\begin{array}{r} \frac{1}{4} \\ +\frac{3}{8} \\ \hline \end{array}$

4. $\begin{array}{r} \frac{2}{3} \\ +\frac{1}{2} \\ \hline \end{array}$

5. $\begin{array}{r} \frac{1}{10} \\ +\frac{2}{5} \\ \hline \end{array}$

6. $\begin{array}{r} \frac{3}{8} \\ +\frac{3}{4} \\ \hline \end{array}$

7. $\begin{array}{r} \frac{1}{2} \\ +\frac{2}{5} \\ \hline \end{array}$

8. $\begin{array}{r} \frac{1}{3} \\ +\frac{3}{8} \\ \hline \end{array}$

9. $\begin{array}{r} \frac{7}{10} \\ +\frac{5}{6} \\ \hline \end{array}$

10. $\begin{array}{r} \frac{2}{3} \\ +\frac{1}{6} \\ \hline \end{array}$

Subtracting fractional numbers is much like adding.

Examples

$$\frac{3}{4} = \frac{9}{12}$$
$$-\frac{1}{6} = \frac{2}{12}$$
$$\frac{7}{12}$$

$$\frac{1}{2} = \frac{4}{8}$$
$$-\frac{1}{8} = \frac{1}{8}$$
$$\frac{3}{8}$$

$$\frac{7}{10} = \frac{21}{30}$$
$$-\frac{1}{6} = \frac{5}{30}$$
$$\frac{16}{30} = \frac{8}{15}$$

Find the differences.

1. $\frac{1}{2}$ $-\frac{2}{5}$

2. $\frac{3}{8}$ $-\frac{1}{4}$

3. $\frac{3}{8}$ $-\frac{1}{3}$

4. $\frac{2}{3}$ $-\frac{1}{2}$

5. $\frac{2}{5}$ $-\frac{1}{3}$

6. $\frac{2}{5}$ $-\frac{1}{10}$

7. $\frac{3}{4}$ $-\frac{3}{8}$

8. $\frac{2}{3}$ $-\frac{1}{4}$

9. $\frac{1}{2}$ $-\frac{3}{10}$

10. $\frac{1}{4}$ $-\frac{1}{5}$

Find the sums and differences.

11. $\frac{3}{4}$ $+\frac{2}{3}$

12. $\frac{1}{2}$ $-\frac{1}{5}$

13. $\frac{7}{10}$ $-\frac{5}{10}$

14. $\frac{1}{8}$ $+\frac{5}{6}$

15. $\frac{2}{5}$ $+\frac{3}{4}$

16. $\frac{9}{10}$ $+\frac{7}{8}$

17. $\frac{2}{3}$ $-\frac{1}{8}$

18. $\frac{3}{8}$ $+\frac{7}{8}$

19. $\frac{5}{8}$ $-\frac{3}{10}$

20. $\frac{9}{10}$ $-\frac{1}{2}$

21. What fraction of a cup would the butter and cherries make combined?

22. If the frosting recipe were doubled, how much cherry juice would be needed? How much chopped cherries?

Frosting
$\frac{1}{6}$ cup butter
$1\frac{3}{4}$ cup confectioner's sugar
$\frac{1}{8}$ cup chopped cherries
1 egg yolk
$\frac{1}{4}$ cup cherry juice
Blend the butter

A flea 1.5 mm tall has been known to jump up to 330 mm. How many times its height is this jump?

If persons 175 cm tall could jump that many times their height, how many meters high could they jump? How many kilometers?

Adding with mixed numerals

An X-ray technician spent $3\frac{1}{2}$ hours taking X-rays of patients and $3\frac{3}{4}$ hours developing the X-ray film. How many hours in all did the X-ray technician work?

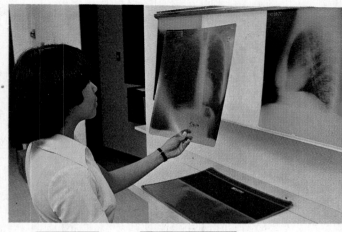

Finding the answer

Mixed numeral addition problem	→	Rewrite the fractions using the least common denominator	→	Add the fractions	→	Add the whole numbers Rename if necessary

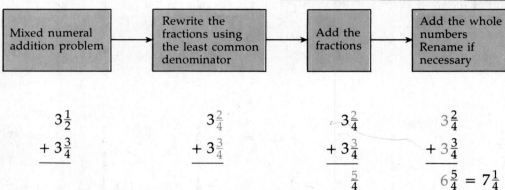

$$3\frac{1}{2}$$
$$+\ 3\frac{3}{4}$$

$$3\frac{2}{4}$$
$$+\ 3\frac{3}{4}$$

$$3\frac{2}{4}$$
$$+\ 3\frac{3}{4}$$
$$\frac{5}{4}$$

$$3\frac{2}{4}$$
$$+\ 3\frac{3}{4}$$
$$6\frac{5}{4} = 7\frac{1}{4}$$

The X-ray technician worked for $7\frac{1}{4}$ hours.

Other examples

$$4\frac{5}{6} = 4\frac{5}{6}$$
$$+\ 2\frac{2}{3} = 2\frac{4}{6}$$
$$6\frac{9}{6} = 7\frac{3}{6} = 7\frac{1}{2}$$

$$3\frac{1}{5} = 3\frac{2}{10}$$
$$+\ 2\frac{3}{10} = 2\frac{3}{10}$$
$$5\frac{5}{10} = 5\frac{1}{2}$$

Find the sums.

1. $5\frac{1}{4}$
$+\ 2\frac{7}{8}$

2. $3\frac{9}{10}$
$+\ 1\frac{2}{5}$

3. $2\frac{1}{2}$
$+\ 3\frac{3}{4}$

4. $6\frac{5}{8}$
$+\ 1\frac{3}{4}$

5. $2\frac{7}{10}$
$+\ 5\frac{1}{2}$

6. $14\frac{1}{4}$
$+\ 7\frac{1}{3}$

7. $26\frac{5}{6}$
$+\ 37\frac{2}{3}$

8. $42\frac{3}{4}$
$+\ 13\frac{5}{6}$

9. $37\frac{2}{3}$
$+\ 14\frac{3}{4}$

10. $53\frac{1}{2}$
$+\ 29\frac{2}{3}$

Find the sums.

1. $4\frac{1}{2}$
$+ 7\frac{1}{3}$

2. $3\frac{2}{3}$
$+ 6\frac{1}{4}$

3. $9\frac{1}{5}$
$+ 7\frac{9}{10}$

4. $8\frac{3}{8}$
$+ 5\frac{1}{2}$

5. $6\frac{5}{6}$
$+ 9\frac{1}{3}$

6. $27\frac{2}{3}$
$+ 43\frac{1}{6}$

7. $82\frac{7}{8}$
$+ 75\frac{1}{2}$

8. $36\frac{5}{6}$
$+ 95\frac{2}{3}$

9. $88\frac{3}{4}$
$+ 14\frac{2}{3}$

10. $17\frac{3}{10}$
$+ 95\frac{3}{4}$

Find the sums.

Example: $\frac{1}{2} = \frac{6}{12}$
$\frac{1}{4} = \frac{3}{12}$
$+ \frac{5}{6} = \frac{10}{12}$
$\frac{19}{12} = 1\frac{7}{12}$

11. $\frac{1}{2}$
$\frac{1}{3}$
$+ \frac{1}{4}$

12. $\frac{1}{4}$
$\frac{2}{3}$
$+ \frac{1}{2}$

13. $\frac{3}{8}$
$\frac{1}{4}$
$+ \frac{1}{2}$

14. $\frac{3}{4}$
$\frac{2}{3}$
$+ \frac{1}{6}$

15. $\frac{1}{2}$
$\frac{3}{10}$
$+ \frac{4}{5}$

16. $\frac{1}{8}$
$\frac{1}{2}$
$+ \frac{1}{4}$

17. $\frac{7}{8}$
$\frac{1}{2}$
$+ \frac{3}{4}$

18. $\frac{5}{6}$
$\frac{1}{8}$
$+ \frac{1}{2}$

19. $\frac{1}{4}$
$\frac{5}{8}$
$+ \frac{1}{6}$

20. $\frac{2}{3}$
$\frac{1}{2}$
$+ \frac{5}{6}$

21. $3\frac{1}{2}$
$4\frac{1}{4}$
$+ 7\frac{1}{2}$

22. $12\frac{3}{4}$
$11\frac{1}{2}$
$+ 14\frac{1}{8}$

23. $23\frac{1}{4}$
$48\frac{1}{2}$
$+ 17\frac{1}{4}$

24. $56\frac{2}{3}$
$75\frac{1}{6}$
$+ 92\frac{1}{3}$

25. $37\frac{5}{6}$
$48\frac{1}{3}$
$+ 16\frac{1}{2}$

26. $27\frac{1}{4}$
$39\frac{3}{8}$
$+ 18\frac{1}{2}$

27. $27\frac{7}{16}$
$28\frac{1}{4}$
$+ 26\frac{5}{8}$

Just for fun, try these.

(Your age) · 21 · 481

(Last two digits of year you were born) · 37 · 273

(Your mass in kilograms) · 91 · 111

28. A lab technician worked with patients for $5\frac{3}{4}$ hours and spent $3\frac{1}{4}$ hours making tests in the lab. How many hours in all did the lab technician work?

More practice, page 388, Set A

Subtracting with mixed numerals

A person's age in years and months
can be written as a mixed numeral.
Bonnie is $13\frac{1}{6}$ years old.
Fred is $11\frac{3}{4}$ years old.
How much older is Bonnie?

Bonnie $13\frac{1}{6}$ years
Fred $11\frac{3}{4}$ years
Susan $12\frac{1}{3}$ years
Tom $12\frac{1}{2}$ years

Finding the answer

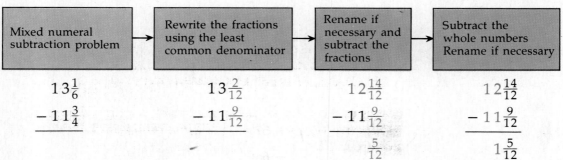

| Mixed numeral subtraction problem | → | Rewrite the fractions using the least common denominator | → | Rename if necessary and subtract the fractions | → | Subtract the whole numbers Rename if necessary |

$$13\frac{1}{6} \qquad\qquad 13\frac{2}{12} \qquad\qquad 12\frac{14}{12} \qquad\qquad 12\frac{14}{12}$$
$$-11\frac{3}{4} \qquad\qquad -11\frac{9}{12} \qquad\qquad -11\frac{9}{12} \qquad\qquad -11\frac{9}{12}$$
$$\overline{\phantom{13\frac{1}{6}}} \qquad\qquad \overline{\phantom{13\frac{2}{12}}} \qquad\qquad \overline{\phantom{12\frac{14}{12}}}\;\frac{5}{12} \qquad\qquad \overline{\phantom{12\frac{14}{12}}}\;1\frac{5}{12}$$

Bonnie is $1\frac{5}{12}$ years older than Fred.

Other examples

$$13\frac{1}{6} = 13\frac{1}{6} = 12\frac{7}{6} \qquad\qquad 16 \;\;= 15\frac{3}{3}$$
$$-12\frac{1}{2} = 12\frac{3}{6} = 12\frac{3}{6} \qquad\qquad -13\frac{2}{3} = 13\frac{2}{3}$$
$$\overline{\;\frac{4}{6} = \frac{2}{3}} \qquad\qquad \overline{\;2\frac{1}{3}}$$

Find the differences.

1. $14\frac{1}{2}$
   $-10\frac{3}{4}$

2. $12\frac{1}{3}$
   $-9\frac{1}{6}$

3. $17\frac{2}{3}$
   $-12\frac{1}{6}$

4. $15\frac{1}{2}$
   $-14\frac{5}{12}$

5. 13
   $-11\frac{5}{6}$

6. $18\frac{1}{12}$
   $-12\frac{2}{3}$

7. $17\frac{1}{4}$
   $-13\frac{1}{2}$

8. $16\frac{1}{2}$
   $-12\frac{5}{6}$

9. $19\frac{1}{6}$
   -16

10. $14\frac{1}{4}$
   $-8\frac{1}{3}$

Find the differences.

1. $26\frac{1}{2}$
   $-13\frac{1}{8}$

2. $83\frac{7}{10}$
   $-56\frac{1}{2}$

3. $70\frac{1}{2}$
   $-12\frac{3}{4}$

4. $143\frac{3}{10}$
   $-71\frac{1}{2}$

5. $62\frac{7}{8}$
   $-18\frac{1}{3}$

6. $91\frac{1}{8}$
   $-43\frac{1}{6}$

7. $53\frac{1}{4}$
   $-52\frac{2}{3}$

8. $76\frac{3}{8}$
   $-14\frac{3}{4}$

9. 241
   $-78\frac{1}{8}$

10. $82\frac{3}{10}$
    $-49\frac{1}{3}$

11. $75\frac{7}{10}$
    $-55\frac{3}{4}$

12. $42\frac{1}{2}$
    $-18\frac{9}{10}$

13. $61\frac{3}{5}$
    $-34\frac{5}{8}$

14. $127\frac{2}{3}$
    $-67\frac{3}{4}$

15. 54
    $-21\frac{1}{6}$

Find the sums and differences.

16. $23\frac{1}{2}$
    $+47\frac{3}{4}$

17. $75\frac{1}{8}$
    $-18\frac{1}{6}$

18. $56\frac{1}{8}$
    $+79\frac{3}{16}$

19. $16\frac{1}{10}$
    $-7\frac{1}{8}$

20. $132\frac{1}{5}$
    $-94\frac{2}{3}$

21. $83\frac{7}{8}$
    $+91\frac{7}{10}$

22. $48\frac{1}{2}$
    $-19\frac{5}{6}$

23. $57\frac{3}{4}$
    $+68\frac{2}{3}$

24. $92\frac{5}{6}$
    $+18\frac{1}{3}$

25. $74\frac{1}{8}$
    $-27\frac{3}{5}$

26. John is $15\frac{1}{3}$ years old. Jan is $13\frac{3}{4}$ years old. How much older is John than Jan?

☆ 27. Sid is $11\frac{2}{3}$ years old. Sid's sister, Ann, was $2\frac{1}{2}$ years old when Sid was born. How old is Ann now?

Begin with any two whole numbers. Start a column and keep adding each sum to the number above it until you have ten numbers. The sum of all ten numbers is 11 times the seventh number. Check it. Try it with two other starting numbers.

2	①
8	②
$\overline{10}$	③
$\overline{18}$	④
$\overline{28}$	⑤
$\overline{46}$	⑥
$\overline{74}$	⑦
$\overline{120}$	⑧
$\overline{194}$	⑨
$\overline{314}$	⑩

More practice, page 388, Set B

Practicing your skills

Add.

1. $\frac{3}{8} + \frac{1}{4}$ 2. $\frac{1}{3} + \frac{1}{2}$ 3. $\frac{3}{4} + \frac{1}{2}$ 4. $\frac{1}{2} + \frac{3}{5}$

5. $\frac{5}{6} + \frac{5}{6}$ 6. $\frac{7}{8} + \frac{3}{4}$ 7. $\frac{3}{10} + \frac{1}{2}$ 8. $\frac{9}{16} + \frac{1}{4}$

9. $\frac{2}{3}$ 10. $\frac{9}{10}$ 11. $\frac{3}{4}$ 12. $\frac{5}{6}$
   $+ \frac{1}{2}$ $+ \frac{1}{4}$ $+ \frac{2}{5}$ $+ \frac{1}{3}$

13. $2\frac{1}{2}$ 14. $3\frac{2}{3}$ 15. $6\frac{7}{8}$ 16. $12\frac{3}{4}$
    $+ 4\frac{1}{4}$ $+ 7\frac{2}{3}$ $+ 5\frac{1}{2}$ $+ 19\frac{3}{4}$

17. $2\frac{1}{3}$ 18. $12\frac{3}{10}$ 19. $32\frac{1}{4}$ 20. $127\frac{1}{2}$
    $3\frac{1}{2}$ $15\frac{1}{2}$ $26\frac{1}{2}$ $156\frac{7}{8}$
    $+ 5\frac{2}{3}$ $+ 9\frac{4}{5}$ $+ 28\frac{3}{4}$ $+ 193\frac{1}{4}$

Subtract.

21. $\frac{9}{10} - \frac{1}{2}$ 22. $\frac{2}{3} - \frac{1}{3}$ 23. $\frac{3}{4} - \frac{5}{8}$ 24. $\frac{9}{10} - \frac{3}{4}$

25. $\frac{2}{3} - \frac{1}{2}$ 26. $\frac{7}{16} - \frac{1}{4}$ 27. $\frac{7}{8} - \frac{3}{4}$ 28. $\frac{5}{6} - \frac{2}{3}$

29. $7\frac{7}{10}$ 30. $18\frac{3}{4}$ 31. 27 32. $37\frac{1}{2}$
    $- 4\frac{1}{2}$ $- 13\frac{1}{4}$ $- 20\frac{3}{8}$ $- 25\frac{1}{3}$

33. $13\frac{3}{4}$ 34. $21\frac{1}{2}$ 35. $56\frac{1}{3}$ 36. $76\frac{3}{10}$
    $- 9$ $- 16\frac{3}{4}$ $- 28\frac{1}{2}$ $- 59\frac{4}{5}$

37. $91\frac{2}{3}$ 38. 127 39. 700 40. $374\frac{3}{8}$
    $- 50\frac{3}{4}$ $- 66\frac{2}{3}$ $- 596\frac{1}{2}$ $- 125\frac{7}{8}$

1. John practiced on his trumpet $\frac{3}{4}$ hour on Monday, $\frac{1}{2}$ hour on Tuesday, and $\frac{3}{4}$ hour on Thursday. How long did he practice in all?

2. Joan watched TV for $1\frac{1}{2}$ hours. Then she did homework for $\frac{3}{4}$ hour. How long did she spend on these activities?

3. A restaurant ordered 20 pies from a bakery. The restaurant sold $17\frac{3}{4}$ of the pies in one day. How much pie was left?

4. Linda drove to the beach in $1\frac{3}{4}$ hours. She took $2\frac{1}{4}$ hours to drive back home. How much longer did she take to drive back home?

5. Terry, Dave, and George shared a large pizza. Terry ate $\frac{1}{3}$ of it. Dave ate $\frac{1}{4}$ of it, and George ate $\frac{1}{3}$ of it. What part of the pizza was left?

Add, subtract, multiply, or divide.

6.
```
   27.6
   38.7
 + 29.5
```

7.
```
   2.78
   0.652
   1.7
 + 4.83
```

8.
```
   6.25
 - 1.89
```

9.
```
   93.06
 - 75.19
```

10.
```
   90
 - 7.83
```

11.
```
   56.3
 ×   27
```

12.
```
   8.27
 ×  0.4
```

13.
```
   52.34
 ×  0.07
```

14.
```
   6.271
 ×   0.3
```

15.
```
   56.8
 × 0.09
```

16. $6\overline{)14.04}$

17. $3.7\overline{)22.94}$

18. $0.8\overline{)0.456}$

19. $35\overline{)842.8}$

20. $16\overline{)5}$

Answers for Self-check 1. $\frac{11}{12}$ 2. $\frac{13}{24}$ 3. $\frac{2}{10}$ or $\frac{1}{5}$ 4. $\frac{1}{8}$ 5. $15\frac{5}{6}$ 6. $9\frac{1}{8}$ 7. $\frac{19}{24}$ 8. $55\frac{1}{4}$
9. $23\frac{7}{12}$ 10. $29\frac{4}{6}$ or $29\frac{2}{3}$ 11. $5\frac{5}{12}$ h 12. $1\frac{1}{4}$ h

Self-check

Find the sums and differences.

1. $\frac{1}{4}$
   $+\ \frac{2}{3}$

2. $\frac{1}{6}$
   $+\ \frac{3}{8}$

3. $\frac{7}{10}$
   $-\ \frac{1}{2}$

4. $\frac{7}{8}$
   $-\ \frac{3}{4}$

5. $7\frac{1}{2}$
   $+\ 8\frac{1}{3}$

6. $3\frac{3}{4}$
   $+\ 5\frac{3}{8}$

7. $\frac{1}{4}$
   $\frac{3}{8}$
   $+\ \frac{1}{6}$

8. $68\frac{3}{4}$
   $-\ 13\frac{1}{2}$

9. $43\frac{1}{4}$
   $-\ 19\frac{2}{3}$

10. $55\frac{1}{6}$
    $-\ 25\frac{1}{2}$

11. On Friday, Pat spent $1\frac{3}{4}$ hours baby-sitting. On Saturday, she baby-sat for $3\frac{2}{3}$ hours. How many hours did she babysit in all?

12. Dave played the piano for $1\frac{1}{4}$ hours. Then he played soccer for $2\frac{1}{2}$ hours. How many more hours did he spend playing soccer?

Answers for Self-check—page 221

Test

Find the sums and differences.

1. $\frac{1}{3}$
   $+\ \frac{3}{4}$

2. $\frac{5}{8}$
   $+\ \frac{1}{6}$

3. $\frac{7}{10}$
   $-\ \frac{1}{4}$

4. $\frac{5}{8}$
   $-\ \frac{1}{4}$

5. $9\frac{1}{6}$
   $+\ 5\frac{2}{3}$

6. $2\frac{7}{8}$
   $+\ 4\frac{1}{4}$

7. $\frac{1}{2}$
   $\frac{5}{6}$
   $+\ \frac{1}{3}$

8. $57\frac{2}{3}$
   $-\ 14\frac{1}{6}$

9. $82\frac{1}{8}$
   $-\ 27\frac{1}{2}$

10. $64\frac{1}{4}$
    $-\ 34\frac{5}{6}$

11. Jim read for $\frac{3}{4}$ hour. Then he watched TV for $1\frac{1}{2}$ hours. How many hours is this in all?

12. Rene spent $2\frac{1}{4}$ hours working on a macrame plant hanger on Wednesday. On Thursday, she worked $1\frac{1}{2}$ hours. How many more hours did she work on Wednesday?

A Tetrahedron Bracelet

1. Make a copy of this pattern on sturdy paper. Each small equilateral triangle should be at least 3 cm on a side.

2. Number the tabs and edges as shown.

3. Cut out the pattern on the solid black lines.

4. Fold the red lines in one direction and the dotted lines in the other.

5. Match the tabs with the edges that have the same number and tape the edges together.

The pattern will form a bracelet of ten tetrahedrons.

The tetrahedrons will rotate when the bracelet is twisted.

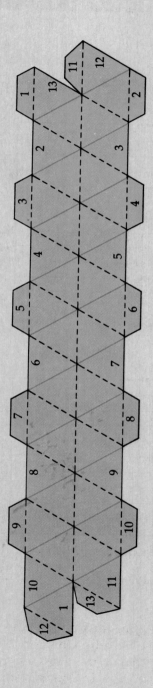

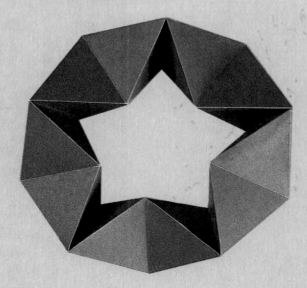

Multiplying and Dividing Fractional Numbers

The examples below compare multiplication
of decimals and multiplication of fractions.

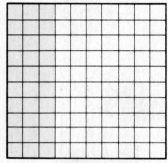 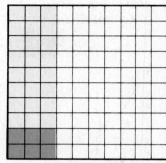 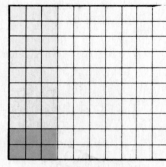

Decimals 0.3 shaded yellow	0.2 of 0.3 shaded orange	0.2 · 0.3 = 0.06
Fractions $\frac{3}{10}$	$\frac{2}{10}$ of $\frac{3}{10}$	$\frac{2}{10} \cdot \frac{3}{10} = \frac{6}{100}$

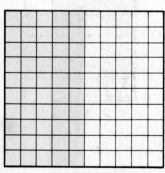 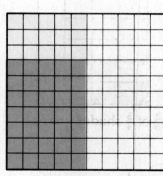 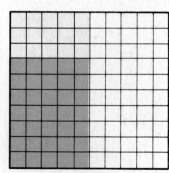

Decimals 0.5 shaded yellow	0.7 of 0.5 shaded orange	0.7 · 0.5 = 0.35
Fractions $\frac{5}{10}$	$\frac{7}{10}$ of $\frac{5}{10}$	$\frac{7}{10} \cdot \frac{5}{10} = \frac{35}{100}$

Find each product. Then rewrite the problem using fractions.

1. 0.2 · 0.7

2. 0.5 · 0.9

3. 0.3 · 0.07

4. 0.8 · 0.09

5. 0.1 · 0.25

6. 0.06 · 0.08

7. 0.2 · 0.006

8. 0.007 · 0.011

Give the missing products.

1.

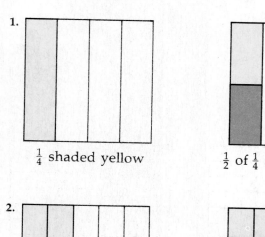

$\frac{1}{4}$ shaded yellow $\frac{1}{2}$ of $\frac{1}{4}$ shaded orange $\frac{1}{2} \cdot \frac{1}{4} = $ ▥

2.

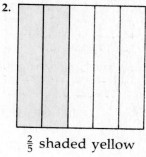 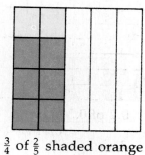 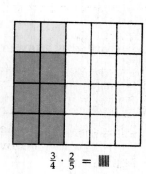

$\frac{2}{5}$ shaded yellow $\frac{3}{4}$ of $\frac{2}{5}$ shaded orange $\frac{3}{4} \cdot \frac{2}{5} = $ ▥

3.

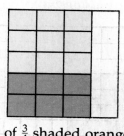 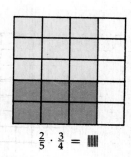

$\frac{3}{4}$ shaded yellow $\frac{2}{5}$ of $\frac{3}{4}$ shaded orange $\frac{2}{5} \cdot \frac{3}{4} = $ ▥

4.

    1   1   1

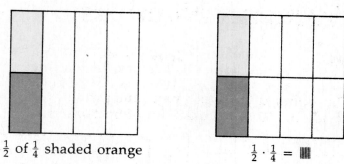

$\frac{1}{4}$ of 3 $\frac{1}{4} \cdot 3 = $ ▥

5.

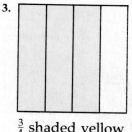

3 times $\frac{1}{4}$

$3 \cdot \frac{1}{4} = $ ▥

6. Give a simple rule for multiplying two fractional numbers.

Multiplying fractional numbers

On Monday, Tony practiced his music for $\frac{3}{4}$ of an hour. On Tuesday, he practiced only $\frac{1}{2}$ that long. What part of an hour did Tony practice on Tuesday?

Finding the answer

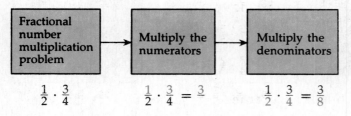

Fractional number multiplication problem	Multiply the numerators	Multiply the denominators

$$\frac{1}{2} \cdot \frac{3}{4} \qquad\qquad \frac{1}{2} \cdot \frac{3}{4} = \frac{3}{} \qquad\qquad \frac{1}{2} \cdot \frac{3}{4} = \frac{3}{8}$$

Tony practiced about $\frac{3}{8}$ of an hour on Tuesday.

Other examples

$$\frac{3}{8} \cdot \frac{4}{5} = \frac{12}{40} = \frac{3}{10} \qquad\qquad \frac{5}{6} \cdot \frac{2}{15} = \frac{10}{90} = \frac{1}{9}$$

Short cut: Divide numerators and denominators by the same number *before* multiplying.

$$\frac{3}{\overset{}{\underset{2}{\cancel{8}}}} \cdot \frac{\overset{1}{\cancel{4}}}{5} = \frac{3}{10} \qquad\qquad \frac{\overset{1}{\cancel{5}}}{\underset{3}{\cancel{6}}} \cdot \frac{\overset{1}{\cancel{2}}}{\underset{3}{\cancel{15}}} = \frac{1}{9}$$

Find the products.

1. $\frac{4}{5} \cdot \frac{2}{3} = d$ **2.** $\frac{2}{7} \cdot \frac{5}{8} = b$ **3.** $\frac{5}{6} \cdot \frac{3}{4} = k$ **4.** $\frac{1}{5} \cdot \frac{2}{3} = g$

5. $\frac{7}{12} \cdot \frac{4}{7} = h$ **6.** $\frac{3}{4} \cdot \frac{2}{5} = p$ **7.** $\frac{3}{10} \cdot \frac{1}{2} = a$ **8.** $\frac{3}{8} \cdot \frac{4}{9} = j$

9. $\frac{1}{2} \cdot \frac{3}{8} = l$ **10.** $\frac{4}{5} \cdot \frac{1}{8} = q$ **11.** $\frac{3}{5} \cdot \frac{5}{6} = f$ **12.** $\frac{1}{4} \cdot \frac{4}{9} = c$

13. $\frac{7}{10} \cdot \frac{2}{5} = e$ **14.** $\frac{3}{4} \cdot \frac{1}{6} = m$ **15.** $\frac{2}{3} \cdot \frac{3}{5} = i$ **16.** $\frac{2}{9} \cdot \frac{5}{8} = n$

Find the products.

1. $\frac{3}{10} \cdot \frac{2}{5} = c$ 2. $\frac{1}{2} \cdot \frac{5}{8} = g$

3. $\frac{3}{4} \cdot \frac{1}{3} = f$ 4. $\frac{3}{5} \cdot \frac{4}{15} = a$

5. $\frac{5}{12} \cdot \frac{4}{5} = j$ 6. $\frac{3}{4} \cdot \frac{2}{9} = l$

7. $\frac{5}{8} \cdot \frac{1}{3} = b$ 8. $\frac{3}{4} \cdot \frac{2}{5} = h$

9. $\frac{2}{3} \cdot \frac{3}{10} = c$ 10. $\frac{7}{9} \cdot \frac{3}{4} = d$

11. $\frac{2}{5} \cdot \frac{3}{8} = i$ 12. $\frac{5}{8} \cdot \frac{4}{5} = k$

Solve the equations.

13. $\frac{5}{12} \cdot \frac{3}{5} = c$ 14. $\frac{3}{8} \cdot \frac{4}{9} = j$

15. $\frac{3}{4} \cdot \frac{3}{5} = g$ 16. $\frac{5}{9} \cdot \frac{3}{8} = b$

17. $\frac{3}{4} \cdot \frac{2}{3} = b$ 18. $\frac{3}{5} \cdot \frac{2}{3} = a$

19. $\frac{3}{10} \cdot \frac{2}{5} = i$ 20. $\frac{1}{2} \cdot \frac{5}{7} = d$

21. $\frac{7}{8} \cdot \frac{3}{4} = f$ 22. $\frac{3}{4} \cdot \frac{4}{15} = l$

23. $\frac{3}{8} \cdot \frac{4}{5} = k$ 24. $\frac{2}{5} \cdot \frac{3}{8} = e$

25. Charles can walk to school in $\frac{2}{3}$ of an hour. He can ride his bicycle to school in $\frac{1}{2}$ that time. What part of an hour does he take when he rides?

26. Karen usually takes $\frac{1}{2}$ hour to eat breakfast. When she is in a hurry, she eats in $\frac{3}{4}$ that time. What part of an hour does she take to eat when she is in a hurry?

Only about 0.125 of an iceberg shows above the surface of the water. A large iceberg may have a mass of 900 000 metric tons. About how many metric tons is the mass of the part of the iceberg that is above the water? What is the mass of the part of the iceberg that is hidden under the water?

Multiplying with mixed numerals

Jerry works as a typist for a scientific company. He estimates that he can type about $5\frac{1}{2}$ of the specialized pages an hour. If Jerry works $7\frac{1}{2}$ hours a day, about how many pages can he type in a day?

Finding the answer

Mixed numeral multiplication problem	Write the mixed numerals as improper fractions	Multiply the improper fractions

$$5\frac{1}{2} \cdot 7\frac{1}{2} \qquad\qquad \frac{11}{2} \cdot \frac{15}{2} \qquad\qquad \frac{11}{2} \cdot \frac{15}{2} = \frac{165}{4} = 41\frac{1}{4}$$

Jerry can type about 41 pages in a day.

Other examples

$$2\frac{3}{5} \cdot 1\frac{2}{3} \qquad\qquad\qquad\qquad 6 \cdot 1\frac{3}{8}$$

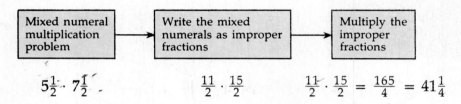

$$\frac{13}{5} \cdot \frac{5}{3} = \frac{13}{3} = 4\frac{1}{3} \qquad\qquad \frac{6}{1} \cdot \frac{11}{8} = \frac{33}{4} = 8\frac{1}{4}$$

Find the products.

1. $1\frac{1}{4} \cdot 2\frac{2}{5} = e$ 2. $5 \cdot 3\frac{1}{3} = b$ 3. $2\frac{3}{8} \cdot 4 = h$ 4. $\frac{2}{3} \cdot 4\frac{1}{5} = d$

5. $3\frac{1}{2} \cdot 2\frac{1}{4} = g$ 6. $3\frac{3}{4} \cdot 2\frac{2}{5} = k$ 7. $8 \cdot 1\frac{1}{8} = a$ 8. $1\frac{2}{3} \cdot \frac{3}{5} = i$

9. $4\frac{1}{8} \cdot 2\frac{2}{3} = c$ 10. $5 \cdot 7\frac{1}{2} = j$ 11. $\frac{2}{3} \cdot 1\frac{1}{2} = l$ 12. $1\frac{1}{3} \cdot 2\frac{1}{4} = f$

13. $\frac{4}{5} \cdot 2\frac{3}{4} = m$ 14. $6\frac{1}{3} \cdot \frac{3}{8} = q$ 15. $6 \cdot 4\frac{1}{3} = n$ 16. $1\frac{2}{3} \cdot 2\frac{3}{4} = p$

	When the product of two numbers is 1, the numbers are **reciprocals** of each other.

Examples:

Since $\frac{2}{3} \cdot \frac{3}{2} = 1$,

$\frac{2}{3}$ is the reciprocal of $\frac{3}{2}$.

$\frac{3}{2}$ is the reciprocal of $\frac{2}{3}$.

Since $4 \cdot \frac{1}{4} = 1$,

4 is the reciprocal of $\frac{1}{4}$.

$\frac{1}{4}$ is the reciprocal of 4.

Give the reciprocal of each number.

1. $\frac{5}{8}$ 2. $\frac{7}{10}$ 3. $\frac{7}{2}$ 4. $\frac{3}{8}$ 5. $\frac{10}{3}$ 6. $\frac{1}{2}$ 7. $\frac{1}{10}$

8. 6   9. 3   10. 7   11. $1\frac{1}{4}$ 12. $2\frac{1}{8}$ 13. 1   14. $4\frac{1}{2}$

Find the products.

15. $\frac{2}{5} \cdot 2\frac{1}{2}$ 16. $\frac{7}{8} \cdot 1\frac{3}{8}$ 17. $1\frac{1}{10} \cdot \frac{10}{11}$ 18. $2\frac{3}{4} \cdot \frac{4}{11}$

19. $\frac{1}{8} \cdot 4$ 20. $1\frac{1}{2} \cdot \frac{2}{3}$ 21. $4\frac{2}{3} \cdot \frac{3}{14}$ 22. $1\frac{3}{4} \cdot \frac{7}{4}$

23. $2\frac{1}{4} \cdot \frac{4}{9}$ 24. $3\frac{4}{5} \cdot \frac{5}{19}$ 25. $1\frac{3}{8} \cdot \frac{9}{8}$ 26. $\frac{7}{8} \cdot 1\frac{1}{7}$

27. In exercises 15 through 26, which pairs of factors are reciprocals of each other?

Calculator problems

Find the decimal reciprocals of these decimals.

28. 0.625   29. 0.64   30. 0.125   31. 0.15625

32. 3.125   33. 6.25   34. 0.3125   35. 3.2

Two numbers are reciprocals of each other. One number is 25 times as large as the other. Find the two numbers.

Dividing fractional numbers

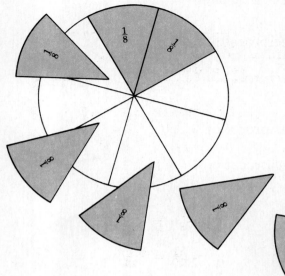

How many of the $\frac{1}{8}$ pieces are needed to exactly cover the $\frac{5}{6}$ piece?

$$\frac{5}{6} \div \frac{1}{8}$$

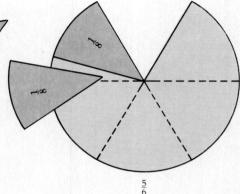

$$\frac{5}{6}$$

The following steps show how a reciprocal can help you find a quotient.

$$\frac{5}{6} \div \frac{1}{8} = \left(\frac{5}{6} \cdot \frac{8}{1}\right) \div \left(\frac{1}{8} \cdot \frac{8}{1}\right)$$

$$= \left(\frac{5}{6} \cdot \frac{8}{1}\right) \div 1 \qquad \boxed{\frac{1}{8} \cdot \frac{8}{1} = 1}$$

$$= \frac{5}{6} \cdot \frac{8}{1}$$

> Multiply both numbers by the reciprocal of the divisor

$$\frac{5}{6} \div \frac{1}{8} = \frac{5}{\overset{}{\underset{3}{6}}} \cdot \frac{\overset{4}{8}}{1} = \frac{20}{3} = 6\frac{2}{3}$$

> Dividing by a number is the same as multiplying by the reciprocal of that number

$6\frac{2}{3}$ of the $\frac{1}{8}$ pieces are needed to exactly cover the $\frac{5}{6}$ piece.

Rewrite each division problem as a multiplication problem.

1. $\frac{2}{3} \div \frac{1}{2}$
2. $\frac{7}{8} \div \frac{1}{4}$
3. $\frac{1}{2} \div \frac{1}{5}$
4. $\frac{5}{9} \div \frac{1}{3}$
5. $\frac{3}{4} \div \frac{1}{6}$
6. $\frac{7}{10} \div \frac{4}{5}$
7. $\frac{1}{6} \div \frac{5}{8}$
8. $\frac{3}{5} \div \frac{3}{4}$

What is $\frac{7}{8} \div \frac{2}{3}$?

Finding the answer

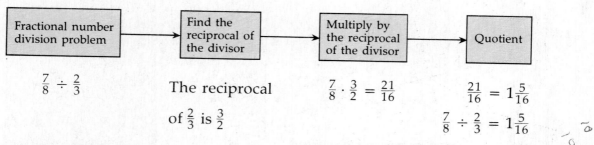

$$\frac{7}{8} \div \frac{2}{3}$$

The reciprocal

of $\frac{2}{3}$ is $\frac{3}{2}$

$$\frac{7}{8} \cdot \frac{3}{2} = \frac{21}{16}$$

$$\frac{21}{16} = 1\frac{5}{16}$$

$$\frac{7}{8} \div \frac{2}{3} = 1\frac{5}{16}$$

Other examples

$$\frac{3}{4} \div \frac{2}{3} = \frac{3}{4} \cdot \frac{3}{2}$$

$$= \frac{9}{8} = 1\frac{1}{8}$$

$$\frac{7}{8} \div \frac{5}{12} = \frac{7}{\underset{2}{8}} \cdot \frac{\overset{3}{12}}{5}$$

$$= \frac{21}{10} = 2\frac{1}{10}$$

$$3\frac{1}{2} \div 2\frac{3}{4}$$

$$\frac{7}{2} \div \frac{11}{4} = \frac{7}{\underset{1}{2}} \cdot \frac{\overset{2}{4}}{11}$$

$$= \frac{14}{11} = 1\frac{3}{11}$$

$$4\frac{1}{6} \div 5$$

$$\frac{25}{6} \div 5 = \frac{25}{6} \cdot \frac{1}{\underset{1}{\overset{5}{5}}}$$

$$= \frac{5}{6}$$

Find the quotients.

1. $\frac{3}{4} \div \frac{1}{6}$

2. $\frac{3}{8} \div \frac{5}{6}$

3. $\frac{1}{2} \div \frac{3}{10}$

4. $\frac{1}{4} \div \frac{7}{12}$

5. $\frac{7}{10} \div \frac{1}{4}$

6. $\frac{9}{10} \div \frac{3}{4}$

7. $\frac{1}{6} \div \frac{5}{8}$

8. $\frac{7}{10} \div \frac{4}{5}$

9. $1\frac{1}{2} \div 2\frac{1}{3}$

10. $2\frac{1}{4} \div 1\frac{1}{5}$

11. $3\frac{1}{2} \div 2\frac{3}{4}$

12. $1\frac{5}{8} \div 2\frac{1}{4}$

13. $3\frac{1}{2} \div 2$

14. $2\frac{5}{6} \div 3$

15. $5 \div 3\frac{1}{5}$

16. $7 \div 3\frac{1}{4}$

$$\frac{10^1 - 7}{3} = \text{▥}$$

$$\frac{10^2 - 7}{3} = \text{▥}$$

$$\frac{10^3 - 7}{3} = \text{▥}$$

$$\frac{10^4 - 7}{3} = \text{▥}$$

Can you extend this
pattern of quotients?

More practice, page 389, Set B

Using recipes

Swiss Steak (6 servings)

○ $\frac{1}{4}$ cup flour

$\frac{3}{4}$ tsp salt

$\frac{1}{2}$ tsp pepper

1 kg round steak

2 tbsp shortening

1 can (250 ml) tomatoes

$\frac{3}{4}$ cup finely chopped onion

○ $\frac{1}{4}$ cup finely chopped
green pepper

Pound flour, salt, and
pepper into both sides of
the round steak. Cut into 6
pieces. Brown meat in the
melted shortening for about
15 minutes. Cover and
simmer over medium heat
1 hour. Add tomatoes,
○ onion, and green pepper.
Simmer 30 minutes longer.

1. The recipe for Swiss steak will serve 6 people.
   List the amount of each ingredient needed to
   serve 12 people.

2. Suppose you wanted to make enough Swiss steak to serve
   15 people. How many times as much of each ingredient
   would be needed?

3. List the amount of each ingredient needed
   to serve 15 people.

4. Suppose you wanted to make enough Swiss steak to serve
   8 people. How many times as much of each ingredient
   would be needed?

5. List the amount of each ingredient needed
   to serve 8 people.

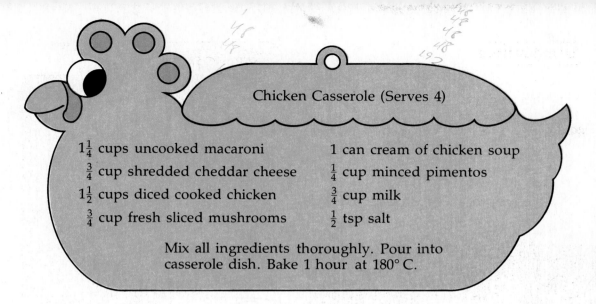

Chicken Casserole (Serves 4)

$1\frac{1}{4}$ cups uncooked macaroni

$\frac{3}{4}$ cup shredded cheddar cheese

$1\frac{1}{2}$ cups diced cooked chicken

$\frac{3}{4}$ cup fresh sliced mushrooms

1 can cream of chicken soup

$\frac{1}{4}$ cup minced pimentos

$\frac{3}{4}$ cup milk

$\frac{1}{2}$ tsp salt

Mix all ingredients thoroughly. Pour into casserole dish. Bake 1 hour at 180° C.

6. The chicken casserole recipe will serve 4 people. List the amount of each ingredient needed to serve chicken casserole to 24 people.

7. List the amount of each ingredient needed to make 10 servings of the chicken casserole.

8. Suppose you wanted to make just enough chicken casserole for 2 people. List the amount of each ingredient needed.

Practicing your skills

Add, subtract, multiply, or divide.

1.	2.	3.	4.	5.
4.83 + 6.785	38.9 + 42.7	7.82 − 1.69	83.42 − 29.56	72 − 13.7

6.	7.	8.	9.	10.
4.83 × 8	67.2 × 18	4.83 × 0.6	787 × 0.09	4.26 × 0.19

11. $4\overline{)10.72}$

12. $4.8\overline{)448.32}$

13. $0.7\overline{)0.4704}$

14. $0.36\overline{)2.016}$

Answers for Self-check 1. $d = \frac{1}{2}$ 2. $b = \frac{1}{10}$ 3. $h = \frac{1}{10}$ 4. $c = \frac{7}{15}$ 5. $g = \frac{27}{8}$ or $3\frac{3}{8}$
6. $e = \frac{55}{6}$ or $9\frac{1}{6}$ 7. $a = \frac{8}{1}$ or 8 8. $f = \frac{13}{3}$ or $4\frac{1}{3}$ 9. 2 10. $\frac{4}{3}$ or $1\frac{1}{3}$ 11. $\frac{5}{7}$ 12. $\frac{3}{13}$ 13. $j = \frac{3}{5}$
14. $m = \frac{5}{2}$ or $2\frac{1}{2}$ 15. $n = \frac{7}{6}$ or $1\frac{1}{6}$ 16. $p = \frac{3}{2}$ or $1\frac{1}{2}$ 17. $k = \frac{11}{4}$ or $2\frac{3}{4}$ 18. $i = \frac{27}{16}$ or $1\frac{11}{16}$
19. $x = \frac{27}{22}$ or $1\frac{5}{22}$ 20. $n = \frac{2}{1}$ or 2

Self-check

Find the products.

1. $\frac{3}{4} \cdot \frac{2}{3} = d$ 2. $\frac{3}{5} \cdot \frac{1}{6} = e$ 3. $\frac{1}{8} \cdot \frac{4}{5} = h$ 4. $\frac{7}{10} \cdot \frac{2}{3} = c$

5. $2\frac{1}{4} \cdot 1\frac{1}{2} = g$ 6. $3\frac{1}{3} \cdot 2\frac{3}{4} = e$ 7. $3 \cdot 2\frac{2}{3} = a$ 8. $6\frac{1}{2} \cdot \frac{2}{3} = f$

Give the reciprocal of each number.

9. $\frac{1}{2}$ 10. $\frac{3}{4}$ 11. $1\frac{2}{5}$ 12. $4\frac{1}{3}$

Find the quotients.

13. $\frac{2}{5} \div \frac{2}{3} = j$ 14. $\frac{5}{6} \div \frac{1}{3} = m$ 15. $\frac{7}{8} \div \frac{3}{4} = n$ 16. $\frac{1}{2} \div \frac{1}{3} = p$

17. $4\frac{1}{8} \div 1\frac{1}{2} = k$ 18. $2\frac{1}{4} \div 1\frac{1}{3} = i$ 19. $3\frac{3}{8} \div 2\frac{3}{4} = x$ 20. $3\frac{1}{5} \div 1\frac{3}{5} = n$

Answers for Self-check—page 233

Test

Find the products.

1. $\frac{4}{5} \cdot \frac{3}{8} = d$ 2. $\frac{7}{8} \cdot \frac{2}{3} = h$ 3. $\frac{9}{10} \cdot \frac{2}{3} = g$ 4. $\frac{1}{5} \cdot \frac{3}{4} = a$

5. $1\frac{1}{4} \cdot 2\frac{1}{2} = b$ 6. $2\frac{1}{4} \cdot 3\frac{2}{3} = m$ 7. $4 \cdot 3\frac{3}{4} = e$ 8. $4\frac{1}{4} \cdot \frac{4}{5} = n$

Give the reciprocal of each number.

9. $\frac{1}{4}$ 10. $\frac{2}{3}$ 11. $2\frac{3}{5}$ 12. $5\frac{1}{2}$

Find the quotients.

13. $\frac{3}{4} \div \frac{3}{5} = i$ 14. $\frac{7}{8} \div \frac{1}{4} = c$ 15. $\frac{1}{2} \div \frac{2}{3} = q$ 16. $\frac{4}{5} \div \frac{1}{3} = k$

17. $3\frac{1}{6} \div 1\frac{2}{3} = f$ 18. $4\frac{1}{5} \div \frac{7}{8} = j$ 19. $2\frac{1}{2} \div 1\frac{1}{4} = s$ 20. $1\frac{4}{5} \div 1\frac{7}{10} = t$

Paper Folding

Start with a large sheet of paper. Fold it in half. Now fold the double sheet in half. Fold in half again. Guess how many times you can do this, if you continue folding as long as you can.

Study the pattern. Give the missing numbers.

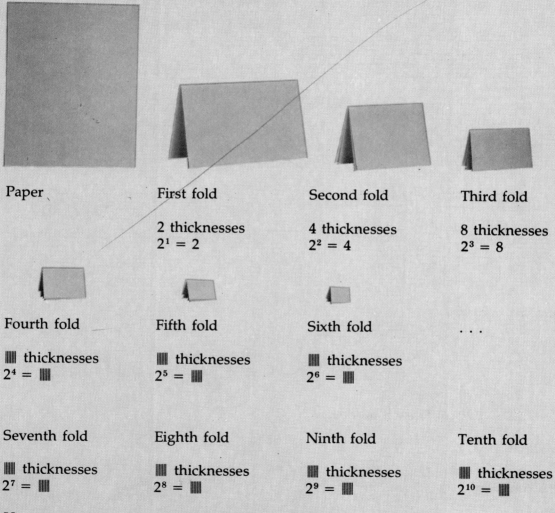

Paper

First fold

2 thicknesses
$2^1 = 2$

Second fold

4 thicknesses
$2^2 = 4$

Third fold

8 thicknesses
$2^3 = 8$

Fourth fold

▨ thicknesses
$2^4 = $ ▨

Fifth fold

▨ thicknesses
$2^5 = $ ▨

Sixth fold

▨ thicknesses
$2^6 = $ ▨

. . .

Seventh fold

▨ thicknesses
$2^7 = $ ▨

Eighth fold

▨ thicknesses
$2^8 = $ ▨

Ninth fold

▨ thicknesses
$2^9 = $ ▨

Tenth fold

▨ thicknesses
$2^{10} = $ ▨

How many times are you able to fold the sheet of paper?
Could you fold a larger sheet of paper more times?
Try to do so.

Ratio and Proportion

You can obtain many different colors of paint by mixing the basic colors, blue, yellow, and red, or shades of these colors. For example, you can get the green shown below by mixing 2 parts of yellow paint with 3 parts of medium blue paint.

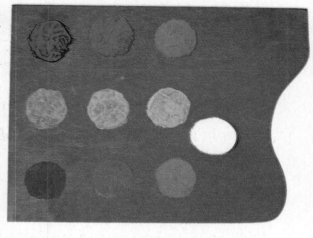

2 to 3
yellow medium blue

The **ratio** of yellow to medium blue is 2 to 3. You can write 2 to 3 as 2:3 or $\frac{2}{3}$.

Write each ratio in two ways.

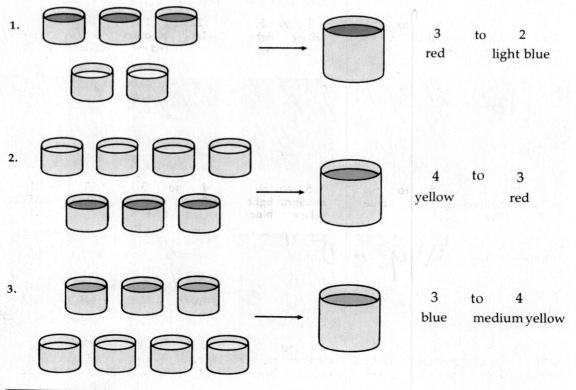

1.
3 to 2
red light blue

2.
4 to 3
yellow red

3.
3 to 4
blue medium yellow

Study these two examples.
Notice that both ratios of
paint give the same color.
What color would you get if
you mixed 6 medium blue
parts with 9 yellow parts?

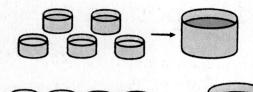

2   to   3
medium   yellow
blue

These ratios are **equal
ratios**.

$$\frac{2}{3} = \frac{4}{6} = \frac{6}{9} = \frac{8}{12} = \frac{10}{15} \cdots$$

4   to   6
medium   yellow
blue

Write the ratio as a lowest-terms fraction for each color.
Then give two other ratios for each.

1.	**2.**	**3.**	**4.**	**5.**
1 to 2 light light yellow red	1 to 1 medium medium yellow red	1 to 3 yellow light red	2 to 1 yellow medium red	4 to 3 medium medium yellow red
6.	**7.**	**8.**	**9.**	**10.**
3 to 4 yellow medium blue	5 to 6 yellow blue	5 to 4 medium light yellow blue	4 to 5 yellow medium blue	3 to 2 yellow medium blue
11.	**12.**	**13.**	**14.**	**15.**
5 to 6 light light red blue	4 to 1 medium medium red blue	6 to 4 medium medium red blue	2 to 3 light medium red blue	2 to 5 medium light red blue

Ratios and proportions

Gary lives 4 km from school. He takes 15 minutes to ride his bicycle to school. The ratio below describes his rate of speed.

4 km to 15 min $\longrightarrow \frac{4}{15}$

Gary rides to school and back home in 30 minutes.

8 km to 30 min $\longrightarrow \frac{8}{30}$

Both ratios describe Gary's riding speed. The ratios are equal. $\frac{4}{15} = \frac{8}{30}$

> A statement that two ratios are equal is called a **proportion**.

A proportion may also be written using special notation.
The ratio $\frac{2}{3} = \frac{6}{9}$ may be written $2:3 = 6:9$

We read: Two is to three as six is to nine.

Read each proportion.

1. $4:5 = 12:15$

2. $7:8 = 14:16$

3. $1:3 = 20:60$

4. $3:2 = 12:8$

5. $1:4 = 25:100$

6. $2:9 = 10:45$

7. $\frac{9}{4} = \frac{27}{12}$

8. $\frac{1}{2} = \frac{4}{8}$

9. $\frac{3}{5} = \frac{12}{20}$

When two ratios form a proportion, the cross products are equal. When the cross products are equal, the ratios are equal.

$$15 \cdot 8 = 4 \cdot 30$$
$$120 = 120$$

Check the cross products to see which pairs of ratios are equal. Write the equal ratios as a proportion.

1. $\frac{3}{16}, \frac{6}{32}$ 2. $\frac{6}{10}, \frac{9}{15}$ 3. $\frac{8}{20}, \frac{12}{30}$

4. $\frac{10}{15}, \frac{17}{16}$ 5. $\frac{6}{16}, \frac{18}{48}$ 6. $\frac{14}{20}, \frac{70}{100}$

Write a proportion for each exercise. Check the cross products for equality.

Example: Pat walks 1 km in 12 minutes. She walks 2 km in 24 minutes.

Answer: $\frac{1}{12} = \frac{2}{24}$, $1 \cdot 24 = 2 \cdot 12$

7. There were 2 music books for every 3 students in a class. There were 16 music books for a class of 24.

8. In 1 can there are 3 tennis balls. In 4 cans there are 12 tennis balls.

9. Bicycle tires were selling at 2 for $7.95. At that rate, 4 tires would be $15.90.

10. There were 5 hot dogs for every 3 people at the party. There were 36 people and 60 hot dogs.

11. Lisa can run 50 meters in 8 seconds. At this rate, she can run 100 meters in 16 seconds.

12. Rich used 3 lemons with 2 ℓ of water for lemonade. He used 6 ℓ of water with 9 lemons.

At the end of one baseball season, these were the ratios of hits to times at bat for the two leaders in the American League.

Brett: $\frac{215}{645}$

McRea: $\frac{175}{527}$

Find a decimal for each ratio to see who won the batting title that year.

Solving proportions

Cheri checked her pulse rate and found that her heart beat 18 times in 15 seconds. At that rate, how many beats would Cheri count in one minute (60 seconds)?

Finding the answer

Write a proportion, using the letter x for the number you want to find	→	Write the cross-product equation	→	Divide to find the number for x

beats
seconds

$\frac{18}{15} = \frac{x}{60}$

$15x = 18 \cdot 60$
$15x = 1080$

$x = 1080 \div 15$
$x = 72$

Cheri would count 72 beats per minute.

Other examples

$\frac{2}{3} = \frac{x}{72}$

$3x = 2 \cdot 72$
$3x = 144$
$x = 144 \div 3$
$x = 48$

$\frac{10}{12} = \frac{x}{42}$

$12x = 10 \cdot 42$
$12x = 420$
$x = 420 \div 12$
$x = 35$

$\frac{2}{3} = \frac{12}{x}$

$2x = 12 \cdot 3$
$2x = 36$
$x = 36 \div 2$
$x = 18$

Solve each proportion.

1. $\frac{3}{4} = \frac{x}{16}$

2. $\frac{2}{5} = \frac{x}{15}$

3. $\frac{1}{3} = \frac{x}{18}$

4. $\frac{3}{8} = \frac{15}{x}$

5. $\frac{5}{6} = \frac{x}{24}$

6. $\frac{10}{16} = \frac{15}{x}$

7. $\frac{12}{15} = \frac{x}{45}$

8. $\frac{3}{12} = \frac{x}{40}$

9. $\frac{10}{15} = \frac{18}{x}$

10. $\frac{6}{20} = \frac{x}{100}$

11. $\frac{6}{12} = \frac{9}{x}$

12. $\frac{4}{6} = \frac{x}{27}$

13. $\frac{14}{16} = \frac{35}{x}$

14. $\frac{27}{30} = \frac{x}{100}$

15. $\frac{15}{18} = \frac{x}{42}$

Write and solve a proportion for each problem.

Example: Dan found that his
pulse beat 15 times
in 12 seconds. How
many times does it
beat in one minute?

$$\frac{15}{12} = \frac{x}{60}$$
$$12x = 15 \cdot 60$$
$$12x = 900$$
$$x = 900 \div 12$$
$$x = 75 \text{ beats per minute}$$

1. Irma's pulse beats 26 times in 20 seconds. How many times does it beat in one minute (60 seconds)?

2. Ted's pulse beats 24 times in 18 seconds. How many times does it beat in one minute?

3. After exercising, Brenda found her pulse beat 28 times in 15 seconds. How many times did her pulse beat in one minute?

4. After running, Don found his pulse beat 39 times in 18 seconds. How many times did it beat in one minute?

5. Mary found that she takes 5 breaths in 15 seconds. How many breaths does she take in a minute?

6. Fred takes 6 breaths in 18 seconds. How many breaths is this per minute?

7. After exercising, Carla breathes 8 times in 10 seconds. What is her breathing rate per minute?

8. Steve breathes 9 times in 12 seconds after swimming. What is his breathing rate per minute after swimming?

☆ 9. Count your own pulse for 10, 12, 15, 18, or 20 seconds. Set up a proportion to find your rate per minute. Check your answer by actually counting for a full minute.

In a contest, a person won $1000 a week for life. How long, in years and weeks, would this person have to live to receive $1 000 000? Use 52 weeks in a year.

More practice, page 390, Set A

Career problems using proportions

Write and solve a proportion for each problem.

1. Personnel worker:
   The ratio of job openings to the number of people applying is 2 to 5. If 30 people applied, how many jobs were open?

2. Paramedic:
   A paramedic squad responded to 135 calls in 1 month. About how many calls would the squad respond to in 3 months?

3. Carpenter:
   A rectangular table has a length of 224 cm. If the ratio of the length to the width is 8:5, what is the width of the table?

4. Department store buyer:
   The ratio of dresses bought to suits bought is 4 to 3. If 96 dresses are bought, how many suits are bought?

5. Counselor:
   The ratio of counselors
   to campers is 2 to 15.
   If there are 135 campers,
   how many counselors are
   needed?

6. Management personnel:
   The ratio of management
   personnel to all employees
   is 3 to 20. In a plant that
   has 500 employees, how
   many are in management?

7. Librarian:
   The ratio of books overdue
   to books loaned is 1 to 20.
   If 460 books are loaned, how
   many are overdue?

☆ 8. Warehouse worker:
   The ratio of cases of
   grape juice ordered to
   cases of lemonade was
   2 to 3. The total order
   was for 120 cases. How
   many of each should
   be shipped?

Scale drawings and ratio

The **scale** of a scale drawing gives the ratio of the dimensions of the drawing to the dimensions of the actual object.

This is a photograph showing the actual size of a baseball.

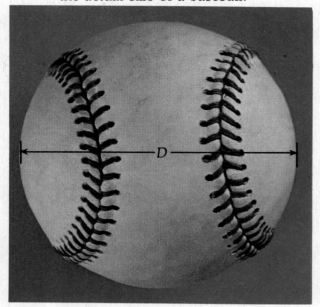

This is a **scale drawing** showing a baseball with diameter at half size.

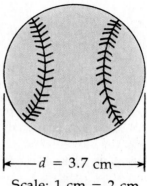

$d = 3.7$ cm

Scale: 1 cm = 2 cm

Find the diameter, D, of the actual baseball.

$$\frac{1}{2} = \frac{3.7}{D}$$
$$1 \cdot D = 2 \cdot 3.7$$
$$D = 7.4 \text{ cm}$$

Sometimes the ratio is given using different units. In the scale drawing of the baseball field, the ratio is 1 cm to 5.7 m or 1 cm to 570 cm. The dimensions of the scale drawing are given to the nearest tenth of a centimeter. Give each dimension below in meters.

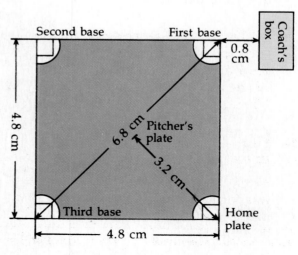

Scale: 1 cm = 5.7 m

1. third base to home plate

2. pitcher's plate to home plate

3. third base to first base

4. first base to coach's box

Maps are also drawn to scale. Use a centimeter ruler and the given proportion to find these actual distances.

1. Anchorage to Fairbanks
2. Fairbanks to Juneau
3. Juneau to Anchorage

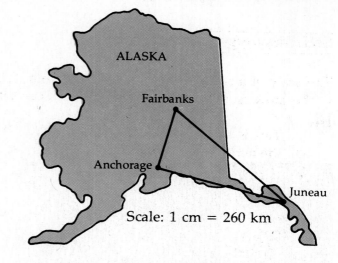

Scale: 1 cm = 260 km

4. Detroit to Cleveland
5. Detroit to Toronto
6. Toronto to Cleveland
7. Toronto to Syracuse
8. Cleveland to Buffalo

Scale: 1 cm = 85 km

Calculator problems

9. Measure the distance d on the drawing of the earth. Find the actual diameter of the earth to the nearest kilometer.

10. Find the actual circumference C of the earth to the nearest kilometer.
$$C = \pi d$$
Use $\pi = 3.1416$

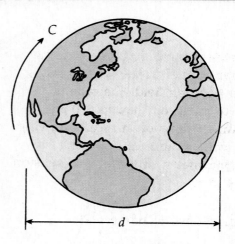

Scale: 1 cm = 2500 km

Answers for Self-check   1. $3:4 = 15:20$ or $\frac{3}{4} = \frac{15}{20}$ 2. $3:1 = 12:4$ or $\frac{3}{1} = \frac{12}{4}$ 3. $x = 21$
4. $x = 20$ 5. $x = 48$ 6. $x = 4$ 7. 90   8. 1100 km

Self-check

Write a proportion for each.

1. There were 3 books
   for every 4 students.
   There were 15 books
   for a class of 20.

2. Melons were selling
   3 for 1 dollar.
   Larry bought 12 for
   4 dollars.

Solve each proportion.

3. $\frac{3}{4} = \frac{x}{28}$

4. $\frac{5}{8} = \frac{x}{32}$

5. $\frac{6}{16} = \frac{18}{x}$

6. $\frac{12}{18} = \frac{x}{6}$

7. Sue found that about
   3 cars passed her school
   every 2 minutes.
   At that rate, how many
   would pass in 1 hour
   (60 minutes)?

8. The scale on a map
   is 1 cm = 250 km.
   What is the actual
   distance if a map
   distance is 4.4 cm?

Answers for Self-check—page 245

Test

Write a proportion for each.

1. There were 4 rulers
   for every 5 students.
   There were 24 rulers
   for a class of 30.

2. Tennis balls were on
   sale at 3 for 2 dollars.
   Joan paid 10 dollars for
   15 balls.

Solve each proportion.

3. $\frac{2}{3} = \frac{x}{24}$

4. $\frac{7}{8} = \frac{21}{x}$

5. $\frac{14}{20} = \frac{x}{50}$

6. $\frac{15}{20} = \frac{x}{12}$

7. Todd found that about
   7 people walked past his
   school every 3 minutes.
   At that rate, how many
   would pass in 1 hour?

8. The scale of a scale drawing
   is 2 cm = 3 m. What is the
   actual length of a room that
   measures 4.5 cm on the scale
   drawing?

Math lab

Gear Ratios

The large spur gear has 30
teeth. The small spur gear
has 15 teeth. While the large
gear makes 1 complete turn,
the small gear must make 2 turns.

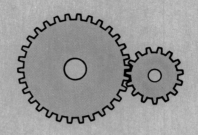

The gear ratio can be found either from
the number of turns or from the number
of teeth of the gears.

Large gear teeth $\longrightarrow \dfrac{30}{15} = \dfrac{2}{1}$ ←—Small gear turns
Small gear teeth ————————————————————————— ←—Large gear turns

Find gear teeth ratios and turn ratios like the ones above for each pair
of spur gears.

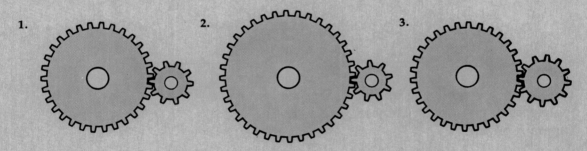

1.   2.   3.

4.

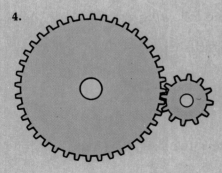

5. Find gear ratios for the chain
    wheel and rear wheel gears
    of a bicycle.

Geometric Relationships

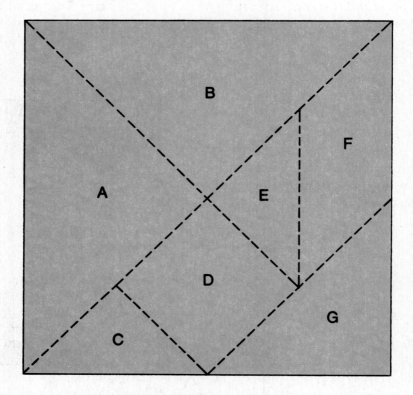

The 7 pieces which make up this square are said to be the pieces of an ancient Chinese puzzle called the Tangram puzzle.

Trace, letter, and cut out the pieces. Use them for the following activities.

1. Find a pair of triangles that have the same size and shape. Find another pair.

2. Find a pair of triangles that have the same shape but not the same size. Find another pair.

3. Put pieces C and E together to form a square the same size and shape as piece D.

4. Use pieces A, B, C, and E to form two squares that are not the same size.

5. Use pieces A, B, C, and E to form two triangles that have the same shape but not the same size.

Two figures are **congruent** to one another if they have the same size and shape.

Two figures are **similar** to one another if they have the same shape but not necessarily the same size.

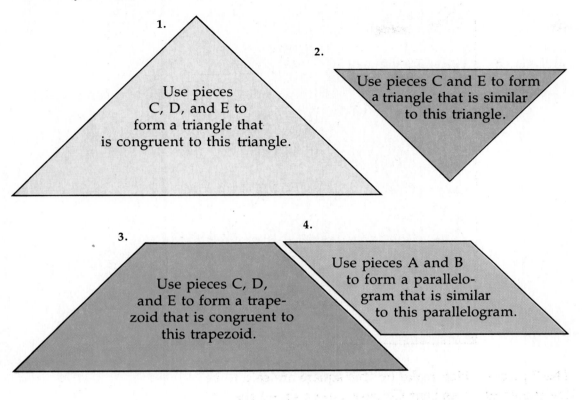

1. Use pieces C, D, and E to form a triangle that is congruent to this triangle.

2. Use pieces C and E to form a triangle that is similar to this triangle.

3. Use pieces C, D, and E to form a trapezoid that is congruent to this trapezoid.

4. Use pieces A and B to form a parallelogram that is similar to this parallelogram.

5. Use pieces C, D, E, F, and G to form a square that is congruent to this square.

6. Use pieces C, E, and G to form a square that is congruent to this square.

Congruent triangles

Two triangles are congruent if they have
the same size and shape. This means that
the vertices of the two triangles can be
matched so that pairs of matching angles
and matching sides are congruent.

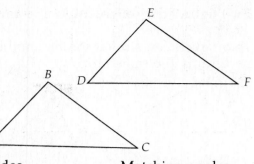

Matching vertices	Matching sides	Matching angles
$A \longleftrightarrow D$	$\overline{AB} \cong \overline{DE}$	$\angle A \cong \angle D$
$B \longleftrightarrow E$	$\overline{BC} \cong \overline{EF}$	$\angle B \cong \angle E$
$C \longleftrightarrow F$	$\overline{AC} \cong \overline{DF}$	$\angle C \cong \angle F$

We write: $\triangle ABC \cong \triangle DEF$

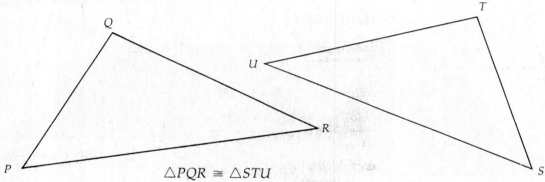

$\triangle PQR \cong \triangle STU$

Copy and complete the following.

1. $\overline{PQ} \cong$ ▦

2. $\overline{QR} \cong$ ▦

3. $\overline{PR} \cong$ ▦

4. $\angle P \cong$ ▦

5. $\angle Q \cong$ ▦

6. $\angle R \cong$ ▦

7. Write a statement of congruence to tell which two of the
following triangles are congruent.

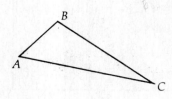

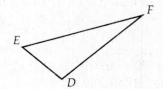

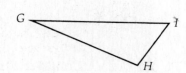

Which pairs of triangles are congruent? (Use tracing or measurement to help you decide.)

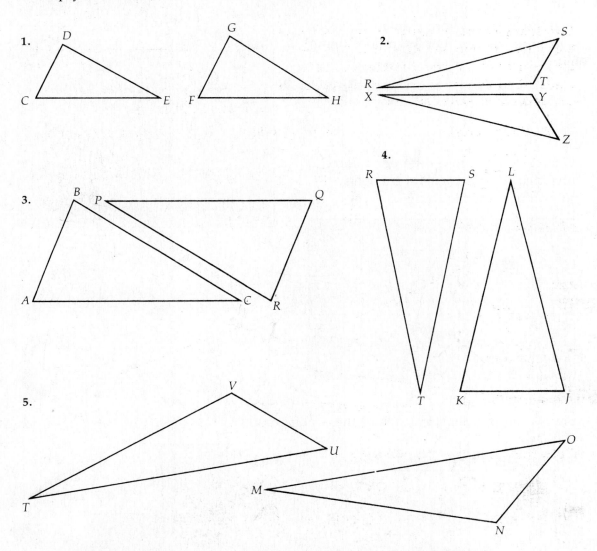

1.

2.

3.

4.

5.

6. Give the pairs of congruent sides and congruent angles for the pairs of triangles that are congruent in exercises 1 through 5.

How old is someone who has lived 1 million hours?
Guess first, without calculating. Then calculate.

A less than 10 years old
C between 25 and 50 years old
E more than 100 years old

B between 10 and 25 years old
D between 50 and 100 years old

✪ Tiling with congruent polygons

A floor-covering store wanted to let its customers design their own floor tiling.

One customer chose different colored tiles that were equilateral triangles to produce this tile design.

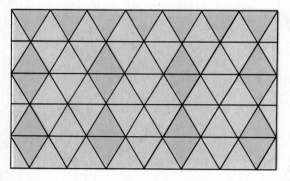

A new idea for tiling !! Mix and match both shapes and colors to design your floor.

Show a tiling design for each of these polygons.

1.

2.

3.

4.

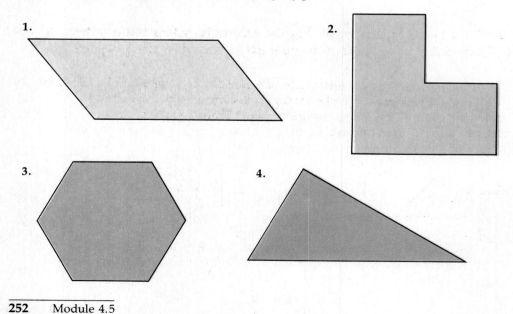

One customer designed this
tiling pattern using squares
and equilateral triangles.

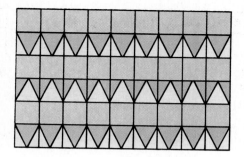

Show a tiling pattern for each combination of polygons.

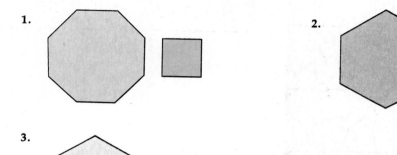

1.

2.

3.

☆ 4. Draw a 15 cm by 20 cm rectangle. Fill the rectangle with a tiling pattern of your
choice. Then color the pattern in an interesting way to make a design.

An equilateral triangle is an example of a **reptile** (for repeating tile) because
four equilateral triangles can be arranged to form a larger equilateral
triangle. Which of these figures are reptiles? Trace 4 of them to show
the larger figure in each case.

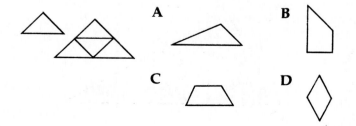

A   B

C   D

Similar triangles

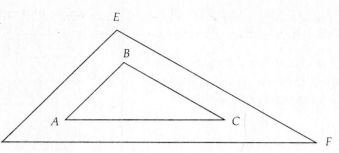

Two triangles are similar
if they have the same shape
but not necessarily the same
size.

This means that the vertices
of the two triangles can be
matched so that the ratios
of the lengths of matching sides
are equal and matching angles
are congruent.

Ratios of lengths
of matching sides

$$\frac{m(\overline{AB})}{m(\overline{DE})} = \frac{m(\overline{BC})}{m(\overline{EF})} = \frac{m(\overline{AC})}{m(\overline{DF})}$$

Matching angles

$\angle A \cong \angle D$
$\angle B \cong \angle E$
$\angle C \cong \angle F$

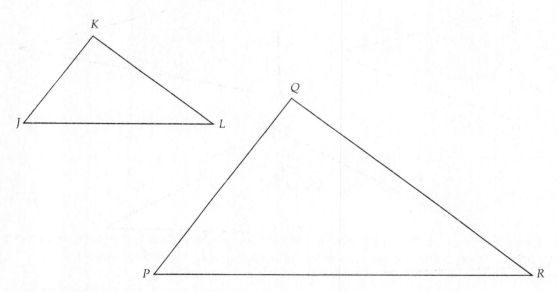

Give the ratios.

1. $\dfrac{m(\overline{JK})}{m(\overline{PQ})} = $ ▦

2. $\dfrac{m(\overline{KL})}{m(\overline{QR})} = $ ▦

3. $\dfrac{m(\overline{JL})}{m(\overline{PR})} = $ ▦

4. Are the ratios of matching sides in exercises 1, 2, and 3 equal?

Copy and complete.

5. $\angle J \cong \angle$ ▦

6. $\angle K \cong \angle$ ▦

7. $\angle L \cong \angle$ ▦

8. Are the triangles similar?

Measure the sides and angles of each pair of triangles below. Tell whether the triangles are similar.

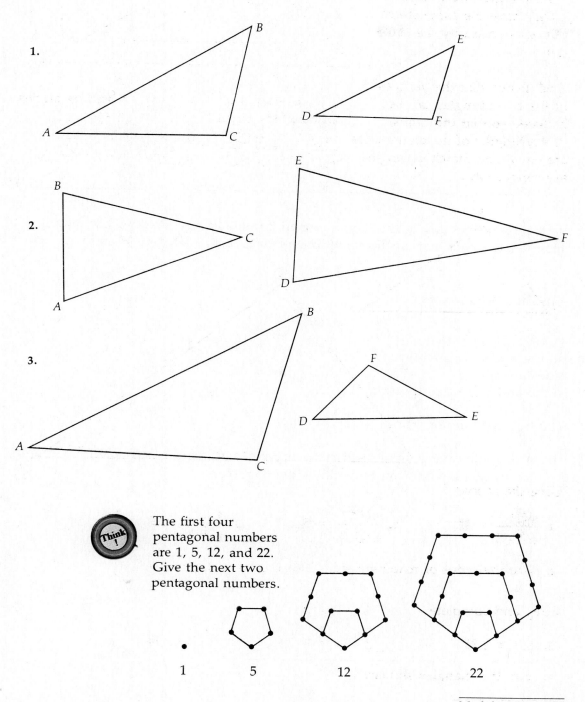

1.

2.

3.

The first four pentagonal numbers are 1, 5, 12, and 22. Give the next two pentagonal numbers.

1   5   12   22

⊛Using similar triangles—indirect measurement

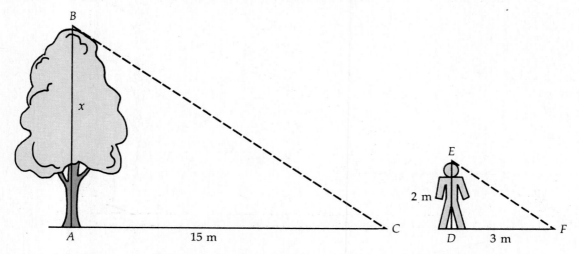

At a certain time during the day, a person 2 m tall casts a shadow 3 m long.
How tall is a tree that, at the same time of day, casts a shadow 15 m long?

Finding the answer

$\triangle ABC$ is similar to $\triangle DEF$,
so the ratios of matching
sides are equal.
Write and solve a proportion.

$$\frac{x}{2} = \frac{15}{3}$$

$$3x = 30$$

$$x = 10$$

The tree is 10 m tall.

1. A flagpole casts a shadow of 30 m at the same time a 1.5 m post
    casts a shadow of 3 m. How tall is the flagpole?

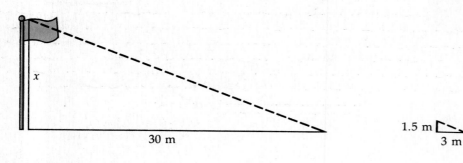

2. △*AEF* is similar to △*ABC*.
How high is the airplane flying?

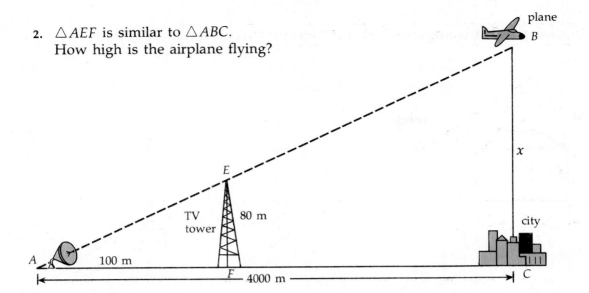

TV tower   80 m

A   100 m   *F*   4000 m   *C*

plane   *B*

x

city

3. △*ABC* is similar to △*DEF*.
What is the approximate
actual length *x* of the
slanted edge?

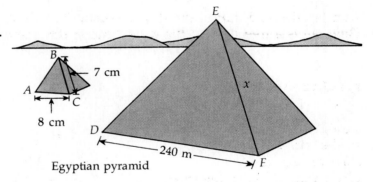

7 cm

8 cm

240 m

Egyptian pyramid

4. The stakes or trees were chosen so that △*ABC* is similar to △*DFC*. $\overline{AB}$ and $\overline{DF}$
are matching sides. So are $\overline{AC}$ and $\overline{DC}$. How far is
it across the river from *A* to *B*?

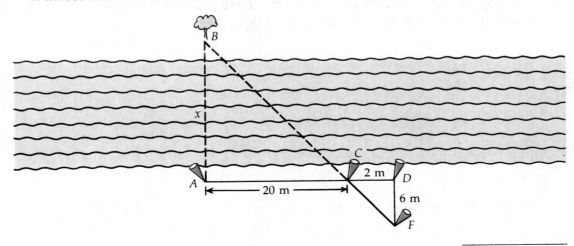

B

x

A   20 m

C   2 m   *D*

6 m

F

Drawing space figures

Think about the real world object and the related space figure.
Then follow the steps and draw each figure.

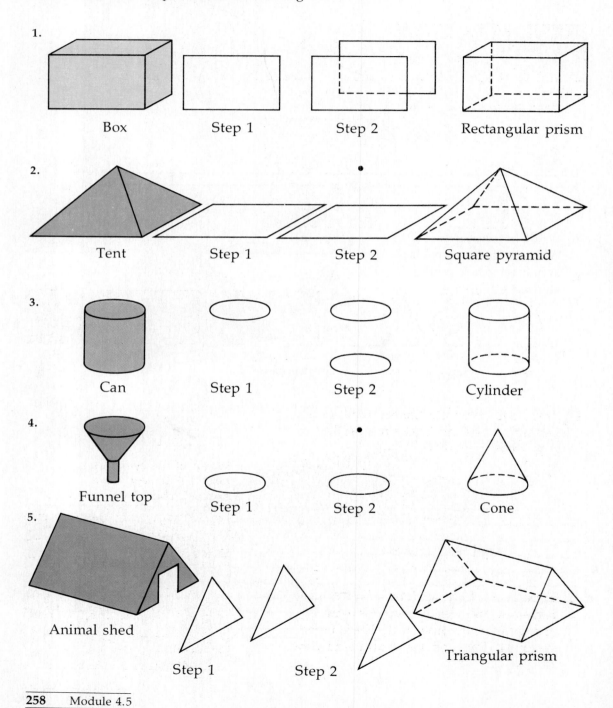

1. Box   Step 1   Step 2   Rectangular prism

2. Tent   Step 1   Step 2   Square pyramid

3. Can   Step 1   Step 2   Cylinder

4. Funnel top   Step 1   Step 2   Cone

5. Animal shed   Step 1   Step 2   Triangular prism

A front view, top view, and side view are given for each of the figures on page 258. Name the figure in each exercise.

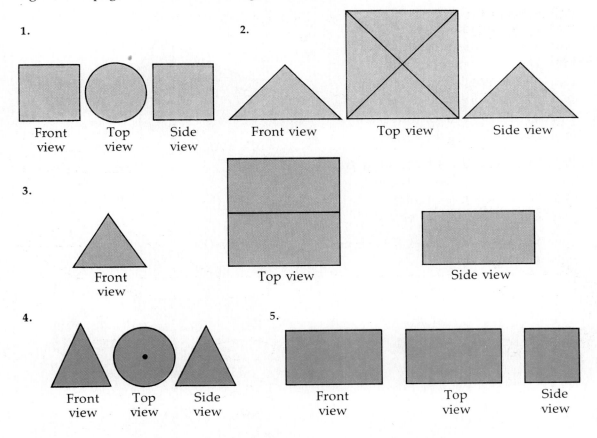

1.

Front view · Top view · Side view

2.

Front view · Top view · Side view

3.

Front view · Top view · Side view

4.

Front view · Top view · Side view

5.

Front view · Top view · Side view

6. Trace and complete this drawing of a pentagonal prism. Show the hidden edges with dotted segments.

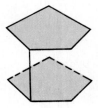

Which of the cylinders is tallest? After you have decided, check by measuring.

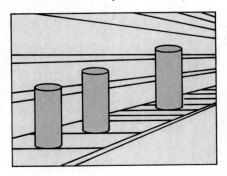

☆ **7.** Choose an object such as a bird house, a glass, a building, a desk, or a table and make a drawing of it. Then show the front view, top view, and side view.

⊛ Polyhedrons

A polyhedron is a space figure
enclosing a region of space. The
boundaries of the polyhedron are
polygons. The polygons are the
faces of the polyhedron. The
common side of two faces is called
an **edge**. The points of intersection
of the edges are called **vertices**.

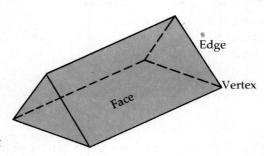

Regular polyhedrons have faces that
are congruent regular polygons.
Patterns for the five regular
polyhedrons are shown below.

*Give the number of faces (F), vertices (V), and edges (E)
for each polyhedron.*

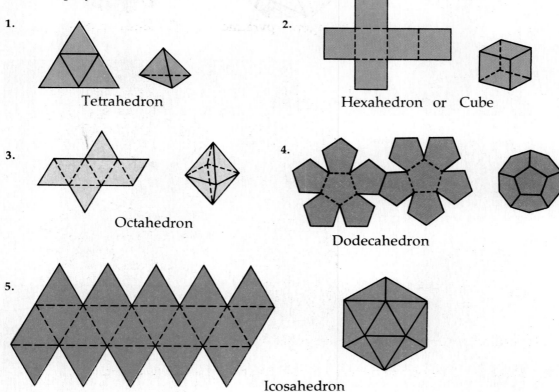

1. Tetrahedron

2. Hexahedron or Cube

3. Octahedron

4. Dodecahedron

5. Icosahedron

6. Find a relationship between the numbers
   F, V, and E for the polyhedrons above.

The mathematician Leonhard Euler (1707–1783) proved that

$V + F - E = 2$

where V is the number of vertices, F the number of faces, and E the number of edges of a polyhedron.

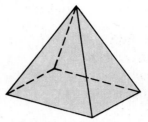

$$\left. \begin{array}{l} V = 5 \\ F = 5 \\ E = 8 \end{array} \right\} \; 5 + 5 - 8 = 2$$

Square pyramid

Find V, F, and E for each polyhedron.
Show that $V + F - E = 2$ for each polyhedron below.

1.

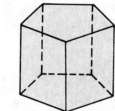

Triangular prism

2.

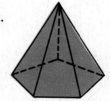

Pentagonal pyramid

3.

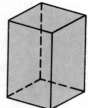

Rectangular prism

4.

Pentagonal prism

5.

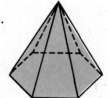

Hexagonal pyramid

6.

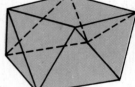

Square antiprism

7.

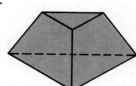

Truncated tetrahedron

8.

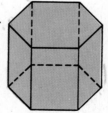

Hexagonal prism

9.

Cube with one corner removed

☆ **10.** Make a model of one or more of the polyhedrons in the lesson.

Answers for Self-check **1.** $\overline{DE}$ **2.** $\overline{EF}$ **3.** $\overline{DF}$ **4.** $\angle D$ **5.** $\angle E$ **6.** $\angle F$ **7.** $\frac{5}{30}$ or $\frac{1}{6}$
8. $\frac{x}{2} = \frac{30}{5}$ or $\frac{2}{x} = \frac{5}{30}$, $x = 12$ **9.** 6 faces, 12 edges, 8 vertices

Self-check

$\triangle ABC \cong \triangle DEF$

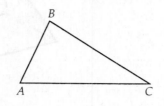

Copy and complete.

1. $\overline{AB} \cong$ ▦
2. $\overline{BC} \cong$ ▦
3. $\overline{AC} \cong$ ▦
4. $\angle A \cong$ ▦
5. $\angle B \cong$ ▦
6. $\angle C \cong$ ▦

$\triangle MNO$ is similar to $\triangle UVW$.

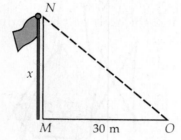

7. Give the ratio of $\dfrac{m(\overline{UW})}{m(\overline{MO})}$.

☆ 8. Write a proportion and use it to find distance x.

☆ 9. Draw a cube. How many faces, edges, and vertices does it have?

Answers for Self-check—page 261

Test

$\triangle PQR \cong \triangle XYZ$

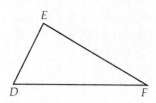

Copy and complete.

1. $\overline{PQ} \cong$ ▦
2. $\overline{QR} \cong$ ▦
3. $\overline{PR} \cong$ ▦
4. $\angle R \cong$ ▦
5. $\angle P \cong$ ▦
6. $\angle Q \cong$ ▦

$\triangle JKL$ is similar to $\triangle RST$.

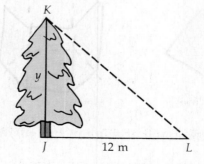
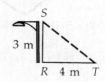

7. Give the ratio of $\dfrac{m(\overline{RT})}{m(\overline{JL})}$.

☆ 8. Write a proportion and use it to find distance y.

☆ 9. Draw a square pyramid. How many faces, edges, and vertices does it have?

Hexominoes and Hexahedrons

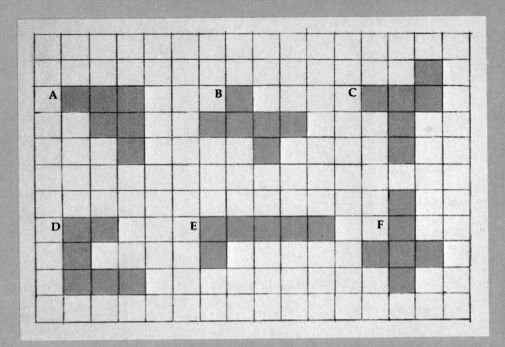

Patterns of six connected squares like the ones above are called hexominoes.

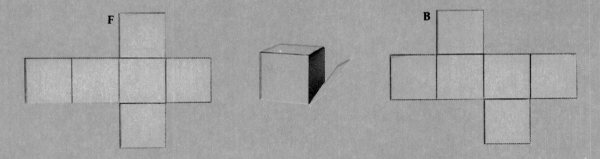

Hexominoes **B**, **C**, and **F** can be folded along the grid lines to form a cube, or **regular hexahedron**.

Altogether, there are 35 hexominoes of different shapes.

How many of these hexominoes can you draw on graph paper?

How many of the hexominoes can be folded to form regular hexahedrons?

Unit 4 review

Write a decimal for each fraction.

1. $\frac{1}{2}$ 2. $\frac{3}{4}$ 3. $\frac{2}{3}$ 4. $\frac{7}{10}$ 5. $\frac{1}{5}$ 6. $\frac{3}{8}$

Write an improper fraction for each mixed numeral.

7. $2\frac{1}{2}$ 8. $4\frac{2}{3}$ 9. $7\frac{1}{4}$ 10. $1\frac{3}{4}$ 11. $8\frac{4}{5}$

Find the sums and differences.

12. $\begin{array}{r} \frac{3}{4} \\ + \frac{1}{2} \\ \hline \end{array}$ 13. $\begin{array}{r} 3\frac{4}{5} \\ + 2\frac{1}{3} \\ \hline \end{array}$ 14. $\begin{array}{r} 8\frac{1}{2} \\ - 6\frac{3}{4} \\ \hline \end{array}$ 15. $\begin{array}{r} 7\frac{1}{3} \\ - 4\frac{1}{4} \\ \hline \end{array}$ 16. $\begin{array}{r} 5\frac{1}{5} \\ - 2\frac{3}{4} \\ \hline \end{array}$

Find the products.

17. $\frac{1}{2} \times \frac{3}{4}$ 18. $\frac{2}{3} \times 1\frac{1}{2}$ 19. $3 \times \frac{4}{5}$ 20. $2\frac{2}{3} \times \frac{9}{10}$

Find the quotients.

21. $\frac{3}{5} \div \frac{1}{2}$ 22. $2\frac{1}{2} \div \frac{3}{4}$ 23. $3\frac{2}{3} \div 1\frac{4}{5}$ 24. $1\frac{3}{4} \div \frac{2}{3}$

Solve each proportion.

25. $\frac{2}{3} = \frac{x}{12}$ 26. $\frac{4}{5} = \frac{x}{15}$ 27. $\frac{1}{2} = \frac{7}{x}$ 28. $\frac{1}{3} = \frac{8}{x}$

29. $\frac{24}{27} = \frac{8}{x}$ 30. $\frac{30}{40} = \frac{x}{4}$ 31. $\frac{12}{18} = \frac{2}{x}$ 32. $\frac{21}{28} = \frac{x}{4}$

33. $\frac{8}{12} = \frac{x}{3}$ 34. $\frac{15}{18} = \frac{5}{x}$ 35. $\frac{7}{8} = \frac{x}{96}$ 36. $\frac{3}{5} = \frac{54}{x}$

37. Each class had a ratio of 5 books to every 3 students. How many books were there for a class of 24 students?

38. A map had a scale of 200 km to 2 cm. What is the actual distance of 8 cm on the map?

Percents
Finding Percents
Using Your Skills
Measuring Volume, Mass, and Temperature

Percents

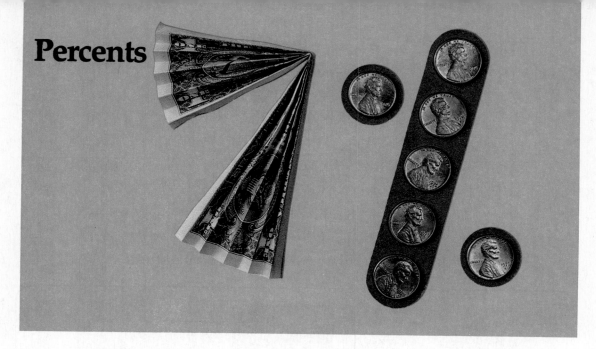

One dollar is 100 cents.
Seven cents is $\frac{7}{100}$ or 0.07 of one dollar.
Seven cents is 7 **percent** of one dollar.

Percent is a special ratio that compares a
number to 100. The symbol for percent is %.
Seven cents is 7% of one dollar.

Each amount is what percent of one dollar?

1.

2.

3.

4.

5.

6.

What percent of each square is shaded?

1.

2.
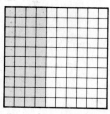

3.
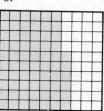

4.
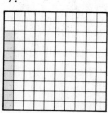

5.
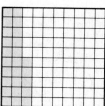

6.
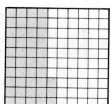

7.

8.
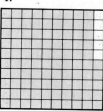

Write each ratio as a percent.

9. 6 out of 100

10. 23 out of 100

11. 74 out of 100

12. 19 to 100

13. 47 to 100

14. 30 to 100

15. 3 to 100

16. 11 to 100

17. 38 to 100

Copy and complete the tables.

	Ratio	Percent
18.	$\frac{17}{100}$	▦
19.	$\frac{9}{100}$	▦
20.	$\frac{26}{100}$	▦
21.	$\frac{58}{100}$	▦
22.	$\frac{83}{100}$	▦
23.	$\frac{37}{100}$	▦

	Ratio	Percent
24.	$\frac{1}{100}$	▦
25.	$\frac{95}{100}$	▦
26.	$\frac{66}{100}$	▦
27.	$\frac{10}{100}$	▦
28.	$\frac{49}{100}$	▦
29.	$\frac{3}{100}$	▦

Decimals and percents

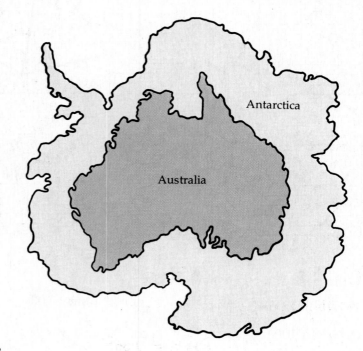

Australia is about 0.54 of the size of Antarctica.

$$0.54 = \frac{54}{100} = 54\%$$

Australia is about 54% of the size of Antarctica.

Other examples

$0.09 = 9\%$ $0.66\frac{2}{3} = 66\frac{2}{3}\%$ $0.2 = 0.20 = 20\%$

$0.24\frac{1}{2} = 24\frac{1}{2}\%$ $0.01 = 1\%$ $0.6 = 0.60 = 60\%$

Write each decimal as a percent.

1. 0.13	2. 0.25	3. 0.45	4. 0.07	5. 0.76
6. 0.34	7. $0.29\frac{1}{2}$	8. 0.06	9. 0.18	10. 0.04
11. 0.7	12. 0.63	13. $0.38\frac{1}{4}$	14. 0.02	15. 0.9
16. 0.27	17. 0.04	18. $0.87\frac{1}{2}$	19. 0.71	20. 0.38
21. $0.41\frac{1}{5}$	22. 0.1	23. 0.99	24. 0.51	25. $0.03\frac{1}{3}$

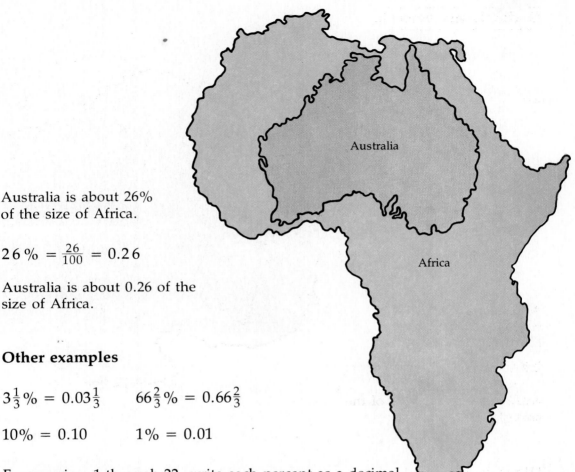

Australia is about 26% of the size of Africa.

$26\% = \frac{26}{100} = 0.26$

Australia is about 0.26 of the size of Africa.

Other examples

$3\frac{1}{3}\% = 0.03\frac{1}{3}$ $66\frac{2}{3}\% = 0.66\frac{2}{3}$

$10\% = 0.10$ $1\% = 0.01$

For exercises 1 through 22, write each percent as a decimal.

1. 23%	2. 47%	3. $33\frac{1}{3}\%$	4. 69%	5. 90%
6. $8\frac{1}{2}\%$	7. 11%	8. 15%	9. 20%	10. $37\frac{1}{4}\%$
11. 2%	12. 50%	13. 72%	14. 63%	15. 80%
16. 12%	17. 85%	18. 97%	19. 4%	20. 7%

21. Australia contains about 5% of the earth's land area.

22. Australia's size is about 32% of the size of North America.

The area of Australia is 7 683 798 km². The population of Australia is about 13 800 000. About how many people, to the nearest tenth, are there to each square kilometer of land in Australia?

Fractions and percents

In one class, 3 out of 25, or $\frac{3}{25}$ of the students are left-handed. What percent of the students are left-handed?

Finding the answer

A fraction	→	Write an equivalent fraction with a denominator of 100	→	Write the percent for the fraction

$$\frac{3}{25} \qquad \frac{3}{25} = \frac{3 \times 4}{25 \times 4} = \frac{12}{100} \qquad\qquad 12\%$$

12% of the students are left-handed.

Other examples

$$\frac{2}{5} = \frac{2 \times 20}{5 \times 20} = \frac{40}{100} = 40\% \qquad\qquad \frac{7}{10} = \frac{7 \times 10}{10 \times 10} = \frac{70}{100} = 70\%$$

Write the percent for each fraction.

1. $\frac{1}{10}$ 2. $\frac{1}{5}$ 3. $\frac{1}{4}$ 4. $\frac{1}{2}$ 5. $\frac{3}{5}$

6. $\frac{4}{10}$ 7. $\frac{3}{4}$ 8. $\frac{9}{10}$ 9. $\frac{2}{10}$ 10. $\frac{3}{20}$

11. $\frac{8}{10}$ 12. $\frac{7}{25}$ 13. $\frac{3}{10}$ 14. $\frac{4}{5}$ 15. $\frac{11}{20}$

16. $\frac{9}{25}$ 17. $\frac{7}{10}$ 18. $\frac{6}{10}$ 19. $\frac{39}{100}$ 20. $\frac{21}{25}$

21. $\frac{4}{20}$ 22. $\frac{17}{100}$ 23. $\frac{5}{10}$ 24. $\frac{17}{50}$ 25. $\frac{49}{50}$

Sometimes you need to find a fraction for a percent.

In one class, 60% of the students were girls. What fractional part of the students were girls?

Finding the answer

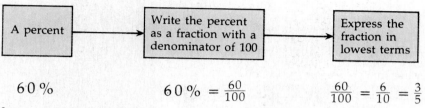

$$60\%$$

$$60\% = \frac{60}{100}$$

$$\frac{60}{100} = \frac{6}{10} = \frac{3}{5}$$

$\frac{3}{5}$ of the students were girls.

Other examples

$$12\% = \frac{12}{100} = \frac{3}{25} \qquad 90\% = \frac{90}{100} = \frac{9}{10} \qquad 35\% = \frac{35}{100} = \frac{7}{20} \qquad 17\% = \frac{17}{100}$$

Write a lowest-terms fraction for each percent.

1. 10%
2. 50%
3. 30%
4. 25%
5. 60%

6. 24%
7. 75%
8. 90%
9. 45%
10. 20%

11. 6%
12. 39%
13. 15%
14. 40%
15. 70%

16. 56%
17. 48%
18. 18%
19. 26%
20. 30%

21. 5%
22. 2%
23. 51%
24. 65%
25. 95%

26. On Friday, 4% of the students in one class were absent. What fractional part of the class was absent?

☆ 27. Make up a percent problem about the students in your class. Solve your problem.

Find the lowest-terms fraction for each.

1. $\frac{231}{924}$
2. $\frac{39}{52}$
3. $\frac{54}{135}$
4. $\frac{888}{1776}$
5. $\frac{101}{1010}$
6. $\frac{49}{245}$

Other fractional numbers and percents

Lynn took 12 pictures. Two of the pictures were blurred. What percent of the pictures were blurred?

Finding the answer

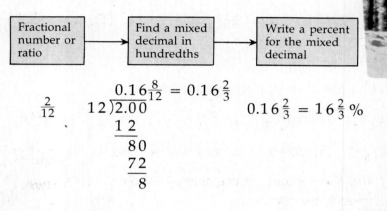

Fractional number or ratio	→	Find a mixed decimal in hundredths	→	Write a percent for the mixed decimal

$$\frac{2}{12} \qquad 12\overline{)2.00} \qquad 0.16\tfrac{8}{12} = 0.16\tfrac{2}{3}$$

$$\begin{array}{r} 0.16\tfrac{8}{12} \\ 12\overline{)2.00} \\ 1\,2 \\ \hline 80 \\ 72 \\ \hline 8 \end{array}$$

$$0.16\tfrac{2}{3} = 16\tfrac{2}{3}\%$$

$16\tfrac{2}{3}\%$ of the pictures were blurred.

Other examples

$$\frac{5}{6} \rightarrow 6\overline{)5.00} \qquad 0.83\tfrac{2}{6} \rightarrow 83\tfrac{1}{3}\%$$

$$\begin{array}{r} 0.83\tfrac{2}{6} \\ 6\overline{)5.00} \\ 4\,8 \\ \hline 20 \\ 18 \\ \hline 2 \end{array}$$

$$\frac{5}{8} \rightarrow 8\overline{)5.00} \qquad 0.62\tfrac{4}{8} \rightarrow 62\tfrac{1}{2}\%$$

$$\begin{array}{r} 0.62\tfrac{4}{8} \\ 8\overline{)5.00} \\ 4\,8 \\ \hline 20 \\ 16 \\ \hline 4 \end{array}$$

Write as percents.

1. $\frac{1}{3}$
2. $\frac{3}{8}$
3. $\frac{1}{6}$
4. $\frac{7}{8}$
5. $\frac{5}{8}$

6. $\frac{5}{9}$
7. $\frac{1}{8}$
8. $\frac{5}{12}$
9. $\frac{9}{16}$
10. $\frac{7}{12}$

11. $\frac{8}{15}$
12. $\frac{7}{16}$
13. $\frac{3}{11}$
14. $\frac{7}{9}$
15. $\frac{8}{13}$

16. $\frac{11}{24}$
17. $\frac{13}{40}$
18. $\frac{15}{32}$
19. $\frac{12}{18}$
20. $\frac{14}{15}$

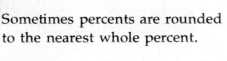

Sometimes percents are rounded to the nearest whole percent.

Examples

$83\frac{1}{3}\% \longrightarrow 83\%$ $\qquad$ $12\frac{1}{2}\% \longrightarrow 13\%$

$\frac{1}{3} < \frac{1}{2}$

$\qquad\qquad\qquad\qquad\qquad 26\frac{3}{4}\% \longrightarrow 27\%$

$83\frac{2}{3}\% \longrightarrow 84\%$ $\qquad$ $52\frac{1}{8}\% \longrightarrow 52\%$

$\frac{2}{3} > \frac{1}{2}$

Round to the nearest whole percent.

1. $6\frac{1}{8}\%$ $\quad$ 2. $19\frac{3}{4}\%$ $\quad$ 3. $76\frac{4}{5}\%$ $\quad$ 4. $51\frac{7}{8}\%$ $\quad$ 5. $32\frac{1}{2}\%$

6. $41\frac{3}{8}\%$ $\quad$ 7. $87\frac{1}{2}\%$ $\quad$ 8. $66\frac{2}{3}\%$ $\quad$ 9. $36\frac{4}{9}\%$ $\quad$ 10. $96\frac{9}{10}\%$

Find the percent, to the nearest whole percent, for each number.

11. $\frac{5}{6}$ $\qquad$ 12. $\frac{7}{12}$ $\qquad$ 13. $\frac{3}{8}$ $\qquad$ 14. $\frac{8}{9}$ $\qquad$ 15. $\frac{5}{11}$

16. $\frac{11}{16}$ $\qquad$ 17. $\frac{10}{17}$ $\qquad$ 18. $\frac{7}{8}$ $\qquad$ 19. $\frac{11}{12}$ $\qquad$ 20. $\frac{13}{16}$

21. $\frac{5}{9}$ $\qquad$ 22. $\frac{13}{18}$ $\qquad$ 23. $\frac{17}{24}$ $\qquad$ 24. $\frac{33}{40}$ $\qquad$ 25. $\frac{19}{35}$

26. $\frac{26}{27}$ $\qquad$ 27. $\frac{17}{29}$ $\qquad$ 28. $\frac{5}{18}$ $\qquad$ 29. $\frac{29}{60}$ $\qquad$ 30. $\frac{35}{45}$

31. Don took 36 pictures. 5 of them did not turn out. What percent of his pictures, to the nearest whole percent, did not turn out?

32. Marie took 12 pictures. 5 of them did not turn out. What percent of her pictures, to the nearest whole percent, did not turn out?

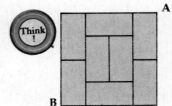

Each of the eight rectangles in the figure is 1 cm by 2 cm. What is the longest path from A to B along the edges of the rectangles? You cannot go through any point more than once.

More practice, page 390, Set B

About 71% of the earth's surface is water.
About 29% of the earth's surface is land.

$71\% + 29\% = 100\%$

$100\% = \frac{100}{100} = 1$

100% of a unit is all of the unit.

The continent of North America has about 16.3% of the earth's land area.
What percent of the land area is on other land masses?

$100\% - 16.3\% = 83.7\%$

Other land masses have 83.7% of the world's land area.

Find the missing percents.

1. $100\% - 30\% = $ ▒▒▒

2. $100\% - 61\% = $ ▒▒▒

3. $100\% - 9\% = $ ▒▒▒

4. $100\% - 22.4\% = $ ▒▒▒

5. $100\% - 46.1\% = $ ▒▒▒

6. $100\% - 37\frac{1}{2}\% = $ ▒▒▒

7. $23\% + 61\% + 16\% = $ ▒▒▒

8. $14.5\% + 6.3\% + 51.4\% + 27.8\% = $ ▒▒▒

9. $38\% + 25\% + $ ▒▒▒ $= 100\%$

10. $11.7\% + 62.4\% + 13.8\% + $ ▒▒▒ $= 100\%$

1. The air around the earth is about 78% nitrogen. What percent of the air is composed of other gases?

2. The crust of the earth is about 28% silicon and 47% oxygen. What percent of the crust is made of other elements?

3. About 99% of the earth's atmosphere is less than 160 km from the earth's surface. About what percent of the atmosphere is at a greater distance from the surface?

4. Only 3% of the earth's water is fresh water. The rest is salt water in oceans and seas. What percent of the earth's water is salt water?

5. About 75% of the earth's fresh water is in the form of ice found in glaciers. What percent of earth's fresh water is not found in glaciers?

6. About 21% of the earth's air is oxygen. What percent of the earth's air is not oxygen?

7. The continent of Asia contains about 58.5% of the world's population. What percent of the world's population is not in Asia?

8. Crops are grown on about 10% of the earth's land area. What percent of the land area is not used for growing crops?

9. Cereal crops such as corn, rice, and wheat occupy 70% of the farm area of the earth. What percent of the farm area is devoted to other crops?

10. Cereal grains provide us with about 52% of our food. What percent of our food does not come from cereal grains?

Percents greater than 100%

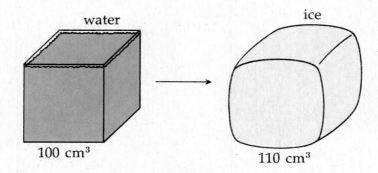

water 100 cm³

ice 110 cm³

When water freezes, it expands.
When 100 cm³ of water freezes,
there will be about 110 cm³
of ice.

$$\frac{\text{ice}}{\text{water}} \qquad \frac{110}{100} = 110\%$$

The volume of ice is 110% of the volume of water.

Other examples

$\frac{137}{100} = 137\%$ $\qquad\qquad$ $2 = 2.00 = 200\%$

$3.15 = 315\%$ $\qquad\qquad$ $1.5 = 1.50 = 150\%$

Write as percents.

1. $\frac{175}{100}$	2. $\frac{213}{100}$	3. $\frac{350}{100}$	4. $\frac{419}{100}$	5. $\frac{107}{100}$
6. 3.00	7. 9.00	8. 6	9. 4	10. 10
11. 1.25	12. 3.75	13. 1.46	14. 2.09	15. 4.13
16. $\frac{120}{100}$	17. 4.75	18. 1.33	19. $\frac{515}{100}$	20. 1.01
21. $4\frac{39}{100}$	22. 6.42	23. $\frac{103}{100}$	24. 1	25. 1.69

The population of San Jose, California in 1970 was 483% of what its population was in 1950.

Write 483% as a decimal.

$$483\% = \frac{483}{100} = 4.83$$

Write as decimals.

1. 165%	2. 350%	3. 268%	4. 104%	5. 600%
6. 193%	7. 409%	8. 119%	9. 750%	10. 229%
11. 110%	12. 500%	13. 199%	14. 1000%	15. 150%
16. 275%	17. 112%	18. 800%	19. 120%	20. 333%
21. 108%	22. 116%	23. 133%	24. 118%	25. 210%

26. A room had 115 people. There were only 100 seats. Express the ratio of people to seats as a percent.

27. A group of salespersons' earnings this week are 152% of their last week's earnings. Express this percent as a decimal.

How many grams of dishwasher detergent do you buy for 1¢ with each size box? Which size is the best buy?

$0.69
567 g

$1.18
992 g

$1.60
1417 g

Self-check

Write each ratio as a percent.

1. $\frac{39}{100}$ 2. $\frac{47}{100}$ 3. $\frac{3}{100}$ 4. $\frac{250}{100}$ 5. $\frac{137}{100}$

Write each decimal as a percent.

6. 0.75   7. 0.04   8. 0.32   9. 1.21   10. 2.00

Write each percent as a decimal.

11. 8%   12. 28%   13. 78%   14. 110%   15. 212%

Find the percent, to the nearest whole percent, for each number.

16. $\frac{3}{4}$ 17. $\frac{7}{8}$ 18. $\frac{5}{9}$ 19. $\frac{2}{3}$ 20. $\frac{1}{6}$

Write each percent as a lowest-terms fraction.

21. 25%   22. 40%   23. 50%   24. About 88% of milk is water. About what percent of milk is not water?

Answers for Self-check—page 277

Test

Write each ratio as a percent.

1. $\frac{23}{100}$ 2. $\frac{57}{100}$ 3. $\frac{2}{100}$ 4. $\frac{150}{100}$ 5. $\frac{207}{100}$

Write each decimal as a percent.

6. 0.17   7. 0.03   8. 0.22   9. 3.15   10. 1.08

Write each percent as a decimal.

11. 6%   12. 53%   13. 36%   14. 225%   15. 100%

Find the percent, to the nearest whole percent, for each number.

16. $\frac{3}{8}$ 17. $\frac{1}{2}$ 18. $\frac{7}{28}$ 19. $\frac{1}{3}$ 20. $\frac{7}{9}$

Write each percent as a lowest-terms fraction.

21. 75%   22. $12\frac{1}{2}$%   23. 60%   24. The human body is about 67% water. About what percent of the body is not water?

Math lab

Making an Ellipse by Paper Folding

An ellipse is an interesting geometric figure. The earth and the other planets travel around the sun in elliptical paths. You can construct an ellipse by folding paper.

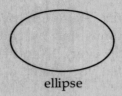

ellipse

Draw a circle about 16 cm in diameter on a sheet of waxed paper. Mark a point P about 2 cm inside the circle.

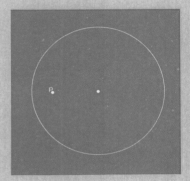

Fold the paper so that a point on the circle falls on point P. Repeat the fold for many points all around the circle.

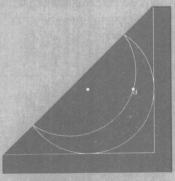

When completed, the fold lines will form the outline of an ellipse.

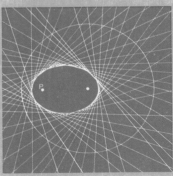

Finding Percents

Have you ever paid a
sales tax on something
you bought?

A sales tax rate of 6% means
that you must pay an additional
6 cents for every 100 cents, or
dollar, that you spend.

Give the missing amounts of sales tax in the table.

	Amount Spent	Sales tax rate	Sales tax
	$1 bill	6%	① ① ① ① ① ①
	two $1 bills	6%	① ① ⑩
1.	$5 bill	6%	▐▐▐
2.	$10 bill	6%	▐▐▐
3.	$20 bill	6%	▐▐▐

Give the missing numbers.

1. 6% of 1 dollar means 6 cents for each dollar,
   or ||||| cents.

2. 6% of 2 dollars means 6 cents for each dollar,
   or ||||| cents.

3. 6% of 3 dollars means 6 cents for each dollar,
   or ||||| cents.

4. 10% of 1 dollar means 10 cents for each dollar,
   or ||||| cents.

5. 10% of 5 dollars means 10 cents for each dollar,
   or ||||| cents.

6. 25% of 1 dollar means 25 cents for each dollar,
   or ||||| cents.

7. 25% of 10 dollars means 25 cents for each dollar,
   or ||||| cents.

Find the amounts.

8. What is 50% of 1 dollar?

9. What is 50% of 4 dollars?

10. What is 50% of 20 dollars?

11. What is 50% of 50 cents?

12. What is 8% of 1 dollar?

13. What is 8% of 10 dollars?

14. What is 8% of 100 dollars?

15. What is 8% of 1000 dollars?

Finding a percent of a number

25% of the students in a class of 36 were born in a state other than the state they live in now. How many students is this?

Finding the answer

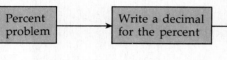

Percent problem	→	Write a decimal for the percent	→	Multiply

25% of 36
means
25% × 36

25% = 0.25

$$\begin{array}{r} 36 \\ \times\,0.25 \\ \hline 180 \\ 72 \\ \hline 9.00 \end{array}$$

9 students were born in other states.

Other examples

Find 6% of 54.5.

$$\begin{array}{r} 54.5 \\ \times\,0.06 \\ \hline 3.270 \end{array}$$

Find 23% of 158.

$$\begin{array}{r} 158 \\ \times\,0.23 \\ \hline 4\,74 \\ 31\,6 \\ \hline 36.34 \end{array}$$

Find the percent of each number.

1. 4% of 75
2. 30% of 80
3. 70% of 150
4. 10% of 62.9
5. 9% of 1000
6. 40% of 350
7. 25% of 60
8. 42% of 5.6
9. 85% of 600
10. 16% of 45
11. 62% of 120
12. 34% of 48

Compute.

1. 90% of 50
2. 20% of 85
3. 50% of 44

4. 25% of 80
5. 75% of 600
6. 30% of 30

7. 2% of 125
8. 6% of 900
9. 5% of 475

10. 12% of 72
11. 33% of 50
12. 21% of 240

13. 4% of 62.4
14. 11% of 35.5
15. 27% of 85.1

16. 65% of 72
17. 83% of 117
18. 98% of 500

Find 1% of each number.

Example: 1% of 856 = 0.01 × 856 = 8.56

19. 275
20. 917
21. 200
22. 4000
23. 100

24. 42.4
25. 196.3
26. 8.9
27. 17.5
28. 0.9

29. 25 000
30. 100 000
31. 63 000
32. 347 000
33. 1 000 000

Find 10% of each number.

Example: 10% of 275 = 0.10 × 275 = 27.50

34. 396
35. 84
36. 257
37. 900
38. 10

39. 537.1
40. 16.53
41. 0.83
42. 2.7
43. 76.9

44. 8000
45. 50 000
46. 189 000
47. 796 500
48. 1 000 000

49. 5% of a class of 40 students have visited another country. How many students is this?

☆ 50. $12\frac{1}{2}$% of 648 students have traveled to at least one state other than the one they live in. How many students is this?

What number gives the same result when multiplied by 3 as when 3 is added to it?

$3 \times n = ?$ $\qquad$ $n + 3 = ?$

More practice, page 391, Set A

Finding the percent one number is of another number

There are 60 musicians in the band. 15 of them play clarinets. What percent of the band members play clarinets? What percent of 60 is 15?

Finding the answer

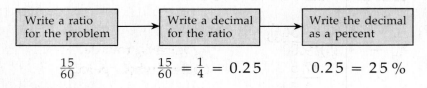

Write a ratio for the problem	Write a decimal for the ratio	Write the decimal as a percent
$\frac{15}{60}$	$\frac{15}{60} = \frac{1}{4} = 0.25$	$0.25 = 25\%$

25% of the band members play clarinets.

15 is 25% of 60.

Other examples

What percent of 20 is 14?

$$\frac{14}{20} = 0.70 = 70\%$$

What percent of 4 is 5?

$$\frac{5}{4} = 1.25 = 125\%$$

4 is what percent of 12?

$$\frac{4}{12} = \frac{1}{3} = 0.33\frac{1}{3} = 33\frac{1}{3}\%$$

3 is what percent of 8?

$$\frac{3}{8} = 0.37\frac{1}{2} = 37\frac{1}{2}\%$$

Find the percents.

1. What percent of 60 is 12?

2. What percent of 25 is 16?

3. What percent of 20 is 16?

4. What percent of 9 is 6?

5. 12 is what percent of 24?

6. 30 is what percent of 600?

Find the percents.

1. What percent of 36 is 9?
2. What percent of 20 is 12?
3. What percent of 15 is 3?
4. What percent of 36 is 18?
5. 40 is what percent of 120?
6. 16 is what percent of 80?
7. 3 is what percent of 300?
8. 6 is what percent of 4?
9. 12 is what percent of 15?
10. 16 is what percent of 40?

Find each percent, rounded to the nearest whole percent.

Example: What percent of 35 is 19?

$$\frac{19}{35} \longrightarrow 35\overline{)19.00}^{\,0.54\frac{10}{35}}$$

$$\begin{array}{r} 17\ 5 \\ \hline 1\ 50 \\ 1\ 40 \\ \hline 10 \end{array}$$

$\frac{19}{35}$ is 54%, rounded to the nearest whole percent.

11. What percent of 42 is 27?
12. What percent of 7 is 6?
13. What percent of 55 is 34?
14. What percent of 96 is 21?
15. What percent of 96 is 90?
16. What percent of 19 is 7?

17. There are 60 members in the band. Three members play French horns. What percent of the band members play French horns?

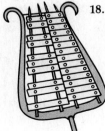

18. One member in the band plays a glockenspiel. What percent of the 60 members of the band play the glockenspiel?

 Start at one of the seven points and trace this figure without retracing any line.

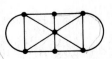

Solving percent equations

64% of the students in a class spent
a week at an outdoor science camp.
16 students went to the camp. What is
the total number of students in the class?

Finding the answer

Think: 64% of the total number in the class = 16
Let n = the total number

Write the equation: $64\% \times n = 16$

Solve the equation: $0.64 \times n = 16$

$$n = 16 \div 0.64 \longrightarrow \begin{array}{r} 25 \\ 0.64\overline{)16.00} \\ \underline{12\,8} \\ 3\,20 \\ \underline{3\,20} \\ 0 \end{array}$$

$n = 25$

The total number of students in the class is 25.

Other examples

15% of what number is 24?

$15\% \times n = 24$
$0.15 \times n = 24$
$\qquad n = 24 \div 0.15$
$\qquad n = 160$

40% of what number is 1.8?

$40\% \times n = 1.8$
$0.40 \times n = 1.8$
$\qquad n = 1.8 \div 0.40$
$\qquad n = 4.5$

Solve the equations.

1. $10\% \times n = 8$

2. $40\% \times n = 10$

3. $75\% \times n = 15$

4. $11\% \times n = 1.87$

5. $6\% \times n = 2.1$

6. $56\% \times n = 22.4$

Solve.

1. $20\% \times n = 12$ 2. $4\% \times n = 10$ 3. $8\% \times n = 4$

4. $12\% \times n = 24$ 5. $16\% \times n = 40$ 6. $1\% \times n = 9$

7. $50\% \times n = 29$ 8. $62\% \times n = 31$ 9. $27\% \times n = 81$

Write and solve an equation for each problem.

10. 60% of what number is 21?   11. 9% of what number is 2.7?

12. 15% of what number is 48?   13. 50% of what number is 38?

14. 22% of what number is 16.5?   15. 31% of what number is 4.65?

16. 95% of what number is 152?   17. 25% of what number is 1?

18. 9% of what number is 33.48?   19. 57% of what number is 17.1?

20. 12% of a group of students took a first aid course. 3 students took the course. How many students were in the group?

☆ 21. $62\frac{1}{2}\%$ of a group of students earn their money from babysitting. 40 students earn their money this way. What is the total number in the group?

How can a 5-minute egg timer and a 7-minute egg timer be used to time exactly 13 minutes of cooking time?

5 minute timer

7 minute timer

Answers for Self-check   1. 30   2. 21.6   3. 12.40   4. 162.00   5. 3.15   6. 84.00   7. 11.2
8. 20.00   9. 25%   10. 8%   11. 75%   12. 30%   13. $n = 50$ 14. $n = 56$ 15. $50\% \times n = 21$, $n = 42$ 16. $65\% \times n = 46.8$, $n = 72$

More practice, page 391, Set B

Self-check

Compute.

1. 60% of 50
2. 30% of 72
3. 8% of 155
4. 27% of 600

5. 1% of 315
6. 35% of 240
7. 10% of 112
8. 1% of 2000

9. 18 is what percent of 72?
10. 6 is what percent of 75?

11. What percent of 112 is 84?
12. What percent of 90 is 27?

Solve.

13. $20\% \times n = 10$
14. $8\% \times n = 4.48$

Write and solve an equation for each problem.

15. 50% of what number is 21?
16. 65% of what number is 46.8?

Answers for Self-check—page 287

Test

Compute.

1. 40% of 85
2. 10% of 718
3. 6% of 850
4. 52% of 925

5. 8% of 500
6. 61% of 4000
7. 1% of 25 000
8. 10% of 400

9. 11 is what percent of 22?
10. 17 is what percent of 85?

11. What percent of 20 is 12?
12. What percent of 80 is 32?

Solve.

13. $90\% \times n = 27$
14. $7\% \times n = 4.2$

Write and solve an equation for each problem.

15. 75% of what number is 66?
16. 18% of what number is 8.1?

Math lab

A Pattern with Primes

Use the flow chart below to find the output numbers for the chart.

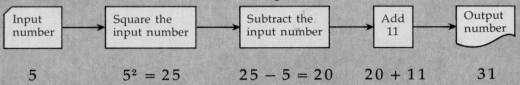

5	$5^2 = 25$	$25 - 5 = 20$	$20 + 11$	31

Input Number	Output Number
1	▥
2	▥
3	▥
4	▥
5	31
6	▥
7	▥
8	▥
9	▥
10	▥

Are each of the output numbers in the chart prime numbers? Do you think the output numbers will always be prime numbers for any input numbers?

Try the numbers from 11 to 20 as input numbers. What do you find?

The first 100 prime numbers									
2	31	73	127	179	233	283	353	419	467
3	37	79	131	181	239	293	359	421	479
5	41	83	137	191	241	307	367	431	487
7	43	89	139	193	251	311	373	433	491
11	47	97	149	197	257	313	379	439	499
13	53	101	151	199	263	317	383	443	503
17	59	103	157	211	269	331	389	449	509
19	61	107	163	223	271	337	397	457	521
23	67	109	167	227	277	347	401	461	523
29	71	113	173	229	281	349	409	463	541

Using Your Skills

An archaeologist is a scientist who finds and studies ancient objects such as buildings, utensils, and tools in order to learn how people lived before the days of recorded history. Many important finds in archaeology have been made by carefully digging and sifting the earth at places where ancient peoples once lived. To a trained archaeologist, a small piece of broken pottery may provide an important clue to understanding the culture of an ancient people.

Picture of
ancient Pompeii

Gold mask
of
King Tutankhamun

1. A skull found in Kenya, Africa, was estimated by an archaeologist to be about 2.5×10^6 years old. How many years old is this?

2. The Rhind papyrus, written about 1700 B.C., was discovered again in 1858. This papyrus scroll was a handbook of Egyptian mathematics. The scroll was 33 cm wide and about 16.5 times as long as it was wide. How many meters long was the scroll?

3. The ancient city of Pompeii had a population of about 20 000 people. The city was covered with ashes from the volcano Vesuvius in 79 A.D. Archaeologists think about 10% of the population was trapped in the city. About how many people was this?

4. Tutankhamun was a king of ancient Egypt. He was born about 1355 B.C. His tomb was opened in 1922 A.D. About how many years later was his tomb opened?

Finding percent scores on tests

Perry got 21 out of 25 problems correct
on a test. What percent of the problems
did Perry work correctly?

Number correct ——————→ $\dfrac{21}{25}$

Number of problems ——————→

$$\begin{array}{r} 0.84 \\ 25\overline{)21.00} \\ \underline{20\ 0} \\ 1\ 00 \\ \underline{1\ 00} \\ 0 \end{array}$$

$0.84 = 84\%$

Perry worked 84% of the problems correctly.
Perry's score may be given as 84%.

Sometimes percent scores are rounded to the nearest whole percent.

What percent score is 29 problems correct out of 30 problems?

Number correct ——————→ $\dfrac{29}{30}$

Number of problems ——————→

$$\begin{array}{r} 0.96\frac{20}{30} \\ 30\overline{)29.00} \\ \underline{27\ 0} \\ 2\ 00 \\ \underline{1\ 80} \\ 20 \end{array}$$

$0.96\frac{20}{30} = 0.96\frac{2}{3}$ Round $0.96\frac{2}{3}$ to 0.97.

$0.97 = 97\%$

To the nearest whole percent, the score is 97%.

Find the percent score.

1. 24 problems correct
   25 problems in all

2. 18 problems correct
   20 problems in all

3. 12 problems correct
   16 problems in all

4. 36 problems correct
   40 problems in all

5. 41 problems correct
   50 problems in all

6. 87 problems correct
   100 problems in all

Find the percent score.
Round all answers to the nearest whole percent.

1. Spelling test:
    Pamela spelled 47 out
    of 50 words correctly.
    What was her score?

2. Homework problems:
    Chris got 8 out of 10
    problems correct.
    What was her score?

3. History quiz:
    Wendy got 10 out of
    12 questions correct.
    What was her score?

4. Social studies test:
    Brian got 23 out of 30
    questions correct.
    What was his score?

5. English quiz:
    Barbara got 13 out of 16 correct.
    What was her score?

6. Who has the higher score?
    Max: 18 out of 21
    William: 24 out of 29

7. True-false test:
    Bill got 72 out of 80
    questions correct.
    What was his score?

8. Multiple-choice test:
    Ralph got 57 correct
    out of 60 questions.
    What was his score?

9. Science test:
    Leslie got 25 out of
    30 questions
    What was her score?

10. Math test:
    Linda got 22 out of 24
    problems correct.
    What was her score?

11. Semester test:
    Jack got 58 out of
    66 problems correct.
    What was his score?

☆ 12. How many of your answers for
    exercises 1 through 11 are
    correct? Find your percent
    score for these problems.

A student took a quiz and missed only
3 questions. The student got a score
of 85%. How many questions were
on the quiz?

Applying sales tax rates

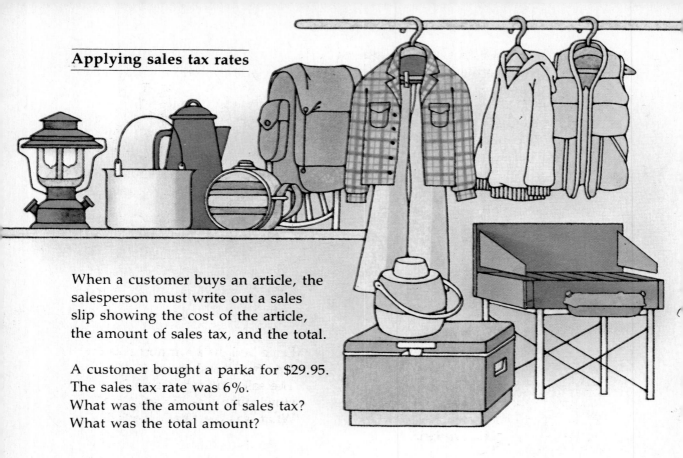

When a customer buys an article, the salesperson must write out a sales slip showing the cost of the article, the amount of sales tax, and the total.

A customer bought a parka for $29.95.
The sales tax rate was 6%.
What was the amount of sales tax?
What was the total amount?

$
\begin{array}{r}
\$\ 29.95 \\
\times\ \ \ 0.06 \\
\hline
\$1.7970
\end{array}
$ ← amount of purchase
← sales tax rate
← sales tax

$1.80 ← sales tax rounded to the nearest cent

$
\begin{array}{r}
\$\ 29.95 \\
+\ \ \ 1.80 \\
\hline
\$31.75
\end{array}
$ ← amount of purchase
← sales tax
← total amount

The sales tax was $1.80.
The total amount was $31.75.

Find the amount of sales tax to the nearest cent.
Then find the total amount.

1. Amount of purchase: $2.50
   Sales tax rate: 4%

2. Amount of purchase: $47.95
   Sales tax rate: 3%

3. Amount of purchase: $16.44
   Sales tax rate: 5%

4. Amount of purchase: $2400
   Sales tax rate: 6%

Find the amount of sales tax to the nearest cent.
Then find the total amount.

1.
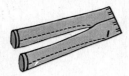
jeans $12.77
Sales tax rate: 5%

2.

knapsack $15.79
Sales tax rate: 6%

3.
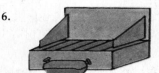
hiking boots $25.99
Sales tax rate: 4%

4.
sleeping bag $36.95
Sales tax rate: 6%

5.
flashlight $4.80
Sales tax rate: 3%

6.
campstove $27.00
Sales tax rate: 6%

7. Jody bought 8 packets of insect
repellent for 19¢ each and a
first aid kit for $4.48. The
sales tax rate was 6%.
How much was the sales tax?
What was the total amount?

8. Dave bought 2 T-shirts for
$3.95 each and 3 pairs of
socks at $1.39 a pair. The
sales tax rate was 4%.
How much was the sales tax?
What was the total amount?

9. Ernie bought a windbreaker for
$14.95 and a shirt for $12.75.
The sales tax rate was 5%.
How much was the sales tax?
What was the total amount?

☆ 10. Find the price of three articles
you would like to buy. Find
out the sales tax rate in your
community. Then find how much
sales tax you would have to pay
and the total amount.

The total amount of purchase,
including sales tax, can be
found by multiplying the
amount of purchase by

1 + sales tax rate

Amount of purchase: $50.00

Sales tax rate: 6%

Total amount = $50.00 × 1.06
= $53

Find the total amount, including
sales tax, for each purchase.

1. Automobile: $4286.00
Sales tax rate: 4%

2. Bicycle: $139.75
Sales tax rate: 5%

3. New coat: $49.95
Sales tax rate: 6%

4. Color TV set: $599.00
Sales tax rate: 3%

Travel problems with percents

Travel agents use mathematics in figuring distances, calculating costs, and planning for time changes and schedules.

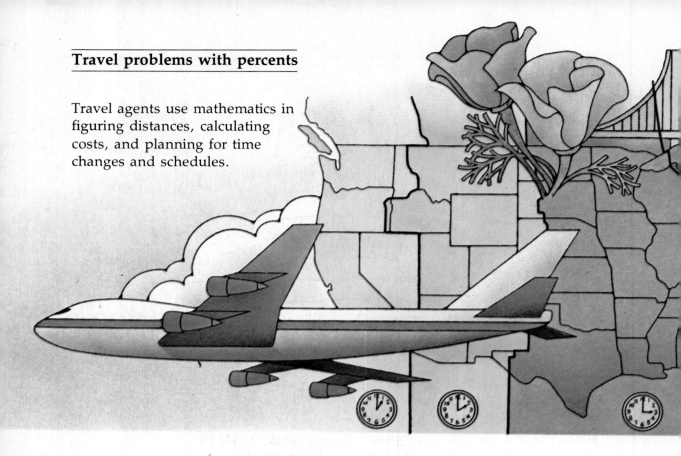

1. Mrs. Brown took a short business trip. Her airfare was $48.15 plus 8% tax. How much was her ticket with tax included?

2. Mr. and Mrs. Lamb took a vacation trip to Miami. Their combined airfare was $487.04 plus 8% tax. How much did they pay for the flight?

3. Jan Lewis took a two-week business trip to 4 cities. The airfares for each part of the trip and back home were $37.04, $45.37, $68.52, $74.07, and $72.22, plus an 8% tax on the total. What was the total cost of her ticket?

4. Mr. Cordoza's Adventure Travel Service makes its money from the airlines, hotels, and other services travelers use. For each airline ticket the travel service sells, it collects 7% of the ticket price. How much would the travel service collect for a ticket costing $263.89 (without tax)?

5. Adventure Travel Service sold these tickets: $703.70, $78.70 $327.78, $429.63, and $216.67. If the travel service's fee was 7% of the total, how much did it make on these tickets?

6. A travel agent was planning a trip from Wichita, Kansas to Boston, Massachusetts. One route traveled 298 km from Wichita to Kansas City and then 2018 km to Boston. Another route traveled 626 km from Wichita to St. Louis and then 1672 km to Boston. Which route is shorter?

☆ 7. Miss Purvis left Philadelphia at 9:30 a.m. (Eastern standard time). She arrived in Los Angeles at 11:50 a.m. (Pacific standard time). There is a 3-hour difference between the times in Philadelphia and Los Angeles. How many hours long was her flight?

☆ 8. Larry Meyer flew east to visit his grandparents. His plane departed at 9:05 a.m. When he arrived, the local time was 2:47 p.m. There was a 2-hour time difference between his home city and his grandparents' home city. How long was the flight?

✦ Road grade percents

Civil engineers apply mathematics to problems about the construction of roads, bridges, airports, water supply systems, and buildings. For example, while working on a road the engineer might measure the steepness of a hill by means of a percent called the **grade** of the hill.

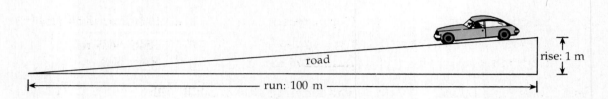

road   rise: 1 m   run: 100 m

A road that rises 1 meter for every 100 meters measured along level ground (run) has a grade of 1%.

$$\text{grade} = \frac{\text{rise}}{\text{run}} = \frac{1}{100} = 1\%$$

Example: A hill has a rise of 12 m and a run of 200 m. What is the percent grade?

$$\frac{\text{rise}}{\text{run}} = \frac{12}{200} = \frac{6}{100} = 0.06 = 6\%$$

Find the percent grade of each hill.

	Rise	Run	% Grade
1.	10 m	250 m	
2.	72 m	1200 m	
3.	35 m	500 m	
4.	7 m	140 m	
5.	16 m	240 m	
6.	18 m	400 m	

Find the percent grade for each hill.

1. Freeway exit ramp:

   Rise: 6 m
   Run: 300 m

2. Country road:

   Rise: 12 m
   Run: 120 m

3. Interstate highway:

   Rise: 12 m
   Run: 800 m

4. Mountain road:

   Rise: 71.5 m
   Run: 650 m

5. Beginners' ski slope:

   Rise: 60 m
   Run: 300 m

6. Average ski slope:

   Rise: 560 m
   Run: 1400 m

7. Steep ski slope:

   Rise: 720 m
   Run: 960 m

8. Cog railroad:

   Rise: 576 m
   Run: 3200 m

9. San Francisco street:

   Rise: 94.5 m
   Run: 300 m

10. Railroad crossing:

    Rise: 1.5 m
    Run: 150 m

11. The drawing shows a hill with a 20% grade.
    What is the rise of the hill?

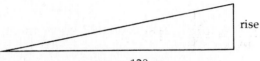

run = 120 m

☆ 12. Estimate the percent grade of some hill in your community. Try to find the actual percent grade of the hill.

Circle graphs and percents

An active person may eat about 650 kg of food in one year. The circle graph shows the different kinds of food that might be eaten and the percent of the total food each kind is. The complete circular region represents 650 kg.

How many kilograms of meat, fish, or poultry might be eaten by an active person in a year?

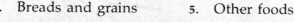

650	total amount of food
× 0.18	percent of meat, fish, and poultry
52 00	
65 0	
117.00	amount of meat, fish, and poultry

An active person might eat about 117 kg of meat, fish, or poultry in a year.

Use the graph above for each exercise. Find the number of kilograms of each kind of food eaten in one year.

1. Dairy products
2. Fats and oils
3. Fruits and vegetables
4. Breads and grains
5. Other foods

The graph gives the percent of each kind of food which would provide a healthful diet. A person might eat a total of 1800 grams of these foods in one day.

Find the number of grams of each kind of food.

1. Cereals and breads

2. Milk and dairy products

3. Meat, fish, or poultry

4. Citrus fruit

5. Green and yellow vegetables

6. Potatoes

7. Other fruits and vegetables

8. Other foods

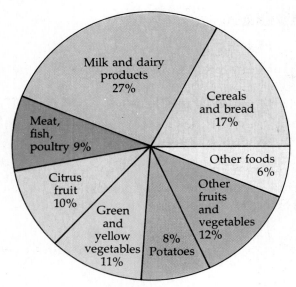

Healthful Foods

Milk contains all the nutrients we need for good health. The circle graphs shows the percent of each nutrient in milk.

9. Does milk contain more carbohydrates or more protein?

10. Which is greater in milk, the percent of fats or the percent of minerals?

11. What percent of milk is made up of proteins, fats, carbohydrates, and minerals?

12. Find the percent of milk that is water.

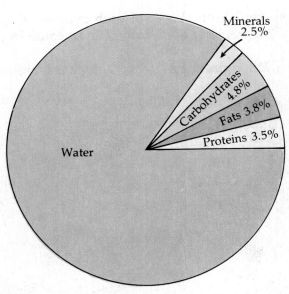

Nutrients in Cow's Milk

Answers for Self-check   1. 95%   2. 80%   3. 70%   4. 75%   5. $0.66, $17.16   6. 20%
7. $64.50   8. $58.05

Self-check

Find the percent of correct answers for the following test scores.

1. 19 out of 20 problems

2. 20 out of 25 problems

3. 7 out of 10 problems

4. 18 out of 24 problems

Find the sales tax to the nearest cent. Then find the total amount.

Find the percent grade for the hill.

5. Amount of purchase: $16.50
   Sales tax rate: 4%

☆ 6.

Rise: 14 m

Run: 70 m

7. Mary Jackson earns $215 a week. She pays 30% of this for housing. How much does she pay for housing each week?

8. From the same $215 she budgets 27% for food. How much money does she budget for food each week?

Answers for Self-check—page 301

Test

Find the percent of correct answers for the following test scores.

1. 43 out of 50 problems

2. 23 out of 25 problems

3. 12 out of 15 problems

4. 72 out of 80 problems

Find the sales tax to the nearest cent. Then find the total amount.

Find the percent grade for the hill.

5. Amount of purchase: $20.00
   Sales tax rate: 6%

☆ 6.

Rise: 5 m

Run: 125 m

7. John Dawson earns $825 a month. He saves 12% of his earnings. What are his monthly savings?

8. From the same $825 he budgets 33% for housing. How much money does the budget allow for housing per month?

Famous Mathematicians

K	A	T	R	P	N	F	E	R	M	A	T
Y	O	U	N	G	O	S	R	E	N	C	E
E	P	V	A	L	E	O	E	U	I	C	L
D	A	U	A	Q	T	M	L	C	A	T	E
E	S	R	G	L	H	E	U	L	M	E	T
S	C	I	N	N	E	R	E	I	R	A	A
C	A	E	E	R	R	V	P	D	E	I	H
A	L	M	S	O	O	I	S	W	G	T	C
R	T	A	I	L	J	L	O	K	C	A	U
T	S	N	I	K	S	L	U	O	A	P	D
E	R	N	O	T	W	E	N	I	T	Y	E
S	D	E	D	E	K	I	N	D	M	H	A

The last names of 18 famous mathematicians are hidden in the square of letters above. Nine of the mathematicians are women and nine are men. The names appear backward, forward, up, down, and diagonally. Make a copy of the puzzle. See how many of the names you can find.

Women Mathematicians

AGNESI, Maria Gaetana (1718–1799)
DU CHATELET, Mme. (1706–1749)
GERMAIN, Sophie (1776–1831)
HYPATIA (died 415 A.D.)
LOVELACE, Ada Byron (1815–1852)
KOVALEVSKAYA, Sofya (1850–1891)
NOETHER, Emmy (1882–1935)
SOMERVILLE, Mary (1780–1872)
YOUNG, Grace Chisholm (1868–1944)

Men Mathematicians

EULER, Leonhard (1707–1783)
DEDEKIND, Richard (1831–1916)
DESCARTES, Rene (1596–1650)
EUCLID (c. 300 B.C.)
FERMAT, Pierre de (1601–1665)
GAUSS, Karl F. (1777–1855)
NEWTON, Isaac (1642–1727)
PASCAL, Blaise (1623–1662)
RIEMANN, G. F. B. (1826–1866)

Find out about one or more of these mathematicians.
Report your findings to the class.

Measuring Volume, Mass, and Temperature

Prisms are named by the shape of their bases.

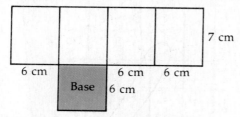

Pattern for a square prism

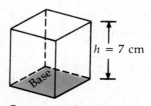

Square prism

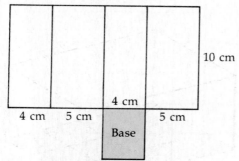

Pattern for a rectangular prism

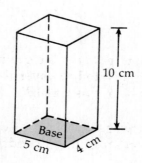

Rectangular prism

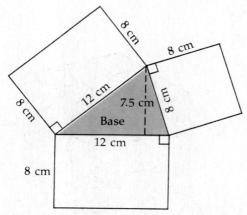

Pattern for a triangular prism

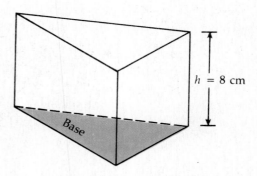

Triangular prism

Which prism do you think will hold the most?

Make models of the prisms. Fill each prism with some material to find which one holds the most.

Volume is the measure of a region of space. A unit for volume is a cube which has 1 unit on each edge. To find volume, we count the number of cubic units.

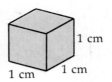 1 cm   1 cubic centimeter
1 cm   1 cm

1. A How many cubes are on the bottom layer?

   B How many layers?

   C The volume is how many cubic centimeters?

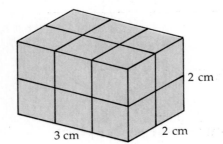
2 cm
3 cm   2 cm

2. A How many cubic centimeters are needed to cover the base of this prism?

   B How many layers of centimeter cubes would be needed?

   C What is the volume of the prism?

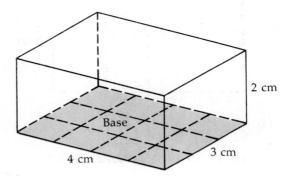
Base
2 cm
4 cm   3 cm

Give the volumes.

3. 1 cm
1 cm   1 cm

4. 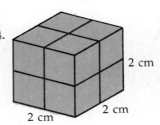 2 cm
2 cm   2 cm

5. 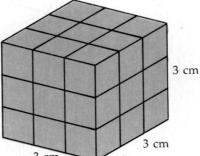 3 cm
3 cm
3 cm

6. 1 cm
1 cm   1 cm

7. 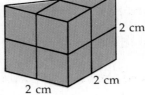 2 cm
2 cm   2 cm

Volume of prisms

This planter box is a rectangular prism.
What is the volume of the
planter box?

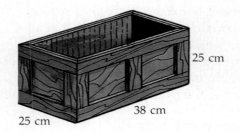

25 cm

38 cm

25 cm

Volume of a rectangular prism = *l*ength × *w*idth × *h*eight.

$V = lwh$
$V = 38 \cdot 25 \cdot 25$
$V = 23\ 750$

The volume is about 23 750 cm³.

Find the volume of each object below.

1.

$l = 43$ cm
$w = 30$ cm
$h = 7$ cm

2.

$l = 43$ cm
$w = 20$ cm
$h = 30$ cm

3.

$l = 70$ cm
$w = 52$ cm
$h = 21$ cm

4.

$l = 35$ cm
$w = 22$ cm
$h = 22$ cm

The volume of any prism is equal to the area of the base, B, times the height, h.

$V = Bh$

What is the volume of the planter box?

$V = 100 \cdot 13 = 1300$

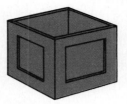

$B = 100$ cm²
$h = 13$ cm

The volume is 1300 cm³.

Find the volume of each prism.

1.

$B = 1886$ cm²
$h = 46$ cm

2.

$B = 2816$ cm²
$h = 22$ cm

3.

$B = 2160$ cm²
$h = 22$ cm

4.

$B = 2432$ cm²
$h = 30$ cm

5.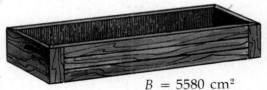

$B = 5580$ cm²
$h = 25$ cm

6.

$B = 1140$ cm²
$h = 38$ cm

☆ 7. Find the length, width, and height of your classroom in meters. Find the volume of your classroom in cubic meters.

More practice, page 392, Set A

✪ Volume of cylinders

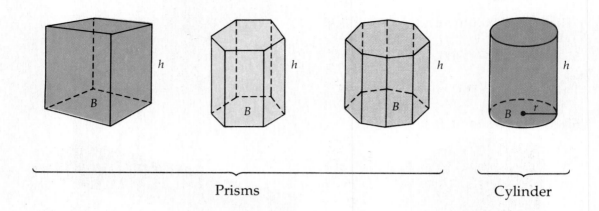

Prisms   Cylinder

The volume of any prism is the area of the base times the height. $V = Bh$
The volume of a cylinder can be found using this same formula.
For the cylinder, the base is a circle, so $B = \pi r^2$.
Therefore, the formula for the volume of a cylinder is $V = \pi r^2 h$.

Find the volume of this cylinder.
Use 3.14 for π.

$V = \pi r^2 h$
$V = 3.14 \cdot 4 \cdot 4 \cdot 12$
$V = 602.88$
The volume is 602.88 cm³.

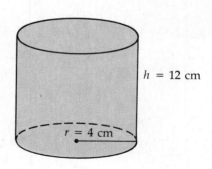

$h = 12$ cm

$r = 4$ cm

Find the volume of each cylinder. Use 3.14 for π.

1. $r = 2$ cm
   $h = 5$ cm

2. $r = 10$ cm
   $h = 10$ cm

3. $r = 1.5$ cm
   $h = 8$ cm

4. $r = 1$ m
   $h = 2.4$ m

5. $r = 9$ cm
   $h = 10$ cm

6. $r = 2.4$ cm
   $h = 5$ cm

7. $r = 3$ m
   $h = 2$ m

8. $r = 2.7$ m
   $h = 3$ m

Find the volume of each cylinder. Use 3.14 for π.

1.
$r = 4$ cm
$h = 10.5$ cm

2.
$r = 2.5$ cm
$h = 9$ cm

3.
$r = 5$ cm
$h = 18$ cm

4.
$r = 4.2$ cm
$h = 13.5$ cm

5.
$r = 3.3$ cm
$h = 7$ cm

6.
$r = 2.8$ cm
$h = 13.5$ cm

7.
$r = 3.3$ cm
$h = 10$ cm

8.
$r = 6.4$ cm
$h = 16$ cm

9.
$r = 3$ cm
$h = 10$ cm

☆ 10.
21.5 cm

28 cm

Make two models of circular cylinders from two sheets of paper 21.5 cm by 28 cm. Make the longer side the height for one cylinder. Make the shorter side the height of the second cylinder. Do the two cylinders have the same volume? Find a way to decide.

More practice, page 392, Set B

✪ Volume and liquid measure

A liter (ℓ) is a unit of liquid measure or capacity.
A milliliter (ml) is a unit used to measure small amounts of liquid.
A kiloliter (kl) is used for larger amounts.

1000 ml = 1 ℓ

1000 ℓ = 1 kl

1 ml = 0.001 ℓ

1 ℓ = 0.001 kl

For any container, when the volume in cubic units is known, the capacity
can be found.

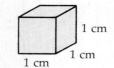

glass
volume: 225 cm³
capacity: 225 ml

1 teaspoon
volume: about 5 cm³
capacity: about 5 ml

volume: 1000 cm³
capacity: 1000 ml = 1 ℓ

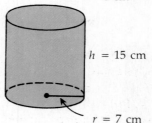

1 cm

1 cm

1 cm

volume: 1 cm³
capacity: 1 ml

What is the capacity of the container in milliliters?

volume = 6 · 4 · 4 = 96 cm³
capacity = 96 ml

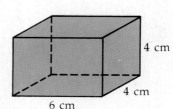

4 cm

4 cm

6 cm

What is the capacity of the cylinder in liters?

$V = \pi r^2 h$
$V = 3.14 \cdot 7 \cdot 7 \cdot 15$
$V = 2307.9$ cm³
$1 \ell = 1000$ cm³
capacity in liters = 2.3079 ℓ

$h = 15$ cm

$r = 7$ cm

Find the capacity of each object in milliliters.

1.

5 cm
3 cm
2 cm

2.
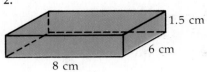
1.5 cm
6 cm
8 cm

3.
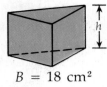
h
$B = 18 \text{ cm}^2$
$h = 10 \text{ cm}$

4.
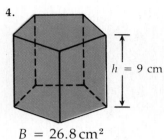
$h = 9 \text{ cm}$
$B = 26.8 \text{ cm}^2$

5.
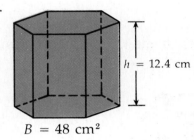
$h = 12.4 \text{ cm}$
$B = 48 \text{ cm}^2$

6.
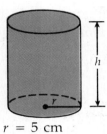
h
$r = 5 \text{ cm}$
$h = 12.74 \text{ cm}$

Find the capacity of each object in liters

7.
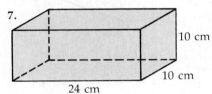
10 cm
10 cm
24 cm

8.
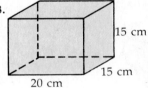
15 cm
15 cm
20 cm

9.
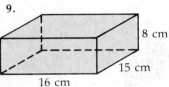
8 cm
15 cm
16 cm

10.
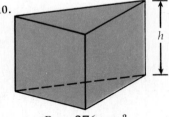
h
$B = 376 \text{ cm}^2$
$h = 20 \text{ cm}$

11.
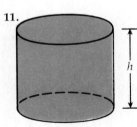
h
$r = 10 \text{ cm}$
$h = 20 \text{ cm}$

12.
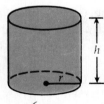
h
$r = 6 \text{ cm}$
$h = 17.7 \text{ cm}$

A cube whose edges are 10 cm long will hold 1 liter. How long should the edges of a cube be to hold 2 liters? Round the answer to the nearest tenth of a centimeter.

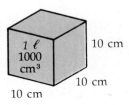
1 ℓ
1000 cm^3
10 cm
10 cm
10 cm

Units of mass

The basic unit of mass
is the **kilogram** (kg).

1 liter of water has
a mass of 1 kg.

1 milliliter of water
has a mass of 1 gram (g).

1 liter
of
water
1 kg

1 milliliter
of
water
1 g

$$1000 \text{ mg} = 1 \text{ g} \qquad 1000 \text{ g} = 1 \text{ kg}$$

nickel   chicken egg   straight pin   book

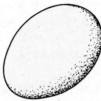  

about 5 g

about 60 g   about 120 mg

about 2 kg

Give the missing numbers.

1. 2000 g = ▓ kg
2. 3174 g = ▓ kg
3. 5 kg = ▓ g
4. 1.8 kg = ▓ g
5. 0.001 kg = ▓ g
6. 0.001 g = ▓ mg
7. 2 g = ▓ mg
8. 500 mg = ▓ g
9. 0.454 kg = ▓ g
10. 0.7 kg = ▓ g
11. 7200 mg = ▓ g
12. 2.938 kg = ▓ g

Give the mass of each amount of water.

13. 3 ℓ
14. 500 ml
15. 1.5 ℓ
16. 27 ml
17. 4.38 ℓ
18. 62 ml
19. 4000 ml
20. 1 ml

Find the number of grams of water each container will hold.

1.

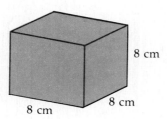

8 cm

8 cm

8 cm

2.

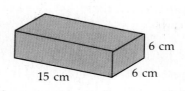

6 cm

15 cm   6 cm

3.

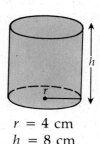

h

r

$r = 4$ cm
$h = 8$ cm

4. The mass of 1 ℓ of water is 1 kg. The mass of 1 ℓ of gasoline is 0.7 kg. What is the mass of 42 ℓ of gasoline?

5. A given amount of mercury has a mass 13.6 times the mass of the same amount of water. What is the mass of 25 ml of mercury?

6. The mass of 1 ℓ of sea water is about 1.03 kg. If 100 ℓ of fresh water and 100 ℓ of sea water are mixed together, what is the total mass of the water?

7. 1 ml of rubbing alcohol has a mass of about 0.8 g. What is the mass of 50 ml of rubbing alcohol?

☆ **9.** An odd-shaped container has a mass of 165 g when empty. When filled with water, the container and water together have a mass of 505 g. How many grams of water does the container hold? How many milliliters of water does it hold?

☆ **8.**

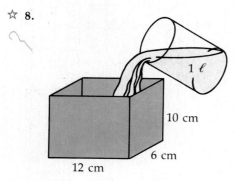

1 ℓ

10 cm

6 cm

12 cm

This plastic box is being filled with water from a full 1 ℓ container. How many grams of water will be left in the pitcher after the box is filled?

The Celsius temperature scale

The Celsius thermometer was invented in 1842 by Anders Celsius, a Swedish astronomer.

The unit of temperature for a Celsius thermometer is the **degree Celsius** (°C). On the Celsius scale, water freezes at 0°C and boils at 100°C.

Some temperatures can be lower than zero degrees. For example, the temperature on a cold winter day may be fifteen degrees colder than zero. This temperature is written:

$$^-15°C$$

and is read as "fifteen degrees below zero" or "negative fifteen degrees."

Use the thermometer to read each temperature.

1. hot soup

2. normal body temperature

3. room temperature

4. boiling point of water

5. freezing point of water

6. cold winter day

7. boiling point of alcohol

8. cool day

9. dangerous fever

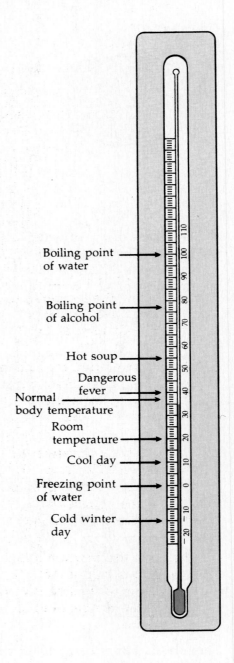

Boiling point of water

Boiling point of alcohol

Hot soup

Dangerous fever

Normal body temperature

Room temperature

Cool day

Freezing point of water

Cold winter day

Solve.

1. Normal body temperature is 63°C below the temperature of boiling water. What is normal body temperature?

2. Oven temperature for baking cookies is 180°C. How much above the temperature of boiling water is this?

3. The hottest temperature on the moon is 17°C above the temperature of boiling water. What is the hottest temperature on the moon?

4. The body temperature of a song-bird is half of the temperature of boiling water. What is the temperature of a song-bird?

5. The coldest weather temperature ever recorded on earth was ⁻88°C, in Antarctica. The coldest temperature on the moon was 75°C colder than the coldest temperature on earth. What was the coldest temperature on the moon?

6. Paper will burn at a temperature of 185°C. Wood will burn when the temperature is 65°C higher than this. At what temperature will wood burn?

7. Mercury in a thermometer freezes at ⁻39°C. Mercury boils at a temperature 396°C higher than this. At what temperature does mercury boil?

8. Butter melts at a temperature about 5°C above normal body temperature. At what temperature does butter melt?

9. The hottest weather temperature ever recorded on earth was 42°C lower than the temperature of boiling water. What was this hottest weather temperature?

☆ 10. The lowest possible temperature, called Absolute Zero, is 373.15°C below the temperature of boiling water. What is the Celsius temperature for absolute zero?

Answers for Self-check   1. 1440 cm³   2. 1005 cm³   3. 360 cm³   4. 4   5. 1   6. 600   7. 1.8
8. 324 ml   9. C   10. B

Self-check

Find the volume of each to the nearest cubic unit.
Use 3.14 for π.

1.
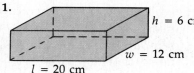
h = 6 cm
w = 12 cm
l = 20 cm

☆ 2.

h
r = 8 cm
h = 5 cm

3.
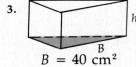
h
B
B = 40 cm²
h = 9 cm

Give the missing numbers.

4. 4000 g = ▓ kg   5. 1000 mg = ▓ g   6. 0.6 kg = ▓ g   7. 1800 g = ▓ kg

☆ 8. Find the capacity in milliliters.
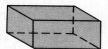
l = 9 cm
w = 6 cm
h = 6 cm

Choose the best estimate of temperature.

9. boiling water   **A** 0°C   **B** 212°C   **C** 100°C

10. normal body temperature   **A** 40°C   **B** 37°C   **C** 34°C

Answers for Self-check—page 315

Test

Find the volume of each to the nearest cubic unit.
Use 3.14 for π.

1.
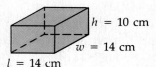
h = 10 cm
w = 14 cm
l = 14 cm

☆ 2.

h
r = 3 cm
h = 8 cm

3.
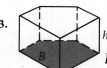
h
B
B = 36.2 cm²
h = 12.5 cm

Give the missing numbers.

4. 3 kg = ▓ g   5. 5 g = ▓ mg   6. 2700 mg = ▓ g   7. 0.8 kg = ▓ g

☆ 8. Find the capacity in milliliters.

h
B
B = 25.8 cm²
h = 10 cm

Choose the best estimate of temperature.

9. freezing point of water   **A** 0°C   **B** 10°C   **C** 32°C

10. comfortable room temperature   **A** 20°C   **B** 30°C   **C** 40°C

Archimedes' Principle

Archimedes (287–212 B.C.) was a famous Greek scientist and mathematician. He discovered the principle that an object floating in water displaces a mass of water equal to the mass of the floating object.

You can check the truth of Archimedes' principle by carrying out an experiment. You will need a metric container that has been marked to show milliliters. You will also need some water and some small objects that float.

1. Fill the container exactly level with some mark.

2. Float a small object such as a block of wood on the surface of the water. Read the new level of the water on the container.

3. Find the number of milliliters of water displaced by the block.

4. Using a metric scale, check the mass of the floating object. The mass of the floating object should be the same as the mass of the displaced water.

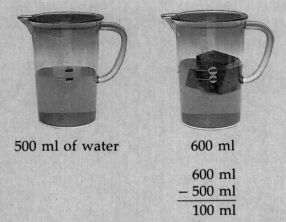

500 ml of water   600 ml

$$\begin{array}{r} 600 \text{ ml} \\ -\ 500 \text{ ml} \\ \hline 100 \text{ ml} \end{array}$$

100 ml of water
has a mass of 100 g.
The floating object has
a mass of 100 g.

Choose some objects of your own. Find their masses using Archimedes' principle.

Unit 5 review

Write each ratio, decimal, or fraction as a percent.

1. $\frac{50}{100}$ 2. $\frac{73}{100}$ 3. $\frac{250}{100}$ 4. 0.45   5. 0.72

6. 2.00   7. 1.50   8. 0.01   9. 0.08   10. 0.10

11. $\frac{1}{2}$ 12. $\frac{3}{4}$ 13. $\frac{1}{8}$ 14. $\frac{2}{5}$ 15. $\frac{7}{8}$

16. $\frac{1}{4}$ 17. $\frac{1}{3}$ 18. $\frac{3}{10}$ 19. $\frac{2}{3}$ 20. $\frac{3}{8}$

Compute.

21. 20% of 60   22. 50% of 3002   23. 42% of 625   24. 12% of 70

25. 1% of 800   26. 10% of 40 000   27. 33% of 450   28. 9% of 5000

29. 25 is what percent of 50?   30. 72 is what percent of 212?

31. What percent of 350 is 200?   32. What percent of 75 is 15?

Solve.

33. $25\% \times n = 30$ 34. $12\% \times n = 48$ 35. $5\% \times n = 8$

36. $90\% \times n = 180$ 37. $75\% \times n = 200$ 38. $32\% \times n = 400$

39. $1\% \times n = 5$ 40. $10\% \times n = 40$ 41. $58\% \times n = 232$

Find the percent score. Round to the nearest whole percent.

42. 18 problems correct
    20 problems in all

43. 21 problems correct
    25 problems in all

44. 9 problems correct
    12 problems in all

45. 11 problems correct
    15 problems in all

46. 26 problems correct
    30 problems in all

47. 15 problems correct
    18 problems in all

Probability
Statistics
Integers
Coordinate Geometry

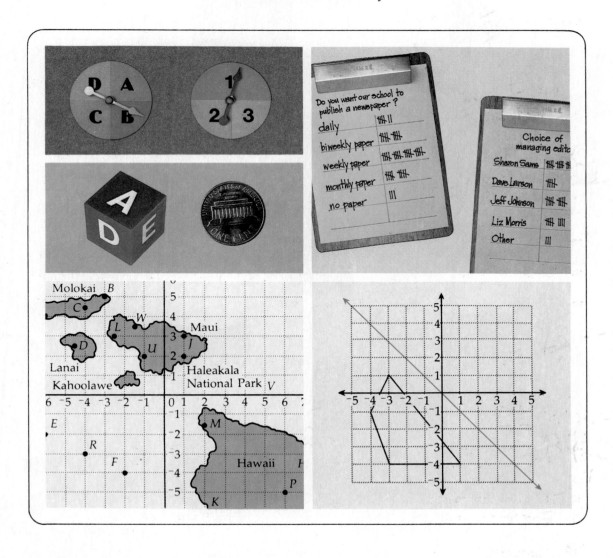

Probability

The faces of three cubes are numbered as shown, for use in a probability game. At each turn a player chooses a cube and rolls it. The top number on the cube is the score for that player. After ten turns the players total their scores. The player with the highest score wins.

1. Study the numbers on the cubes.
   Which cube would you choose?

2. Here are 10 tosses of the blue cube.

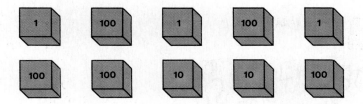

   What is the score?

3. Do you think someone could beat this
   score using the red cube?

4. Here are 10 tosses of the red cube.

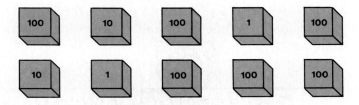

   Does this score beat the blue score above?

5. Is it **possible** that someone could toss this red cube score?

6. Is it very **likely** that someone would toss the red cube score shown above?
   Why or why not?

7. Here are 10 tosses of the green cube.
   Is this score **possible**
   with the green cube?

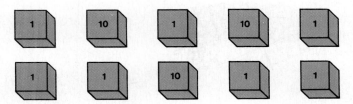

8. Is this score very **likely** to happen?

9. Which cube is most likely to give you the highest score? Next highest? Lowest?

Equally likely outcomes

100 on 2 faces
10 on 2 faces
1 on 2 faces

Each face of the cube has the same chance of appearing on top when the cube is tossed. The top number tossed is called an **outcome**.

When each of the possible outcomes for an experiment has the same chance of occurring, the outcomes are said to be **equally likely** outcomes.

In 100 tosses of the cube we would expect that each of the three numbers would appear about 33 times. The table shows the results of an actual experiment.

Outcomes	Occurrences	
100	~~JHT~~ ~~JHT~~ ~~JHT~~ ~~JHT~~ ~~JHT~~ IIII	29 hundreds
10	~~JHT~~ ~~JHT~~ ~~JHT~~ ~~JHT~~ ~~JHT~~ ~~JHT~~ III	33 tens
1	~~JHT~~ ~~JHT~~ ~~JHT~~ ~~JHT~~ ~~JHT~~ ~~JHT~~ ~~JHT~~ III	38 ones

1. A penny is tossed.
   What are the possible outcomes?
   Are the outcomes equally likely?

2. What are the possible outcomes for this spinner? Are the outcomes equally likely?

3. What are the possible outcomes for this spinner? Are the outcomes equally likely?

Copy and complete the table.

Experiment	Outcomes	Are the outcomes equally likely?	Most likely outcome (if there is one)
Tossing a cube with faces numbered 1 through 6	1, 2, 3, 4, 5, 6	yes	none
Drawing a marble from a box that has 2 blue and 7 red marbles in it			
Spinning this spinner			
Tossing a cube that has **A** on 3 faces, **B** on 2 faces, and **C** on 1 face			
Drawing a ball from a box that has 1 yellow ball, 2 green balls, and 1 black ball in it			

 This is a magic multiplication square.
The products in any row (↔), column (↕),
or diagonal (↘, ↗) are the same.
Find the missing numbers.

		24
	48	
96		6

Probability

Lisa and Tom were playing a board game using one die. Tom was ready to take his turn. He knew that if he tossed a 4 or a 6, he would win. What were the chances of Tom tossing a 4 or a 6? What was the **probability** of Tom tossing a 4 or a 6?

Equally likely outcomes	Successful outcomes	Chances	Probability
1, 2, 3, 4, 5, 6	4 or 6	There are 2 chances in 6 of tossing a 4 or a 6.	The probability of a successful outcome is $\frac{2}{6}$ or $\frac{1}{3}$.

What is the probability of getting an odd number with this spinner?

Equally likely outcomes	Successful outcomes	Chances	Probability
1, 2, 3, 4, 5	1, 3, or 5	There are 3 chances in 5 of getting an odd number.	The probability of a successful outcome is $\frac{3}{5}$.

Spinning a spinner

1. What is the probability that you will spin a 2?

2. What is the probability that you will spin an even number?

3. What is the probability that you will spin a number less than 5?

Drawing from a box without looking

4. What is the probability of drawing a red ball?

5. What is the probability of drawing a blue ball?

6. What is the probability of drawing a green ball?

Tossing a cube

7. Give the probability of tossing an **A**.

8. Give the probability of tossing a **B**.

9. What is the probability of tossing an **A** or a **C**?

10. What is the probability of tossing one of the first 3 letters of the alphabet?

A on 3 faces
B on 2 faces
C on 1 face

Think
!

Use four 5's, any of the symbols +, −, ×, ÷, and parentheses to write a name for 30. There are at least two ways to do this.

Pairs in probability

Suppose you toss a penny and a nickel, and use
a chart to keep the results. In 100 trials, about
how many of each of these outcomes would
you expect? Study the chart of outcomes below.

Outcomes	Tally
Two heads	卌 卌 卌 卌 ‖
Two tails	卌 卌 卌 卌 卌 ‖‖
Penny heads, nickel tails	卌 卌 卌 卌 卌 ‖
Penny tails, nickel heads	卌 卌 卌 卌 ‖‖‖

Look at the possible outcomes below. There are
four equally likely outcomes.

Two heads   One tail
One head

One head
One tail   Two tails

One head
One tail   Two tails

1. What is the probability of getting two heads?

2. What is the probability of getting two tails?

3. What is the probability of getting a head with the
   nickel and a tail with the penny?

4. What is the probability of getting one head and
   one tail?

Tossing a cube and a penny

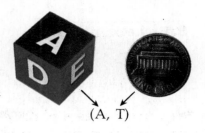

(A, T)

The faces of the cube are labeled **A**, **B**, **C**, **D**, **E**, and **F**.

One possible outcome is an **A** on the cube and tails on the penny. Write (A, T) for the outcome.

There are 12 possible outcomes.

1. List all the possible outcomes.

2. What is the probability of getting an **F** and heads?

3. What is the probability of getting an outcome with a **B**?

4. What is the probability of getting an outcome with tails?

5. What is the probability of getting an outcome with an **A** or **E**?

Tossing a pair of dice

The grid shows all the possible outcomes for tossing a pair of dice.

Each dot represents one of the 36 possible outcomes.

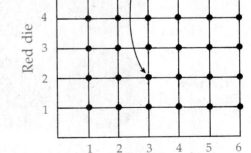

(3, 2)

6. How many ways can you toss a sum of 12 (6, 6)? What is the probability of tossing a sum of 12?

7. One way of tossing a sum of 5 is (3, 2). How many different ways can you toss a sum of 5? What is the probability of tossing a sum of 5?

8. What is the probability of tossing a sum of 7?

9. What is the probability of tossing a sum of 10, 11, or 12?

☆ 10. What is the probability that the blue die will be a 3?

☆ 11. What is the probability that one die or both dice will be a 1?

Answers for Self-check 1. 1, 2, or 3; yes 2. **A**, **B**, or **C**; no 3. $\frac{1}{6}$ 4. $\frac{3}{6}$ or $\frac{1}{2}$
5. (T, T), (H, T), (T, H), (H, H) 6. $\frac{1}{4}$ 7. $\frac{2}{4}$ or $\frac{1}{2}$

Self-check

1. What are the possible outcomes
for this spinner?
Are they equally likely?

2. What are the possible outcomes
for this spinner?
Are they equally likely?

Suppose you toss a cube that has faces numbered 1 through 6.

3. What is the probability of tossing a 3?

4. What is the probability of tossing an odd number?

A penny and a dime are tossed together.

5. List all possible outcomes.

6. What is the probability of getting a head with a penny and
a tail with the dime?

7. What is the probability of getting one head and one tail?

Answers for Self-check—page 327

Test

1. What are the possible outcomes for tossing a cube with faces
numbered 1 through 6? Are they equally likely?

2. What are the possible outcomes for tossing a cube with **A** on 3 faces,
B on 2 faces, and **C** on 1 face? Are they equally likely?

Suppose you spin this spinner.

3. What is the probability of spinning a 4?

4. What is the probability of spinning an even number?

This red spinner and this blue spinner are spun at the same time.

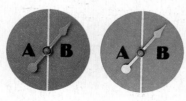

5. List all possible outcomes.

6. What is the probability of getting an **A** on the
red spinner and a **B** on the blue spinner?

7. What is the probability of getting one **A** and one **B**?

Math lab

Balance Beam

You can make your own balance scales to check
out the relationship stated below.

Put a loop of string around
a meter stick.

 A

 B

Tack a light plastic bag to each end
of the meter stick.

Now you are ready to try out the relationship between the mass of
objects in the plastic bags (**A** and **B**) and their distance from the point
of balance (string).

> The scales should balance if the mass at **A** times its
> distance from the string is equal to the mass at **B** times
> its distance from the string.

Try this with some known masses.

Example:

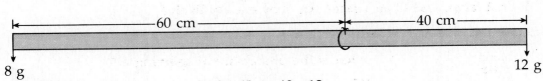

$$8 \cdot 60 = 40 \cdot 12$$

Find m for each problem.

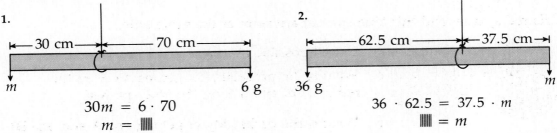

1.

$$30m = 6 \cdot 70$$
$$m = \text{▥}$$

2.

$$36 \cdot 62.5 = 37.5 \cdot m$$
$$\text{▥} = m$$

Statistics

Some students were interested in starting
a school newspaper. To find out what other
students thought of the idea, they took
a survey. The results are shown below.

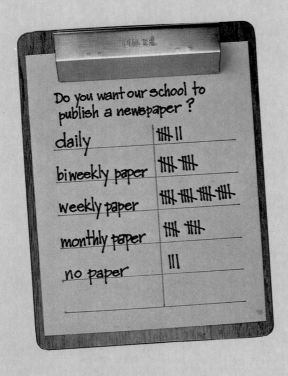

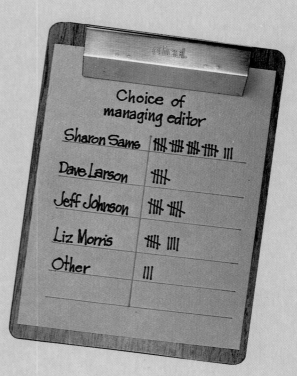

What are some things that you can conclude from the
results of the survey?

1. Which number of hours was chosen most often in the data shown at the right? This number is called the **mode** of the data.

2. Which number of hours was chosen least often?

3. How many total hours of work could the students who chose 3, 4, or 5 hours a week give to the newspaper?

4. How many total hours of work could the students who chose 1 or 2 hours a week give?

5. The number of copies are given in intervals of 25 copies (0-25, 26-50, etc.). Which interval was chosen most often?

6. Give the mode of the data.

7. Which interval was selected least often?

8. If the number of copies sold is in the most frequently selected interval, the newspaper sales will be between what two amounts?

☆ 9. Use one of these questions. Make a survey of your class or the students in your school.

A How many hours a day do you watch TV?

B How long does it take you to get to school?

C How many letters are in your last name?

D A question of your own

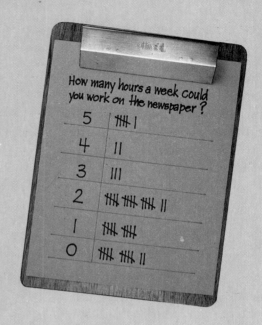

How many hours a week could you work on the newspaper?

5	ⅢⅠⅠ
4	ⅠⅠ
3	ⅠⅠⅠ
2	ⅢⅠ ⅢⅠ ⅢⅠ ⅠⅠ
1	ⅢⅠ ⅢⅠ
0	ⅢⅠ ⅢⅠ ⅠⅠ

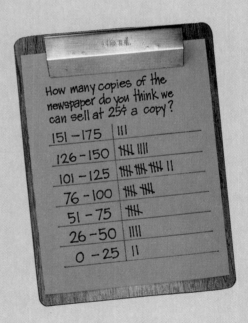

How many copies of the newspaper do you think we can sell at 25¢ a copy?

151 –175	ⅠⅠⅠ
126 –150	ⅢⅠ ⅠⅠⅠⅠ
101 –125	ⅢⅠ ⅢⅠ ⅢⅠ ⅠⅠ
76 –100	ⅢⅠ ⅢⅠ
51 –75	ⅢⅠ
26 –50	ⅠⅠⅠⅠ
0 –25	ⅠⅠ

Frequency distributions—bar graphs

A school paper editor made a survey of student hobbies. The information is shown by a **frequency distribution**. The **frequency** of each hobby is the number of persons who listed that hobby.

Hobby	Tally	Frequency
Collections	JHT JHT IIII	14
Reading or Writing	JHT II	7
Crafts	JHT JHT II	12
Sports	JHT JHT	10
Music	JHT III	8
Other	JHT	5

The same information given in the frequency distribution can be presented by a bar graph.

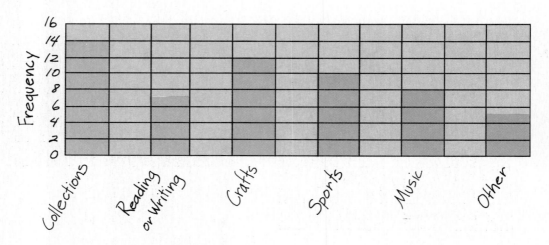

1. Give the frequency for each hobby.

2. Find the total of all the frequencies. What does this number represent?

3. Which hobby had the greatest frequency?

4. Which hobby had next to the greatest frequency?

5. If you were the manager of a hobby store, what two kinds of items would the survey suggest that you might sell most often?

Make a bar graph of each frequency distribution.

1.

School Mascot	
Mascot	Tally
Lion	ЖЖ ///
Dolphin	ЖЖ ///
Tiger	//
Cardinal	///
Owl	ЖЖ ///
Colt	ЖЖ ЖЖ /
Other	ЖЖ /

2.

School Colors	
Color	Tally
Red & white	ЖЖ
Red & blue	ЖЖ //
Blue & white	////
Green & white	ЖЖ ЖЖ
Green & blue	//
Gold & green	ЖЖ ЖЖ ///
Gold & red	///
Red & black	ЖЖ /

3.

Favorite School Subject	
Art	ЖЖ ЖЖ /
Math	ЖЖ ЖЖ
Science	ЖЖ ////
English	////
Social science	ЖЖ //
Other	///

4.

Birthday Seasons	
Spring	ЖЖ /
Summer	ЖЖ ЖЖ ///
Fall	ЖЖ ЖЖ ЖЖ
Winter	ЖЖ ////

☆ **5.** Collect in a frequency distribution, data about one of the following topics. Make a bar graph of the data.

A Favorite TV program   **C** Favorite car

B Favorite ice cream flavor   **D** A topic of your own

Line segment graphs—arithmetic mean

A science class spent some time studying weather. For a week they collected data about local weather. They made line segment graphs to show the number of hours of sunshine each day.

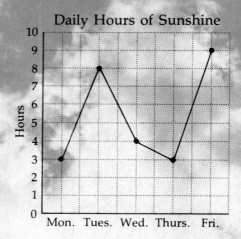

Daily Hours of Sunshine

1. Which day of the week had the most hours of sunshine? The fewest?

2. Which three days of the week were the most cloudy?

3. How many more hours of sunshine were there on Friday than on Wednesday?

The students also used this data to find the **arithmetic mean** or **average** number of hours of sunshine a day.

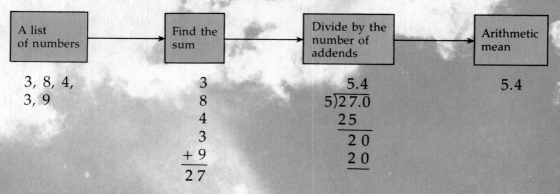

The mean number of hours of sunshine a day was 5.4 hours.

Find the mean of each list of numbers.

4. 42, 56, 34, 48

5. 168, 160, 157, 155, 147

6. 26, 19, 30, 12, 16, 11

7. 43, 58, 35, 62, 57, 23, 47, 51

This graph shows both daily high and low temperatures for five days.

1. Give the daily high temperature for each day.

2. Give the daily low temperature for each day.

3. Which day of the week had the greatest difference between the high and low temperature?

4. Which day had the smallest difference between the high and low temperature?

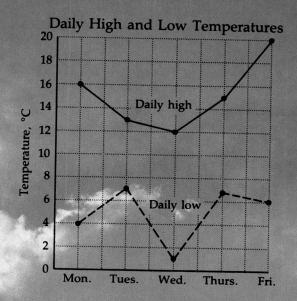

Daily High and Low Temperatures

The **mean daily temperature** = $\dfrac{\text{high temperature} + \text{low temperature}}{2}$

5. Find the mean daily temperature for each day given by the graph.

6. Construct a line segment graph of the mean daily temperatures you have found.

☆ 7. What is the mean temperature for the 5 days? (Find the mean of the mean daily temperatures.)

☆ 8. Find the high and low daily temperatures for your community for a week. Make a line segment graph to show the data. Find the mean temperature for each day.

Pictographs

The students in a school planned a banquet to raise funds to help with a city improvement plan. The pictograph shows the number of banquet tickets each class sold.

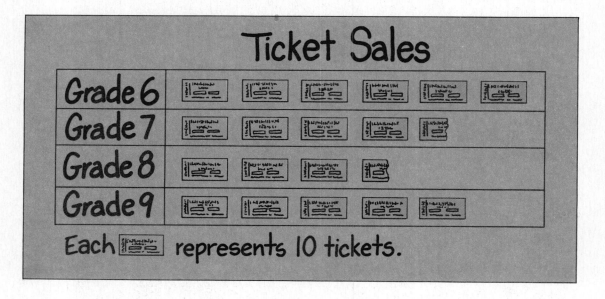

1. Give the number of tickets sold by each grade.

2. How many tickets were sold in all?

3. If each ticket cost $4.25, how much was collected from the sale of the tickets?

4. If food and other banquet expenses cost $2.45 per person, how much profit was made from the banquet?

5. Suppose each represents 20 tickets and the following numbers were sold:

   7th grade: 112
   8th grade: 78
   9th grade: 54

Round the numbers to the nearest 10 and make a pictograph to display the data.

As another city improvement project, the students collected empty cans to be recycled. This pictograph shows the results.

Empty Cans

Grade 6	🥫 🥫 🥫
Grade 7	🥫 🥫 🥫 🥫 🥫
Grade 8	🥫 🥫 🥫 🥫 🥫 🥫
Grade 9	🥫 🥫 🥫 🥫 🥫 🥫

Each 🥫 represents 2 kg of cans.

1. How many kilograms of cans were collected by each grade?

2. How many kilograms of cans were collected in all?

As part of the improvement plan, the city park department planted new trees. This pictograph shows how many trees were planted.

3. Give the number of trees planted each day.
4. How many trees were planted in all?
☆ 5. Choose one of these topics. Collect data and make a pictograph to display your data.

A Number of students in each grade of your school

B Number of cars passing a school corner during a week

C Number of hours spent by the class viewing some TV programs

✪ Circle graphs

The school newspaper used a circle graph
to show the results of the student council
presidential election. The complete circular
area represents 100% of the votes.

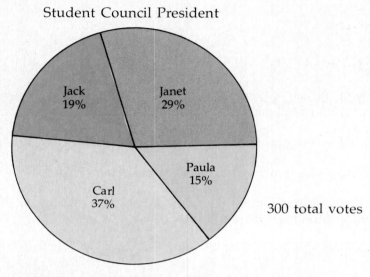

Student Council President

300 total votes

If there were 300 votes, how many votes
did Carl get?

$$37\% \cdot 300 = 0.37 \cdot 300 = 111$$

Carl received 111 votes.

Find the number of votes for each student.

1. Janet   2. Jack   3. Paula

Paula received 15% of the votes.
The central angle of the sector of the
circle representing Paula's votes is:

$$15\% \cdot 360° = 0.15 \cdot 360° = 54°.$$

Find the central angle on the circle graph
for each student.

4. Janet   5. Carl   6. Jack

This circle graph shows the reading choices of 80 students.

Find the number of students who chose each kind of book.

1. Mystery

2. Adventure

3. Science fiction

4. Biography

5. Other

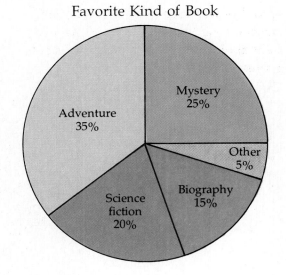

Favorite Kind of Book

Mystery 25%

Adventure 35%

Other 5%

Biography 15%

Science fiction 20%

Find the central angle for each kind of book.

6. Mystery

7. Adventure

8. Science fiction

9. Biography

10. Other

Make a circle graph showing the data in each chart.

11. Yearly Household Solid Waste Total: 6600 kg	
Paper	30%
Food	20%
Yard waste	18%
Glass	10%
Metals	9%
Wood, plastic, leather, textiles	11%
Other	2%

12. Annual Use of Electricity in Homes Total: 13 000 kWh	
Food preparation	15%
Refrigeration	12%
Laundry	9%
Water heating	35%
Air conditioning	15%
Lighting	14%

✪ Finding the median

Team heights (cm)
170
168
166
160
158
153
150
148
148
142
138

The heights of eleven girls on a soccer team are given in the table. The **median** height is the middle height in the list.

What is the median height?

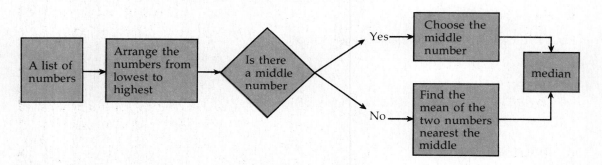

There are 11 heights listed in order.
The median height is the sixth number, 153.

Find the median of each list of numbers.

1.	2.	3.	4.	5.
68	1.2	37	$21.66	69¢
77	2.6	43	32.49	69¢
84	3.7	26	27.95	63¢
76	1.6	50	25.00	72¢
91	5.3	38	27.50	66¢
75	2.7	27		75¢
86	6.0			61¢
98				72¢
66				

1. What is the median score for the Cougars?

2. What is the median score for the opponents?

3. Find the mean score for the Cougars.

4. Find the mean score for the opponents.

Soccer Scores		
Game	Cougars	Opponents
1	7	4
2	3	2
3	3	5
4	4	1
5	3	4
6	6	4

5. Find the median score of the winners.

6. Find the mean score of the winners.

7. Find the difference between the median and mean scores of the winners.

8. What was the mean score of the losers?

World Cup Soccer Scores				
Year	Winner		Loser	
1930	Uruguay	4	Argentina	2
1934	Italy	2	Czechoslovakia	1
1938	Italy	4	Hungary	2
1950	Uruguay	2	Brazil	1
1954	West Germany	3	Hungary	2
1958	Brazil	5	Sweden	2
1962	Brazil	3	Czechoslovakia	1
1966	England	4	West Germany	2
1970	Brazil	4	Italy	1
1974	West Germany	2	The Netherlands	1

☆ 9. Choose one of these topics, collect the data, and find the mean and the median.

A Heights of the students in your class

B Heights of the players on the school basketball team

C Masses of the members of the school football team

Answers for Self-check   1. Rock, 10   2. 1°C   3. 9   4. 6 h   5. mean; 9, median: 8, mode: 7

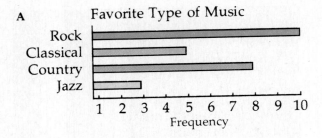

A Favorite Type of Music

Rock
Classical
Country
Jazz

Frequency

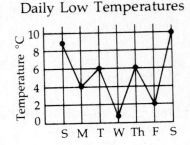

B Daily Low Temperatures

Temperature °C

S M T W Th F S

C Average Number of Single Records
Bought by a Student

Jan ⊙ ⊙ ⊙
Feb ⊙ ⊙
Mar ⊙ ☾
Apr ⊙
May ⊙
June ⊙

Each ⊙ represents 6 records

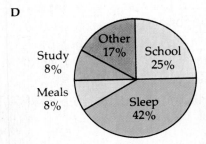

D

Other 17% School 25%
Study 8%
Meals 8%
Sleep 42%

Time Spent during a 24-hour Day

Self-check

1. Graph **A**: Which type of music has the greatest frequency of votes? How many?

2. Graph **B**: What was the lowest temperature of the week?

3. Graph **C**: How many records were bought in March?

☆ 4. Graph **D**: How many hours are spent in school, according to the graph?

☆ 5. Find the mean (to the nearest whole number), median, and mode of this set of data: {4, 6, 7, 7, 7, 8, 8, 9, 12, 14, 16}

Answers for Self-check—page 341

Test

1. Graph **A**: Which type of music has the lowest frequency of votes? How many?

2. Graph **B**: What was the temperature on Saturday?

3. Graph **C**: In what month were the fewest records purchased? How many?

☆ 4. Graph **D**: How many hours are spent studying, according to the graph?

☆ 5. Find the mean, median, and mode of this set of data: {9, 12, 15, 24, 29, 29, 36}

Estimating Sizes

Estimate your size for each item in the table to the nearest centimeter.
Record your estimate. Then measure and record the actual size.
How close was your estimate to each actual measurement?

Size	Estimate	Actual measurement	Difference between estimate and actual measurement
Ring size	▥ cm	▥ cm	▥ cm
Wristwatch size	▥ cm	▥ cm	▥ cm
Hat size	▥ cm	▥ cm	▥ cm
Collar size	▥ cm	▥ cm	▥ cm
Belt size	▥ cm	▥ cm	▥ cm
Shoe size	▥ cm	▥ cm	▥ cm

Sum of differences = ▥ cm

Integers

Integers are numbers that help us describe things that are opposites of each other. Give the missing integers.

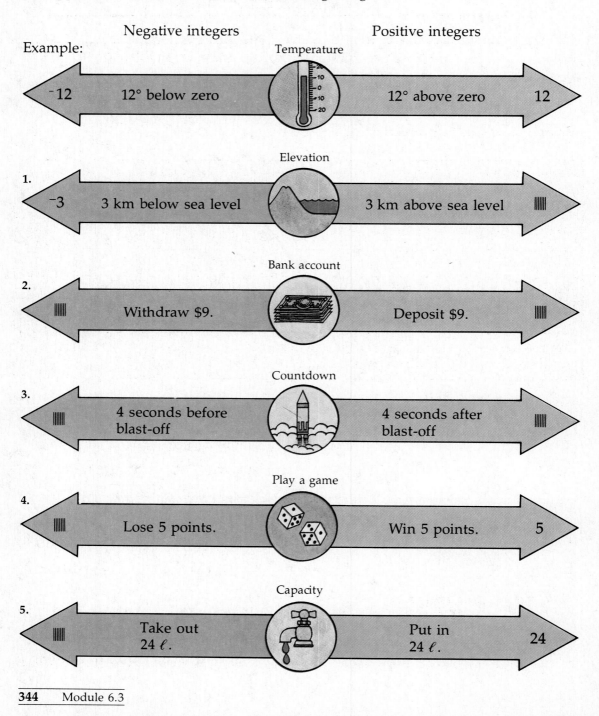

Negative integers   Positive integers

Example:

Temperature

‾12   12° below zero   12° above zero   12

1.

Elevation

‾3   3 km below sea level   3 km above sea level

2.

Bank account

Withdraw $9.   Deposit $9.

3.

Countdown

4 seconds before blast-off   4 seconds after blast-off

4.

Play a game

Lose 5 points.   Win 5 points.   5

5.

Capacity

Take out 24 ℓ.   Put in 24 ℓ.   24

The number line shows that every integer has an opposite.

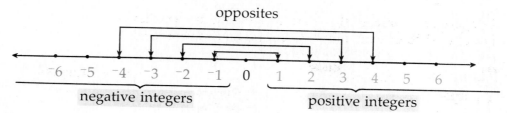

opposites

negative integers   positive integers

The opposite of 2 is ⁻2.
The opposite of ⁻3 is 3.

Basic principles for addition of integers

Zero principle	For every integer a, $a + 0 = a$.	Examples: $\\ ⁻3 + 0 = ⁻3 \\ 5 + 0 = 5$
Commutative principle	For all integers a and b, $a + b = b + a$.	$7 + ⁻3 = ⁻3 + 7$ $⁻6 + ⁻9 = ⁻9 + ⁻6$
Associative principle	For any three integers a, b, and c, $(a + b) + c = a + (b + c)$.	$(3 + ⁻5) + ⁻7 = 3 + (⁻5 + ⁻7)$ $⁻1 + (⁻2 + 6) = (⁻1 + ⁻2) + 6$
Opposites principle	The sum of any integer and its opposite is zero.	$2 + ⁻2 = 0$ $⁻8 + 8 = 0$

Give the opposite of each integer.

1. ⁻6   **2.** 4   **3.** ⁻10   **4.** ⁻1   **5.** 7   **6.** ⁻2   **7.** ⁻15   **8.** 11

9. 13   **10.** ⁻20   **11.** 6   **12.** ⁻19   **13.** ⁻99   **14.** 72   **15.** ⁻63   **16.** ⁻80

Give the sum.

17. $4 + ⁻4$ **18.** $⁻7 + 7$ **19.** $6 + ⁻6$ **20.** $⁻10 + 10$

21. $⁻15 + 0$ **22.** $0 + ⁻7$ **23.** $8 + 0$ **24.** $⁻17 + 0$

Give the missing integer.

25. $6 + ⁻3 = \text{▥} + 6$ **26.** $⁻7 + ⁻4 = ⁻4 + \text{▥}$

27. $8 + (⁻5 + ⁻3) = (8 + \text{▥}) + ⁻3$ **28.** $(⁻9 + ⁻1) + 1 = \text{▥} + (⁻1 + 1)$

Adding integers

You can use different colored dots or counters to help you add integers.

Think of the two colors as opposites.

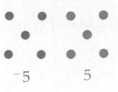

$$^-5 \qquad 5$$

Examples

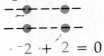

$$^-2 + 2 = 0$$

$$5 + {}^-2 = 3$$

$$^-6 + 4 = {}^-2$$

Find the sums.

1.

$$5 + {}^-3 = n$$

2.

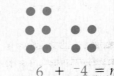

$$3 + {}^-4 = n$$

3.

$$^-5 + 2 = n$$

4.

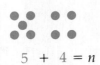

$$4 + {}^-4 = n$$

5.

$$6 + {}^-4 = n$$

6.

$$1 + {}^-3 = n$$

7.

$$^-6 + 2 = n$$

8.

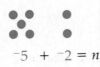

$$^-3 + 4 = n$$

9.

$$^-2 + {}^-3 = n$$

10.

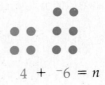

$$5 + 4 = n$$

11.

$$^-5 + {}^-2 = n$$

12.

$$3 + {}^-6 = n$$

13.

$$^-2 + 3 = n$$

14.

$$^-1 + 1 = n$$

15.

$$4 + {}^-6 = n$$

Find the sums.

1.

$2 + {}^-6 = n$

2.

${}^-4 + 5 = n$

3.

${}^-3 + 2 = n$

4.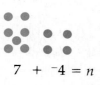

${}^-1 + 4 = n$

5.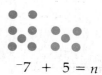

$4 + {}^-5 = n$

6.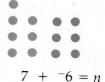

${}^-6 + 5 = n$

7.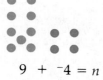

$7 + {}^-4 = n$

8.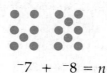

${}^-2 + {}^-8 = n$

9.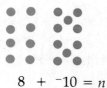

${}^-7 + 5 = n$

10.

$9 + {}^-4 = n$

11.

${}^-7 + {}^-8 = n$

12.

${}^-5 + 9 = n$

13.

$8 + {}^-10 = n$

14.

${}^-2 + 9 = n$

15.

$7 + {}^-6 = n$

Which is the greater amount of money?

1. A bag of dimes with the same mass as yourself
   (A dime has a mass of 2 g.)

2. 50¢ a day for every day you have lived since you were born.

Estimate first. Then calculate each amount.
Was your estimate correct?

More about adding integers

To add integers,

you can think about counters   *or*   you can think about basic principles.

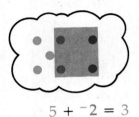

$$5 + {}^-2 = 3$$

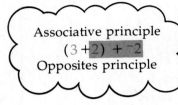

Associative principle
$(3 + 2) + {}^-2$
Opposites principle

$$5 + {}^-2 = 3$$

Find the sums.

1. $7 + {}^-3 = n$

2. $9 + {}^-4 = n$

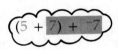

3. $12 + {}^-7 = n$

$({}^-2 + (2 + 7)$

4. ${}^-2 + 9 = n$

${}^-8 + (8 + 7)$

5. ${}^-8 + 15 = n$

${}^-10 + (10 + 14)$

6. ${}^-10 + 24 = n$

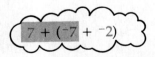

7. ${}^-8 + 3 = n$

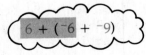

8. ${}^-13 + 7 = n$

9. ${}^-17 + 4 = n$

$7 + ({}^-7 + {}^-2)$

10. $7 + {}^-9 = n$

$6 + ({}^-6 + {}^-9)$

11. $6 + {}^-15 = n$

$13 + ({}^-13 + {}^-12)$

12. $13 + {}^-25 = n$

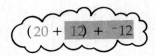

13. $32 + {}^-12 = n$

$({}^-13 + {}^-11) + 11$

14. ${}^-24 + 11 = n$

${}^-24 + (24 + 26)$

15. ${}^-24 + 50 = n$

Find the sums.

1. $8 + {}^-3 = n$ 2. $9 + {}^-5 = n$ 3. $12 + {}^-8 = n$

4. ${}^-9 + 2 = n$ 5. ${}^-6 + 4 = n$ 6. ${}^-15 + 7 = n$

7. $12 + {}^-5 = n$ 8. $19 + {}^-4 = n$ 9. $8 + {}^-5 = n$

10. ${}^-17 + 8 = n$ 11. $16 + {}^-5 = n$ 12. $24 + {}^-10 = n$

13. ${}^-23 + 8 = n$ 14. ${}^-17 + 6 = n$ 15. $25 + {}^-6 = n$

16. ${}^-9 + {}^-8 = n$ 17. $36 + {}^-9 = n$ 18. ${}^-45 + 5 = n$

19. ${}^-8$
    $+\ 3$

20. 5
    $+\ {}^-7$

21. ${}^-9$
    $+\ 8$

22. ${}^-3$
    $+\ 10$

23. 12
    $+\ {}^-5$

24. ${}^-9$
    $+\ 11$

25. 4
    $+\ {}^-8$

26. 6
    $+\ {}^-13$

27. 9
    $+\ {}^-16$

28. ${}^-4$
    $+\ {}^-9$

Calculator problems

29. $396 + {}^-139 = n$ 30. $702 + {}^-956 = n$

31. ${}^-324 + 246 = n$ 32. ${}^-555 + {}^-438 = n$

33. ${}^-478 + 946 = n$ 34. ${}^-213 + {}^-195 = n$

35. $843 + {}^-568 = n$ 36. ${}^-674 + 832 = n$

 In Puzzle A, the sum of the integers along
the path is equal to the sum at the end.
Find such a path for Puzzle B. You can move
only horizontally or vertically.

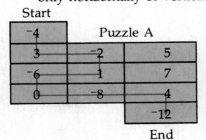

Subtracting integers

Just as with whole numbers, you can think of subtracting integers as finding the missing addend.

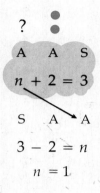

$$? $$

A   A   S

$$n + 2 = 3$$

S   A   A

$$3 - 2 = n$$

$$n = 1$$

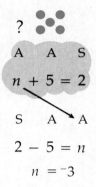

$$?$$

A   A   S

$$n + 5 = 2$$

S   A   A

$$2 - 5 = n$$

$$n = {}^-3$$

When you have found the missing addend in the first equation, you will have found the difference in the second equation. Write the second equation with the correct difference.

1.

$$n + {}^-3 = 2$$
$$2 - {}^-3 = n$$

2.

$$n + {}^-4 = {}^-7$$
$${}^-7 - {}^-4 = n$$

3.

$$n + 2 = {}^-3$$
$${}^-3 - 2 = n$$

4.

$$n + 3 = 2$$
$$2 - 3 = n$$

5.

$$n + {}^-4 = 1$$
$$1 - {}^-4 = n$$

6.

$$n + 1 = {}^-5$$
$${}^-5 - 1 = n$$

Find the sums and differences.

7.
$$3 + {}^-8 = n$$
$${}^-8 + 3 = n$$
$${}^-5 - {}^-8 = n$$
$${}^-5 - 3 = n$$

8.
$$6 + {}^-4 = n$$
$${}^-4 + 6 = n$$
$$2 - {}^-4 = n$$
$$2 - 6 = n$$

9.
$${}^-5 + {}^-4 = n$$
$${}^-4 + {}^-5 = n$$
$${}^-9 - {}^-4 = n$$
$${}^-9 - {}^-5 = n$$

Find the differences. Thinking of addends (A) and a sum (S) may help you.

	S	A	A
1.	3	−	$^-2 = n$

	S	A	A
2.	$^-4$	−	$^-3 = n$

	S	A	A
3.	3	−	$7 = n$

	S	A	A
4.	$^-4$	−	$5 = n$

	S	A	A
5.	$^-8$	−	$^-10 = n$

	S	A	A
6.	$^-6$	−	$2 = n$

7. $2 - {^-7} = n$

8. $0 - 4 = n$

9. $5 - {^-2} = n$

10. $2 - 8 = n$

11. $^-5 - 8 = n$

12. $^-7 - {^-9} = n$

13. $^-7 - {^-1} = n$

14. $14 - {^-6} = n$

15. $^-7 - 13 = n$

16. $^-9 - 3 = n$

17. $^-4 - 10 = n$

18. $0 - {^-5} = n$

19. $^-6 - {^-8} = n$

20. $^-11 - {^-6} = n$

21. $8 - 12 = n$

22. $12 - {^-4} = n$

23. $17 - {^-8} = n$

24. $4 - {^-11} = n$

Use this rule to find the differences below.

> **To subtract a number, add its opposite.**

Examples: $^-1 - 6 = {^-1} + {^-6} = {^-7}$
$^-5 - {^-8} = {^-5} + 8 = 3$

25. $^-3 - 7$

26. $2 - 8$

27. $^-8 - 2$

28. $5 - {^-3}$

29. $^-6 - 9$

30. $15 - {^-6}$

31. $^-4 - {^-2}$

32. $^-2 - 8$

33. $^-3 - {^-5}$

34. $^-8 - 12$

Frank spends 6 hours each day in school. He watches TV an average of 3 hours a day. In 12 years (365 days per year), does he spend more time in school or watching TV? How much more? (Note: Frank goes to school 180 days a year.)

More practice, page 393, Set B

Multiplying integers

Complete each flow chart and equation
to see how to multiply integers.

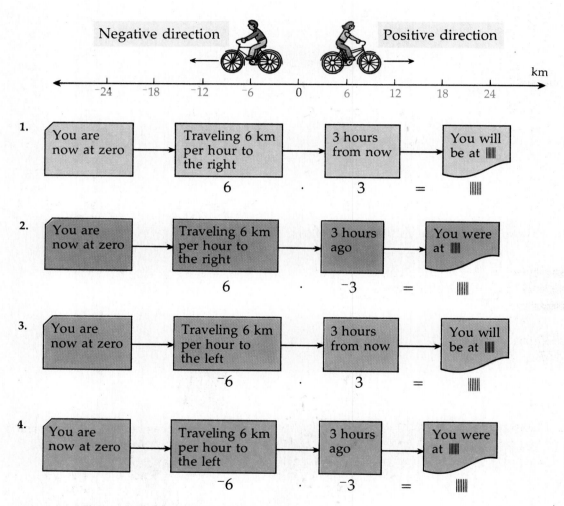

1. You are now at zero → Traveling 6 km per hour to the right → 3 hours from now → You will be at ▓
   6 · 3 = ▓

2. You are now at zero → Traveling 6 km per hour to the right → 3 hours ago → You were at ▓
   6 · ⁻3 = ▓

3. You are now at zero → Traveling 6 km per hour to the left → 3 hours from now → You will be at ▓
   ⁻6 · 3 = ▓

4. You are now at zero → Traveling 6 km per hour to the left → 3 hours ago → You were at ▓
   ⁻6 · ⁻3 = ▓

Complete the following statements.

5. The product of a positive integer and a negative integer
   is a ___?___ integer.

6. The product of a negative integer and a negative integer
   is a ___?___ integer.

Copy these equations in columns, giving the correct products. Notice the pattern of the products.

1. $6 \cdot 2 = n$
    $6 \cdot 1 = n$
    $6 \cdot 0 = n$
    $6 \cdot {}^-1 = n$
    $6 \cdot {}^-2 = n$

2. $^-6 \cdot 2 = n$
    $^-6 \cdot 1 = n$
    $^-6 \cdot 0 = n$
    $^-6 \cdot {}^-1 = n$
    $^-6 \cdot {}^-2 = n$

Find the products.

3. $^-4 \cdot 3$

4. $8 \cdot 7$

5. $^-5 \cdot 4$

6. $7 \cdot {}^-6$

7. $^-6 \cdot {}^-4$

8. $9 \cdot {}^-9$

9. $7 \cdot {}^-8$

10. $^-9 \cdot 6$

11. $^-8 \cdot {}^-5$

12. $^-7 \cdot 3$

13. $4 \cdot {}^-9$

14. $^-8 \cdot 6$

15. $^-6 \cdot {}^-8$

16. $^-8 \cdot 1$

17. $^-7 \cdot 0$

18. $6 \cdot {}^-10$

19. $^-12 \cdot 3$

20. $^-24 \cdot {}^-4$

21. $7 \cdot 13$

22. $^-18 \cdot 6$

23. $^-21 \cdot {}^-5$

24. $^-36 \cdot {}^-4$

25. $42 \cdot {}^-9$

26. $^-7 \cdot 15$

27. $^-9 \cdot {}^-28$

28. $^-54 \cdot 3$

29. $^-46 \cdot {}^-2$

30. $^-95 \cdot {}^-4$

Give an example of each basic principle for multiplication of integers.

☆ 31. **1 principle**
For any integer a,
$a \cdot 1 = a$

☆ 32. **Commutative principle**
For integers a and b,
$a \cdot b = b \cdot a$

☆ 33. **Associative principle**
For integers a, b, and c,
$(a \cdot b) \cdot c = a \cdot (b \cdot c)$

☆ 34. **Distributive principle**
For integers a, b, and c,
$a \cdot (b \cdot c) = (a \cdot b) + (a \cdot c)$

Find two values, one negative and one positive, for each equation.
Example: $x^2 = 16$
Since $4 \cdot 4 = 16$ and
$^-4 \cdot {}^-4 = 16$,
$x = 4$ or $x = {}^-4$

1. $y^2 = 81$

2. $a^2 = 169$

3. $b^2 = 1089$

4. $r^2 = 4356$

5. $c^2 = 3025$

6. $s^2 = 0.25$

7. $t^2 = 2116$

8. $z^2 = 9801$

More practice, page 394, Set A

Dividing integers

Just as with whole numbers, you can find the quotient of two integers
by finding the missing factor.

$$\begin{array}{ccc} \text{F} & \text{F} & \text{P} \\ 7 \cdot 8 & = & 56 \end{array}$$

$$\begin{array}{ccc} \text{P} & \text{F} & \text{F} \\ 56 \div 8 & = & 7 \end{array}$$

$$\begin{array}{ccc} \text{F} & \text{F} & \text{P} \\ 4 \cdot {}^-6 & = & {}^-24 \end{array}$$

$$\begin{array}{ccc} \text{P} & \text{F} & \text{F} \\ {}^-24 \div {}^-6 & = & 4 \end{array}$$

$$\begin{array}{ccc} \text{F} & \text{F} & \text{P} \\ {}^-8 \cdot {}^-6 & = & 48 \end{array}$$

$$\begin{array}{ccc} \text{P} & \text{F} & \text{F} \\ 48 \div {}^-6 & = & {}^-8 \end{array}$$

Find the quotients. Think about missing factors.

1.
$$\begin{array}{ccc} \text{F} & \text{F} & \text{P} \\ {}^-4 \cdot {}^-3 & = & 12 \end{array}$$

$$\begin{array}{ccc} \text{P} & \text{F} & \text{F} \\ 12 \div {}^-3 & = & n \end{array}$$

2.
$$\begin{array}{ccc} \text{F} & \text{F} & \text{P} \\ {}^-3 \cdot 8 & = & {}^-24 \end{array}$$

$$\begin{array}{ccc} \text{P} & \text{F} & \text{F} \\ {}^-24 \div 8 & = & n \end{array}$$

3.
$$\begin{array}{ccc} \text{F} & \text{F} & \text{P} \\ 6 \cdot {}^-7 & = & {}^-42 \end{array}$$

$$\begin{array}{ccc} \text{P} & \text{F} & \text{F} \\ {}^-42 \div {}^-7 & = & n \end{array}$$

4. $n \cdot 9 = {}^-18$

$\quad {}^-18 \div 9 = n$

5. $n \cdot {}^-8 = 56$

$\quad 56 \div {}^-8 = n$

6. $n \cdot {}^-9 = {}^-72$

$\quad {}^-72 \div {}^-9 = n$

7. $n \cdot 7 = {}^-63$

$\quad {}^-63 \div 7 = n$

8. $n \cdot {}^-8 = 48$

$\quad 48 \div {}^-8 = n$

9. $n \cdot {}^-6 = {}^-54$

$\quad {}^-54 \div {}^-6 = n$

Solve the equations.

10. $9 \cdot {}^-5 = n$
$\quad {}^-5 \cdot 9 = n$
$\quad {}^-45 \div {}^-5 = n$
$\quad {}^-45 \div 9 = n$

11. ${}^-6 \cdot {}^-7 = n$
$\quad {}^-7 \cdot {}^-6 = n$
$\quad 42 \div {}^-7 = n$
$\quad 42 \div {}^-6 = n$

12. ${}^-8 \cdot 5 = n$
$\quad 5 \cdot {}^-8 = n$
$\quad {}^-40 \div 5 = n$
$\quad {}^-40 \div {}^-8 = n$

Find the quotients. Think about missing factors.

1. $81 \div {}^-9 = n$ 2. $28 \div {}^-4 = n$ 3. $54 \div {}^-6 = n$ 4. $24 \div {}^-8 = n$

5. ${}^-21 \div {}^-7 = n$ 6. ${}^-24 \div 8 = n$ 7. $56 \div {}^-7 = n$ 8. $72 \div {}^-9 = n$

9. $63 \div 9 = n$ 10. ${}^-28 \div 4 = n$ 11. $21 \div {}^-7 = n$ 12. $45 \div {}^-5 = n$

13. ${}^-81 \div 9 = n$ 14. $49 \div {}^-7 = n$ 15. ${}^-72 \div 8 = n$ 16. $63 \div {}^-9 = n$

17. ${}^-35 \div 7 = n$ 18. ${}^-40 \div 8 = n$ 19. $35 \div {}^-7 = n$ 20. $40 \div {}^-8 = n$

21. $64 \div {}^-8 = n$ 22. $48 \div 8 = n$ 23. $40 \div {}^-5 = n$ 24. ${}^-42 \div {}^-7 = n$

25. Check Jeri's paper by multiplying integers. Which problems did she miss?

Give the correct solution to the problems Jeri worked incorrectly.

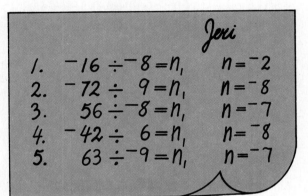

Jeri

1. $^-16 \div {}^-8 = n,$ $n = {}^-2$
2. $^-72 \div 9 = n,$ $n = {}^-8$
3. $56 \div {}^-8 = n,$ $n = {}^-7$
4. $^-42 \div 6 = n,$ $n = {}^-8$
5. $63 \div {}^-9 = n,$ $n = {}^-7$

Solve the equations.

26. $({}^-24 \div {}^-6) \div 2 = n$

27. ${}^-24 \div ({}^-6 \div 2) = n$

28. $({}^-36 + 24) \div {}^-4 = n$

29. $({}^-36 \div {}^-4) + (24 \div {}^-4) = n$

30. ${}^-48 \div ({}^-6 + 2) = n$

31. $({}^-48 \div {}^-6) + ({}^-48 \div 2) = n$

32. $({}^-10 + {}^-18) \div (10 + {}^-3) = n$

The squares in each row and column are to be filled with 4-digit numerals. The clue for each numeral shows the correct digits, but the order of the digits must be changed.

Fill in the squares with correct numerals.

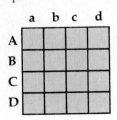

Across		Down	
A	1356	a	2468
B	2477	b	0179
C	1889	c	1374
D	0244	d	2458

More practice, page 394, Set B

Module 6.3   355

⊛ Comparing integers

Thinking about some of the uses of integers can help you compare them.
Complete each sentence. Then give the correct sign, > or <, for each ●.

1.

A temperature of 20 degrees
above zero is _____?_____ than
            (higher, lower)
a temperature of 25 degrees
below zero.

20 ● ⁻25

2.

A place 100 m below sea level is
_____?_____ than a place 200 m
(higher, lower)
below sea level.

⁻100 ● ⁻200

3.

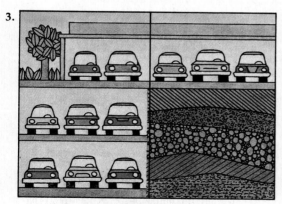

An elevator 2 floors below
ground level is _____?_____ than
            (higher, lower)
an elevator 1 floor above
ground level.

⁻2 ● 1

4.

If you owe $75 you are
_____?_____ off financially than
(better, worse)
if you owe $50.

⁻75 ● ⁻50

The integer that is farther to the right on the number line
is the greater of two integers.

```
◄──•──•──•──•──•──•──•──•──•──•──•──•──•──•──•──•──•──•──•──•──•──•──•──•──•──►
  ⁻12 ⁻11 ⁻10 ⁻9 ⁻8 ⁻7 ⁻6 ⁻5 ⁻4 ⁻3 ⁻2 ⁻1  0  1  2  3  4  5  6  7  8  9 10 11 12
```

Think about the number line and give the correct
symbol, >, <, or =, for each .

1. 9 ⬤ ⁻2

2. 5 ⬤ ⁻17

3. 0 ⬤ 5

4. ⁻3 ⬤ 0

5. ⁻1 ⬤ ⁻5

6. 1 ⬤ ⁻1

7. ⁻2 ⬤ 2

8. ⁻12 ⬤ ⁻15

9. ⁻23 ⬤ 14

10. ⁻67 ⬤ ⁻24

11. 5 ⬤ ⁻39

12. 8 ⬤ ⁻9

13. 8 · ⁻2 ⬤ ⁻9 · ⁻2

14. 7 · 4 ⬤ ⁻7 · ⁻4

15. ⁻4 · 3 ⬤ 6 · 2

16. 4 · ⁻7 ⬤ ⁻7 · 4

17. ⁻3 · ⁻6 ⬤ ⁻9 · ⁻2

18. ⁻4 · 12 ⬤ ⁻3 · 11

19. 7 · 7 ⬤ ⁻8 · ⁻8

20. 6 · 8 ⬤ ⁻5 · ⁻4

21. 2 · ⁻5 ⬤ ⁻3 · ⁻4

Use **greater than** or **less than** to complete each sentence.

22. Any positive integer is _____?_____ zero.

23. Any negative integer is _____?_____ zero.

24. Any positive integer is _____?_____ any negative integer.

25. Any negative integer is _____?_____ any positive integer.

26. Any integer is _____?_____ another integer that is to the right of it
on the number line.

If the smallest possible square were drawn
around 4 touching nickels, what would be
the area of the square in mm²?

Approximately what percent of the square
would be covered by nickels?

(Information: Diameter of a nickel is 21 mm.
Area of a circle = $\pi \cdot r^2$, where r is the
radius of the circle.
Area of a square = s^2, where s is the
length of the side.
Use π = 3.14.)

Answers for Self-check 1. 5 2. ⁻11 3. ⁻2 4. 9 5. 5 6. ⁻4 7. ⁻21 8. ⁻3 9. ⁻9
10. ⁻8 11. ⁻13 12. 11 13. ⁻4 14. 21 15. ⁻12 16. ⁻20 17. 40 18. ⁻42 19. ⁻48
20. 63 21. ⁻9 22. 8 23. ⁻6 24. ⁻6 ☆ 25. > ☆ 26. < ☆ 27. < ☆ 28. >

Self-check

Find the sums.

1. $7 + {}^-2$
2. ${}^-8 + {}^-3$
3. ${}^-6 + 4$
4. ${}^-3 + 12$

5. $13 + {}^-8$
6. $11 + {}^-15$
7. ${}^-12 + {}^-9$
8. $7 + {}^-10$

Find the differences.

9. ${}^-16 - {}^-7$
10. $3 - 11$
11. ${}^-5 - 8$
12. $2 - {}^-9$

13. $8 - 12$
14. $7 - {}^-14$
15. ${}^-6 - 6$
16. ${}^-13 - 7$

Find the products.

17. $5 \cdot 8$
18. ${}^-6 \cdot 7$
19. $8 \cdot {}^-6$
20. ${}^-9 \cdot {}^-7$

Find the quotients.

21. $63 \div {}^-7$
22. ${}^-48 \div {}^-6$
23. ${}^-54 \div 9$
24. $42 \div {}^-7$

Give the correct symbol, $<$, $>$, or $=$, for each ●.

☆ 25. 18 ● ${}^-26$ ☆ 26. ${}^-7$ ● 0 ☆ 27. ${}^-64$ ● ${}^-32$ ☆ 28. ${}^-12$ ● ${}^-15$

Answers for Self-check—page 357

Test

Find the sum.

1. $13 + {}^-6$
2. ${}^-9 + {}^-7$
3. ${}^-15 + 8$
4. ${}^-7 + 21$

7. ${}^-8 + {}^-11$
6. $8 + {}^-14$
7. ${}^-7 + 9$
8. $3 + {}^-7$

Find the differences.

9. ${}^-4 - {}^-9$
10. $7 - {}^-4$
11. ${}^-12 - 8$
12. ${}^-15 - {}^-7$

13. $8 - {}^-10$
14. $6 - 10$
15. ${}^-7 - 11$
16. ${}^-3 - 2$

Find the products.

17. ${}^-9 \cdot 6$
18. $12 \cdot {}^-3$
19. ${}^-8 \cdot {}^-9$
20. $4 \cdot {}^-8$

Find the quotients.

21. $56 \div {}^-8$
22. ${}^-32 \div {}^-4$
23. ${}^-63 \div 9$
24. $36 \div {}^-4$

Give the correct symbol, $<$, $>$, or $=$, for each ●.

☆ 25. 3 ● ${}^-12$ ☆ 26. ${}^-17$ ● ${}^-12$ ☆ 27. ${}^-48$ ● ${}^-49$ ☆ 28. ${}^-15$ ● 18

Math lab

Geoboard Problems

Pictures A, B, and C each show a **convex** polygon.
A convex polygon has no dents in it.

A

B

C

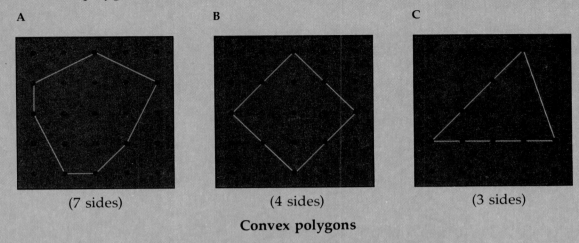

(7 sides)

(4 sides)

(3 sides)

Convex polygons

Pictures D, E, and F each show a **non-convex** polygon.
A non-convex polygon is also called a **concave** polygon.

D

E

F

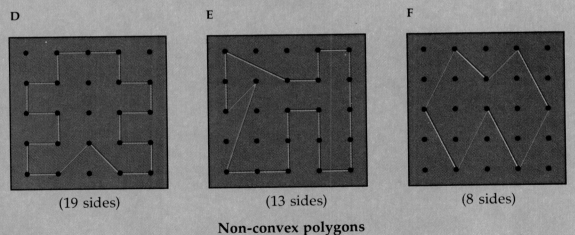

(19 sides)

(13 sides)

(8 sides)

Non-convex polygons

Use dot paper.

1. Show a convex polygon with 8 sides.

2. Show a non-convex polygon with 22 sides.

3. Show a convex polygon with 9 sides.

4. Show a non-convex polygon with 24 sides.

Coordinate Geometry

Canadian and United States Parks

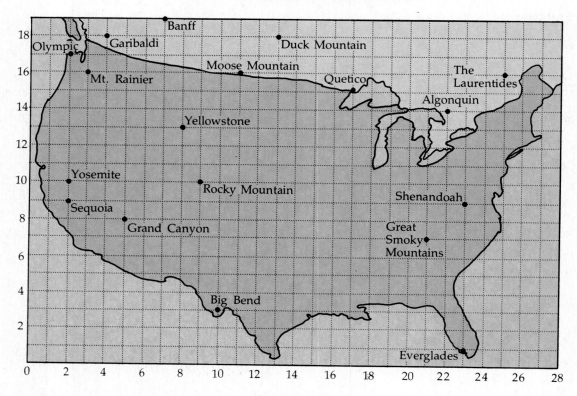

Find Grand Canyon Park. The coordinates (5, 8) give the approximate location of the park on the map.

Give the coordinates of the approximate locations of these parks.

1. Yosemite

2. Big Bend

3. Algonquin

4. Mt. Rainier

5. Duck Mountain

6. Great Smoky Mountains

7. Garibaldi

8. Rocky Mountain

9. Moose Mountain

10. Banff

11. Yellowstone

12. Everglades

You can graph a geometric figure by graphing the vertex points and connecting them in the order given.

Example:

Graph a pentagon with these vertices:

(2, 3), (4, 9), (6, 9), (8, 3), (5, 2), (2, 3)

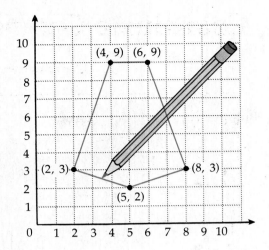

Graph each polygon.

1. Isosceles triangle
   (2, 2), (4, 8), (6, 2)

2. Octagon
   (1, 3), (1, 6), (2, 7), (5, 7)
   (6, 6), (6, 3), (5, 2), (2, 2)

3. Right triangle
   (1, 3), (1, 8), (5, 8)

4. Hexagon
   (3, 4), (4, 6), (7, 6), (8, 4),
   (7, 2), (4, 2)

5. Quadrilateral
   (3, 4), (6, 6), (7, 3), (6, 2)

6. Trapezoid
   (0, 0), (2, 3), (7, 3), (9, 0)

7. Rectangle
   (1, 3), (5, 7), (7, 5), (3, 1)

8. Pentagon
   (3, 3), (6, 5), (9, 3), (8, 1), (4, 1)

9. Parallelogram
   (5, 3), (2, 9), (7, 10), (10, 4)

10. Square
    (2, 1), (2, 8), (9, 8), (9, 1)

Negative and fractional coordinates

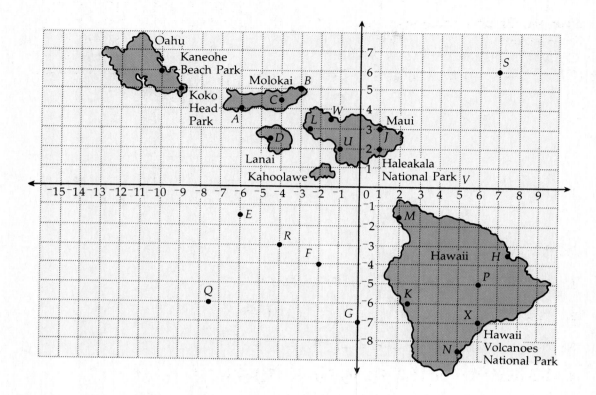

The coordinates of some points on this map are negative integers or fractional numbers.

The coordinates for point E are $\left(^-6,\ ^-1\frac{1}{2}\right)$.

The coordinates for Hawaii Volcanoes National Park at point X are $(6,\ ^-7)$.

Give the coordinates of each point.

1. A 2. B 3. C 4. D 5. F

6. H 7. J 8. K 9. L 10. M

11. N 12. P 13. Q 14. R 15. S

16. Kaneohe Beach Park   17. Haleakala National Park

18. Koko Head Park

Polygons may be graphed using coordinates which include integers or fractional numbers.

Example: Graph a rhombus with these vertices:

$(^-3, 3)$, $\left(1\frac{1}{2}, 1\frac{1}{2}\right)$, $(3, ^-3)$, $\left(^-1\frac{1}{2}, ^-1\frac{1}{2}\right)$

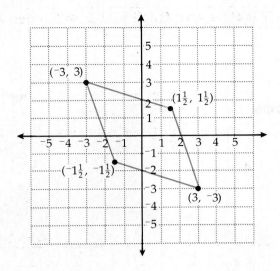

Graph each polygon.

1. Isosceles right triangle: $(^-4, 4)$, $(2, 4)$, $(2, ^-2)$

2. Pentagon: $(^-4, 3)$, $(2, 4)$, $(5, ^-1)$, $\left(\frac{1}{2}, ^-5\frac{1}{2}\right)$, $\left(^-4\frac{1}{2}, ^-3\right)$

3. Scalene triangle: $(^-4, ^-2)$, $(^-3, 2)$, $(4, 3)$

4. Isosceles trapezoid: $\left(^-2, 4\frac{1}{2}\right)$, $\left(4, 2\frac{1}{2}\right)$, $\left(4, ^-1\frac{1}{2}\right)$, $\left(^-2, ^-3\frac{1}{2}\right)$

5. Equilateral triangle: $\left(^-4\frac{1}{2}, 3\frac{1}{2}\right)$, $\left(3\frac{1}{2}, \frac{1}{2}\right)$, $(^-3, ^-5)$

6. Convex polygon: $(^-5, 1)$, $(^-4, 4)$, $(0, 5)$, $\left(5, 3\frac{1}{2}\right)$, $(4, ^-4)$, $(0, ^-5)$, $\left(^-3, ^-2\frac{1}{2}\right)$

7. Non-convex quadrilateral: $(^-4, 1)$, $\left(\frac{1}{2}, 1\right)$, $(3, 5)$, $\left(3, ^-2\frac{1}{2}\right)$

8. A "kite": $(^-3, 0)$, $(^-3, 4)$, $(1, 4)$, $(5, ^-4)$

9. A 5-pointed star: $(^-3, ^-4)$, $\left(0, 5\frac{1}{2}\right)$, $(3, ^-4)$, $(^-5, 2)$, $(5, 2)$

10. A 6-pointed star: $(^-5, 3)$, $\left(^-1\frac{1}{2}, 3\right)$, $(0, 6)$, $\left(1\frac{1}{2}, 3\right)$, $(5, 3)$, $\left(3\frac{1}{2}, 0\right)$,
    $(5, ^-3)$, $\left(1\frac{1}{2}, ^-3\right)$, $(0, ^-6)$, $\left(^-1\frac{1}{2}, ^-3\right)$, $(^-5, ^-3)$, $\left(^-3\frac{1}{2}, 0\right)$

☆ 11. Graph and connect these points in the order given.

$(^-14, 5)$ $(^-9, 10)$ $\left(^-7, 10\frac{1}{2}\right)$ $(^-7, 13)$ $(^-5, 10)$ $\left(^-6, 11\frac{3}{4}\right)$ $(^-5, 13)$ $\left(^-4, 10\frac{1}{2}\right)$
$(4, 3)$ $(4, 1)$ $\left(2\frac{1}{2}, 1\right)$ $(3, 0)$ $\left(2, ^-\frac{1}{2}\right)$, $(^-4, 2)$ $(^-5, 2)$ $(^-6, 1)$ $(^-8, ^-2)$

☆ 12. Graph an interesting figure of your own.

✪ Graphing symmetric figures

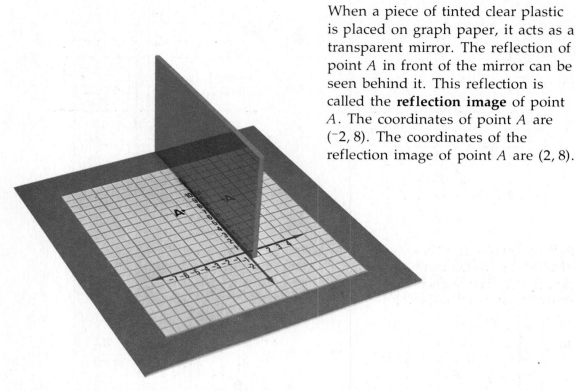

When a piece of tinted clear plastic is placed on graph paper, it acts as a transparent mirror. The reflection of point A in front of the mirror can be seen behind it. This reflection is called the **reflection image** of point A. The coordinates of point A are (⁻2, 8). The coordinates of the reflection image of point A are (2, 8).

Think of the red line in each exercise as a mirror.
Give the coordinates of the reflection image of each point.

1.

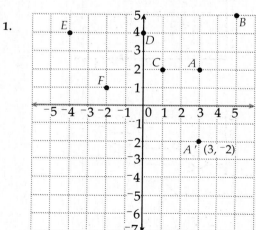

2.

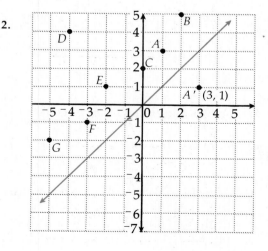

Example: The coordinates of the reflection image of point A are (3, ⁻2).

Find the coordinates of the reflection images of the indicated points and draw the reflection image of each figure.

1.

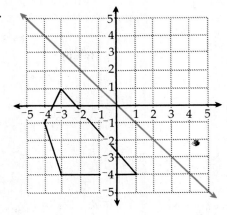

2.

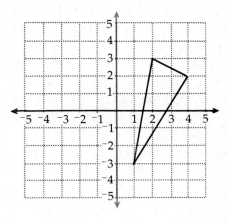

A figure made up of a set of points and the reflection images of those points is called a **symmetric figure**. Mark the given points and their reflection images on your graph paper and draw the symmetric figure.

3.

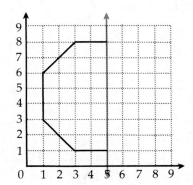

4.

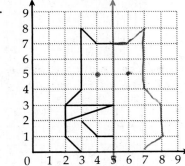

5.

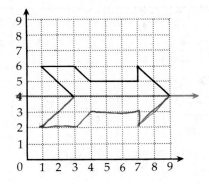

6.

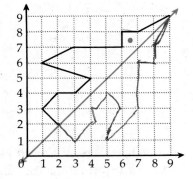

✴ Graphing similar figures

You can graph a figure similar to a given figure
by using graph paper with larger squares.

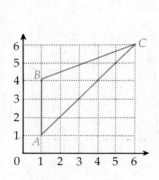

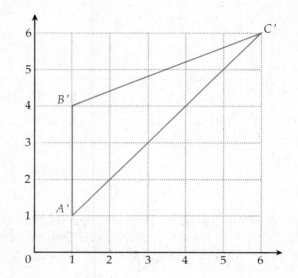

$$\triangle ABC \sim \triangle A'B'C'$$

Use centimeter graph paper to graph figures similar to these.

1.

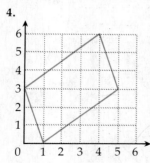

2.

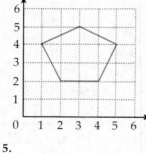

3.

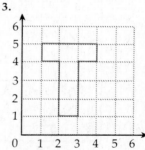

4.

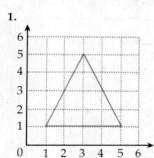

5.

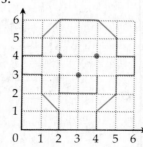

6.

☆ 7. What is the approximate ratio of the lengths of matching
sides in each pair of similar figures in exercises 1–6?

A figure similar to a given figure may be graphed by multiplying each of the coordinates of the given figure by the same number.

The coordinates of points A, B, and C were each multiplied by 3. The new coordinates were used to draw the larger triangle.

Original coordinates:
A (1, 1), B (1, 2), C (3, 1)

New coordinates:
A' (3, 3), B' (3, 6), C' (9, 3)

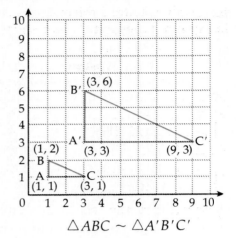

$$\triangle ABC \sim \triangle A'B'C'$$

Copy each figure on a grid with numbers on each axis up to 12. Multiply each of the coordinates by the number given and graph the similar figure.

1.

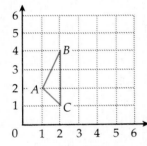

Multiply by 2.

2.

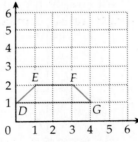

Multiply by 3.

3.

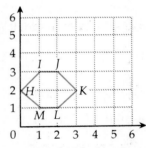

Multiply by 4.

4.

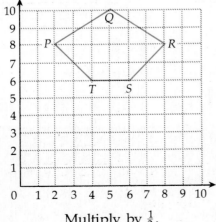

Multiply by $\frac{1}{2}$.

5.

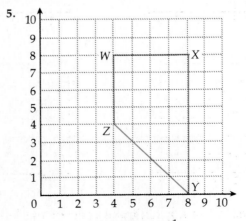

Multiply by $\frac{1}{4}$.

✪ Graphing relationships

Hillary placed masses on a spring and measured the distance the spring stretched for each mass.

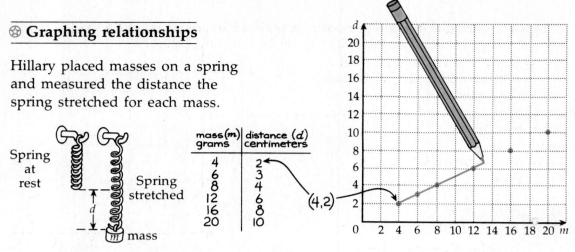

Spring at rest

Spring stretched

mass (m) grams	distance (d) centimeters
4	2
6	3
8	4
12	6
16	8
20	10

(4,2)

m mass

Then she recorded the results in a table, graphed each pair of coordinates, and connected the points to show the relationship between the masses and the stretch of the spring.

Copy each grid, graph the coordinates in each table, and connect the points. Tell whether the graph appears to be a straight line or a curve.

1.

2.

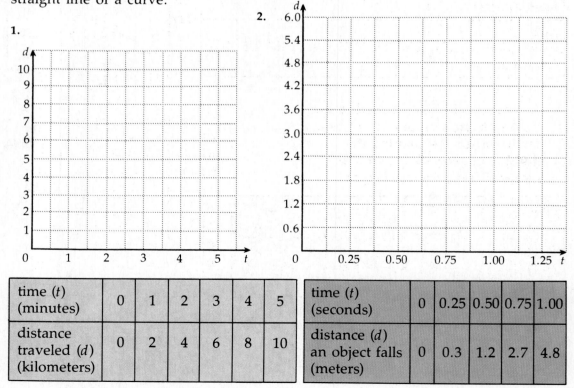

time (t) (minutes)	0	1	2	3	4	5
distance traveled (d) (kilometers)	0	2	4	6	8	10

time (t) (seconds)	0	0.25	0.50	0.75	1.00
distance (d) an object falls (meters)	0	0.3	1.2	2.7	4.8

Copy each grid, graph the coordinates in each table, and connect the points.

1. A super ball is dropped from a height of 100 cm. It will bounce several times.

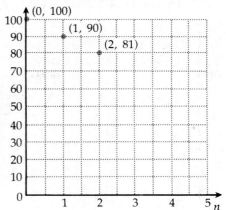

number (n) of bounce	0	1	2	3	4	5
height (h) of bounce (centimeters)	100	90	81	73	66	59

2. This table shows the average heights in centimeters of boys and girls from ages 7 to 14. Use the same grid for both sets of data.

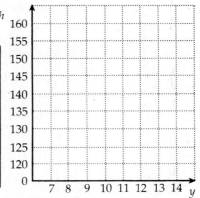

age (y)	7	8	9	10	11	12	13	14
boys' height (h) (centimeters)	122	125	130	135	140	147	152	160
girls' height (h) (centimeters)	121	124	130	135	142	148	155	160

3. A model rocket is launched. Using marks on the side of a tower as a guide, observers counted the number of seconds it took the rocket to reach certain heights.

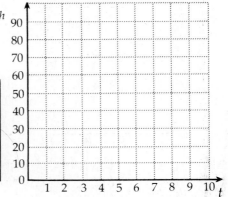

time (t) (seconds)	0	1	2	4	6	7	8
height (h) of rocket (meters)	0	50	70	80	70	50	0

☆ 4. Collect data on the relationship between the length of a pendulum and the number of swings per minute. Record the results in a table and make a graph of the data.

✸ Graphing equations

The equation $d = 5t$ states that the distance (d) traveled on a walk is 5 times the number of hours (t) a person has been walking. To graph this equation, first use the equation to make a table.

t	d	$d = 5 \cdot t$
1	5	← $d = 5 \cdot 1$, or 5
2	10	← $d = 5 \cdot 2$, or 10
3	15	← $d = 5 \cdot 3$, or 15
4	20	← $d = 5 \cdot 4$, or 20
5	25	← $d = 5 \cdot 5$, or 25

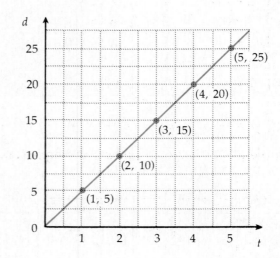

Now use the coordinates from the table to graph the equation $d = 5t$.

Complete each table and graph the equation.

1.

x	y	$y = 2x + 1$
0	1	← $y = 2 \cdot 0 + 1$, or 1
1	3	← $y = 2 \cdot 1 + 1$, or 3
2	5	← $y = 2 \cdot 2 + 1$, or 5
3		
4		
5		
6		

2.

s	A	$A = s + 3$
0	3	← $A = 0 + 3$, or 3
1	4	← $A = 1 + 3$, or 4
2	5	← $A = 2 + 3$, or 5
3		
4		
5		
6		

Make a table and graph each equation.

3. $y = x + 3$

4. $p = 2x + 2$

5. $d = 2t$

6. $y = 10 - x$

7. $s = 3t - 1$

8. $y = \frac{x}{2}$

9. $y = 3 \cdot (x - 1)$

10. $p = q + 5$

11. $y = 2x + 3$

You can graph equations using integer coordinates.

n	T	$T = n + 2$
$^-4$	$^-2$	$\longleftarrow T = {}^-4 + 2$, or $^-2$
$^-3$	$^-1$	$\longleftarrow T = {}^-3 + 2$, or $^-1$
$^-2$	0	$\longleftarrow T = {}^-2 + 2$, or 0
$^-1$	1	$\longleftarrow T = {}^-1 + 2$, or 1
0	2	$\longleftarrow T = 0 + 2$, or 2
1	3	$\longleftarrow T = 1 + 2$, or 3
2	4	$\longleftarrow T = 2 + 2$, or 4

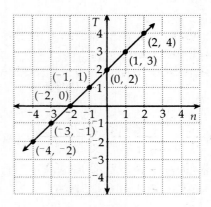

Complete each table and graph the equation.

1.

x	y	$y = x + {}^-2$
$^-2$	$^-4$	$\longleftarrow y = {}^-2 + {}^-2$, or $^-4$
$^-1$	$^-3$	$\longleftarrow y = {}^-1 + {}^-2$, or $^-3$
0		
1		
2		
3		

2.

p	q	$q = 3 - p$
$^-1$	▦	$\longleftarrow q = 3 - {}^-1$, or 4
0	▦	$\longleftarrow q = 3 - 0$, or 3
2		
3		
4		
5		

Make a table and graph each equation.

3. $y = 2x - 3$

4. $p = \dfrac{12}{m}$

5. $A = s^2 - 9$

Find the value of each equation for five different values of x.
Try $x = 1$, $x = 2$, $x = 3$, $x = 4$, and $x = 5$.

$x^2 = n_1$

$x^2 + x = n_2$

$x^3 + x^2 + x = n_3$

$x^4 + x^3 + x^2 + x = n_4$

Answers for Self-check   1. $(3, 2)$ 2. $(1, {}^-3)$ 3. $({}^-3, 1)$ 4. $(0, 3)$ 5. $({}^-2, {}^-2)$ 6. $(0, {}^-2)$

☆ 7.   ☆ 8.   ☆ 9. d ☆ 10.

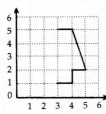

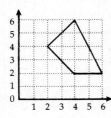

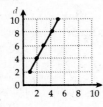

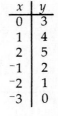

x	y
0	3
1	4
2	5
$^-1$	2
$^-2$	1
$^-3$	0

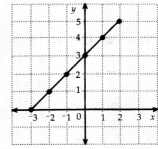

Self-check

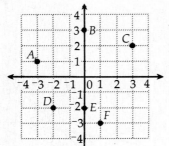

Give the
coordinates
of each point.

1. C 2. F
3. A 4. B
5. D 6. E

☆ 7. Graph the reflection image
of this figure.

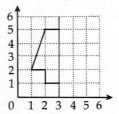

☆ 8. Multiply the coordinates by 2.
Graph the similar figure.

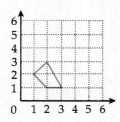

☆ 9. Graph the coordinates in this
table and connect the points.

time (t) (seconds)	1	2	3	4	5
distance (d) (kilometers)	2	4	6	8	10

☆ 10. Make a table and graph the
equation $y = x + 3$.

Answers for Self-check—page 371

Test

Give the
coordinates ▸
of each point.

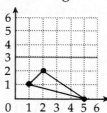

1. A 2. C
3. E 4. B
5. F 6. D

☆ 7. Graph the reflection image
of this figure.

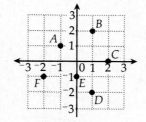

☆ 8. Multiply the
coordinates by 3.
Graph the similar
figure.

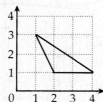

☆ 9. Graph the coordinates in this
table and connect the points.

Number of points (p) on a circle	1	2	3	4	5
Number of chords (c) possible	0	1	3	6	10

☆ 10. Make a table and graph the
equation $q = 2p + 1$.

Math lab

Curves of Constant Width

A circle is an example of a **curve of constant width.** This means that a circle of diameter d can roll between two parallel lines which are d units apart, touching both lines continuously.

You may find it surprising that there are other curves besides circles which have this same property. The construction of one such curve is shown below.

Step 1

Draw arc BC with radius r and center A.

Step 2

Draw arc AD with radius r and center B.

Step 3

Locate point E which is the intersection of arcs with radius r and centers at D and C.

Step 4

Draw arc AE with center C.
Draw arc DC with center E.
Draw arc BE with center D.

The closed curve $AEBCD$ is a curve of constant width. It will roll between two parallel lines which are r units apart and will always be touching both lines.

Make a larger copy of the curve of constant width. Can you make it roll between two parallel lines?

Unit 6 review

1. A cube has faces lettered **A**, **B**, **C**, **D**, **E**, **F**. When it is tossed, what is the probability of getting an **A** or an **F**?

2. A spinner has sections labeled 1, 2, 3, 4. When it is spun, what is the probability of the spinner landing on an even number?

Find the mean (to the nearest whole number), the median, and the mode for each list of numbers.

3. 23, 21, 24, 22, 21, 26

4. 100, 98, 99, 97, 97, 97, 98

Find the sums or differences.

5. $^-4 + ^-2$
6. $7 + ^-3$
7. $^-8 + 5$
8. $^-11 + 9$

9. $12 + ^-18$
10. $^-24 + 12$
11. $23 + ^-14$
12. $^-31 + 24$

13. $6 - ^-2$
14. $^-11 - 8$
15. $^-12 - ^-5$
16. $8 - ^-10$

17. $^-15 - ^-11$
18. $16 - ^-8$
19. $^-25 - 8$
20. $9 - ^-11$

Find the products or quotients.

21. $^-4 \cdot 8$
22. $^-12 \cdot ^-2$
23. $^-5 \cdot 4$
24. $9 \cdot ^-3$

25. $^-6 \cdot ^-6$
26. $^-8 \cdot 5$
27. $7 \cdot ^-6$
28. $^-9 \cdot ^-9$

29. $45 \div ^-9$
30. $^-72 \div ^-8$
31. $64 \div ^-8$
32. $^-56 \div ^-7$

33. $^-70 \div 7$
34. $54 \div ^-6$
35. $^-12 \div 3$
    $35 \div ^-5$

Appendix

Add.

| 1. | 62
+ 49 | 2. | 453
+ 76 | 3. | 581
+ 643 | 4. | 7654
+ 728 | 5. | 382
+ 548 |

| 6. | 6731
+ 4851 | 7. | 18 465
+ 9 372 | 8. | 4536
+ 5299 | 9. | 95 437
+ 62 849 | 10. | 8547
+ 6869 |

| 11. | 37 615
+ 45 938 | 12. | 453 297
+ 87 589 | 13. | 69 328
+ 542 768 | 14. | 56 374
+ 28 387 | 15. | 9456
+ 8657 |

| 16. | 436
217
4133
+ 516 | 17. | 287
3475
2754
+ 9235 | 18. | 1 475
132 526
378
+ 1 495 | 19. | 2643
7751
368
+ 4291 | 20. | 3584
7621
6675
+ 4339 |

21. 27 + 6 + 244 + 1376

22. 3672 + 4511 + 357 + 21

23. 38 465 + 2645 + 521 + 316

24. 65 721 + 8419 + 527 653

Add.

| 1. | 3.75
+ 4.36 | 2. | 7.56
+ 0.389 | 3. | 12.536
+ 9.483 | 4. | 0.075
+ 5.778 | 5. | 26.78
+ 0.59 |

| 6. | 0.543
+ 0.727 | 7. | 64.329
+ 27.89 | 8. | 8.76
+ 0.398 | 9. | 82.075
+ 8.659 | 10. | 0.757
+ 25.638 |

| 11. | 26.078
+ 9.58 | 12. | 54.302
+ 7.058 | 13. | 64.374
+ 28.949 | 14. | 126.08
+ 57.936 | 15. | 9.3765
+ 4.6635 |

| 16. | 2.74
3.63
+ 5.03 | 17. | 0.566
0.973
+ 0.481 | 18. | 13.762
0.54
+ 39.176 | 19. | 28.37
0.581
+ 15.438 | 20. | 65.215
3.984
+ 24.896 |

21. 3.54 + 2.6 + 5.439

22. 5.66 + 0.437 + 2.741

23. 5.034 + 285.6 + 0.755

24. 84.56 + 3.725 + 25.029

Subtract.

1.	43 − 26	**2.**	526 − 379	**3.**	602 − 438	**4.**	328 − 157	**5.**	854 − 277
6.	750 − 362	**7.**	948 − 565	**8.**	401 − 123	**9.**	530 − 226	**10.**	613 − 328
11.	3022 − 1431	**12.**	4326 − 1418	**13.**	8037 − 5269	**14.**	7002 − 4136	**15.**	5135 − 2186
16.	2000 − 1732	**17.**	6040 − 3728	**18.**	5000 − 3724	**19.**	8460 − 4583	**20.**	3001 − 2265
21.	5734 − 4568	**22.**	7030 − 2639	**23.**	3500 − 1761	**24.**	4205 − 2518	**25.**	9001 − 3827
26.	9007 − 2838	**27.**	8000 − 6637	**28.**	7486 − 3789	**29.**	6020 − 5379	**30.**	4070 − 3385

Subtract.

1.	72.5 − 36.8	**2.**	0.843 − 0.269	**3.**	62.2 − 48.7	**4.**	3.761 − 0.583	**5.**	456.1 − 239.8
6.	54.03 − 27.68	**7.**	9.304 − 1.826	**8.**	0.702 − 0.464	**9.**	630.5 − 78.9	**10.**	2.000 − 0.385
11.	600.00 − 437.28	**12.**	40.06 − 28.48	**13.**	17.057 − 9.578	**14.**	8.714 − 3.938	**15.**	300.01 − 25.76
16.	25.142 − 9.368	**17.**	542.3 − 238.6	**18.**	31.06 − 15.79	**19.**	0.850 − 0.372	**20.**	40.03 − 22.47
21.	0.604 − 0.328	**22.**	9.000 − 3.174	**23.**	70.00 − 48.22	**24.**	43.70 − 18.93	**25.**	507.06 − 358.47

26. 84.1 − 38.67   **27.** 42 − 26.85   **28.** 51.43 − 37.88

Find the sums.

1.	57.38 + 9.764	**2.**	36.041 + 25.58	**3.**	6.707 + 0.879	**4.**	25.09 + 78.56	**5.**	83.291 + 176.89
6.	9.327 + 0.698	**7.**	5.037 + 0.6895	**8.**	378.02 + 742.39	**9.**	54.76 + 8.579	**10.**	6.008 + 15.906
11.	47.65 + 380.592	**12.**	705.09 + 8.963	**13.**	56.47 + 9.807	**14.**	27.64 + 93.78	**15.**	8.527 + 1.603
16.	62.58 + 7.078	**17.**	8.037 + 23.706	**18.**	43.716 + 118.98	**19.**	71.005 + 36.09	**20.**	22.75 + 59.93

21. 0.5 + 0.35 + 0.167 **22.** 15.8 + 27.6 + 0.33 **23.** 300 + 42.7 + 0.399

24. 6.48 + 27.031 + 0.82 **25.** 500.01 + 0.07 + 0.006 **26.** 36.52 + 5.781 + 1.483

27. 7.28 + 6.79 **28.** 14.8 + 2.07 + 7 **29.** 21.6 + 0.84 + 6.5

Find the differences.

30.	43.72 − 7.68	**31.**	5.076 − 0.857	**32.**	72.08 − 7.99	**33.**	614.3 − 29.8	**34.**	7.005 − 3.987
35.	36.02 − 19.74	**36.**	0.903 − 0.358	**37.**	5.006 − 2.643	**38.**	22.03 − 9.7	**39.**	407.2 − 36.7
40.	0.082 − 0.037	**41.**	54.035 − 19.368	**42.**	6.07 − 3.298	**43.**	7.06 − 0.099	**44.**	9.72 − 5.865
45.	73.8 − 28.64	**46.**	1.037 − 0.98	**47.**	8.005 − 7.469	**48.**	0.09 − 0.027	**49.**	60.07 − 49.93

50. 32 − 15.6 **51.** 0.06 − 0.054 **52.** 700 − 25.6

53. 7.06 − 4.378 **54.** 22.5 − 3.98 **55.** 4.06 − 0.0081

56. 37.8 − 22.99 **57.** 5.731 − 2.565 **58.** 8.372 − 2.605

Set A   For use after page 73

Multiply.

1.	2.	3.	4.	5.	6.
53 × 7	28 × 2	44 × 5	2073 × 8	5607 × 3	3871 × 2

7.	8.	9.	10.	11.	12.
36 × 44	72 × 27	90 × 26	61 × 58	87 × 34	15 × 86

13.	14.	15.	16.	17.	18.
47 × 64	54 × 32	83 × 46	75 × 57	39 × 63	66 × 76

19.	20.	21.	22.	23.	24.
215 × 35	704 × 43	638 × 22	459 × 52	813 × 65	522 × 29

25.	26.	27.	28.	29.	30.
726 × 36	308 × 63	437 × 73	506 × 82	644 × 51	829 × 24

Set B   For use after page 75

Multiply.

1.	2.	3.	4.	5.	6.
4134 × 25	2516 × 7	7049 × 8	3291 × 45	6432 × 37	5804 × 56

7.	8.	9.	10.	11.	12.
324 × 703	706 × 425	480 × 297	522 × 308	826 × 562	259 × 732

13.	14.	15.	16.	17.	18.
407 × 634	514 × 705	920 × 252	735 × 602	393 × 475	619 × 373

19.	20.	21.	22.	23.	24.
2053 × 308	6437 × 225	7304 × 549	3008 × 624	8720 × 416	4217 × 703

25.	26.	27.	28.	29.	30.
5142 × 275	4236 × 933	8605 × 348	2700 × 572	6483 × 403	7964 × 612

Multiply.

1. 54.3 × 2.1	**2.** 246 × 0.33	**3.** 7.54 × 0.8	**4.** 36.8 × 45	**5.** 0.412 × 0.5	**6.** 6.22 × 3.4
7. 435 × 0.005	**8.** 60.7 × 5.26	**9.** 0.948 × 0.3	**10.** 8.56 × 2.4	**11.** 389 × 0.54	**12.** 0.712 × 9
13. 3.174 × 2.6	**14.** 5.66 × 4.3	**15.** 82.6 × 1.34	**16.** 48.6 × 6.21	**17.** 6.03 × 3.75	**18.** 728 × 0.42
19. 92.5 × 0.34	**20.** 4.07 × 7.3	**21.** 1.629 × 8.1	**22.** 0.47 × 59	**23.** 28.87 × 0.05	**24.** 0.34 × 6.6
25. 0.806 × 9.4	**26.** 7.3 × 4.9	**27.** 0.68 × 0.79	**28.** 39.7 × 40	**29.** 22.04 × 9.6	**30.** 379 × 0.08

Multiply.

1. 0.07 × 0.06	**2.** 0.8 × 0.04	**3.** 0.43 × 0.03	**4.** 0.024 × 0.5	**5.** 0.536 × 0.014	**6.** 0.038 × 0.28
7. 2.8 × 0.0007	**8.** 0.05 × 0.08	**9.** 0.06 × 0.4	**10.** 0.47 × 0.002	**11.** 2.56 × 0.03	**12.** 1.6 × 0.014
13. 0.25 × 0.24	**14.** 0.0075 × 0.7	**15.** 5.03 × 0.67	**16.** 0.045 × 0.073	**17.** 0.38 × 0.05	**18.** 4.2 × 0.009
19. 0.0034 × 0.06	**20.** 82 × 0.0007	**21.** 3.037 × 0.054	**22.** 0.736 × 0.244	**23.** 0.0521 × 0.76	**24.** 0.009 × 0.068
25. 7.17 × 0.0046	**26.** 382 × 0.0085	**27.** 0.059 × 0.03	**28.** 16.3 × 0.0024	**29.** 0.0653 × 82	**30.** 0.088 × 0.044

Estimate. Then find the sums and differences.

1.	2.	3.	4.	5.	6.
346 + 157	1803 − 1099	5632 + 2711	7493 + 3851	25 206 − 14 391	4382 − 1336

7.	8.	9.	10.	11.	12.
$ 0.57 − 0.38	$ 40.00 − 28.05	$ 35.20 + 22.60	$ 30.00 − 18.00	$ 0.61 − 0.28	$ 7384 + 4628

13.	14.	15.	16.	17.	18.
$ 736.62 − 458.23	$ 2643 + 8195	$ 0.86 − 0.55	$ 41.99 + 32.00	$ 6372 + 8951	$ 34.75 − 18.63

19.	20.	21.	22.	23.	24.
176 344 308 + 565	$ 23.00 46.52 50.09 + 18.20	$ 950 130 250 + 418	$ 17.65 21.75 32.60 + 17.00	7060 4372 5800 + 2500	$ 325.10 486.20 309.50 + 756.30

Choose the best estimate.

1. 4.6×33
   - A 120
   - B 150
   - C 200

2. 65×2.1
   - A 140
   - B 180
   - C 120

3. 0.83×4.5
   - A 4.0
   - B 0.4
   - C 3.2

4. 0.36×0.21
   - A 0.008
   - B 0.8
   - C 0.08

5. 73.2×0.051
   - A 0.350
   - B 3.50
   - C 35.0

6. 0.362×0.077
   - A 2.4
   - B 0.24
   - C 0.024

7. 43.6×28.2
   - A 3000
   - B 1500
   - C 1200

8. 8.2×0.964
   - A 8
   - B 7.2
   - C 0.6

9. 0.361×0.071
   - A 0.28
   - B 0.028
   - C 0.21

10. 56×7.2
    - A 420
    - B 350
    - C 480

11. 0.56×0.93
    - A 0.54
    - B 5.4
    - C 0.054

12. 7.72×0.64
    - A 4.2
    - B 4.8
    - C 3.6

13. 95×2.7
    - A 180
    - B 300
    - C 500

14. 0.84×3.5
    - A 3.2
    - B 2.4
    - C 36

15. 26.5×0.27
    - A 210
    - B 9.0
    - C 21.0

16. 63.7×5.4
    - A 360
    - B 300
    - C 400

17. 48.3×26.7
    - A 1000
    - B 800
    - C 1500

18. 0.83×0.96
    - A 0.8
    - B 0.08
    - C 8

19. 8.6×0.38
    - A 0.36
    - B 3.6
    - C 2.4

20. 8.2×0.864
    - A 0.72
    - B 72
    - C 7.2

Find the perimeter of each rectangle.

1. $l = 4.73$ m
   $w = 2.06$ m

2. $l = 21.6$ m
   $w = 7.4$ m

3. $l = 8.84$ m
   $w = 7.36$ m

4. $l = 31.3$ m
   $w = 18.7$ m

5. $l = 6.43$ cm
   $w = 3.22$ cm

6. $l = 13.6$ cm
   $w = 7.8$ cm

7. $l = 5.73$ m
   $w = 2.2$ m

8. $l = 18.6$ m
   $w = 4.6$ m

9. $l = 9.71$ m
   $w = 3.2$ m

10. $l = 10.5$ m
    $w = 1.5$ m

11. $l = 5.61$ m
    $w = 3.79$ m

12. $l = 14.79$ m
    $w = 5.21$ m

13. $l = 9.3$ m
    $w = 4.62$ m

14. $l = 20.2$ cm
    $w = 8.3$ cm

15. $l = 7.3$ m
    $w = 3.2$ m

Find the perimeter of each triangle.

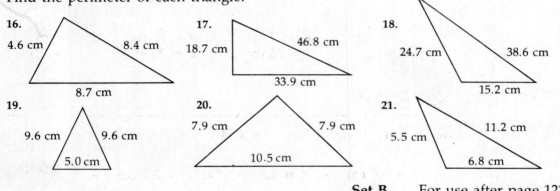

16. 4.6 cm, 8.4 cm, 8.7 cm

17. 18.7 cm, 46.8 cm, 33.9 cm

18. 24.7 cm, 38.6 cm, 15.2 cm

19. 9.6 cm, 9.6 cm, 5.0 cm

20. 7.9 cm, 7.9 cm, 10.5 cm

21. 5.5 cm, 11.2 cm, 6.8 cm

Find the area of each rectangle.

1. $l = 15.7$ cm
   $w = 7.2$ cm

2. $l = 73$ m
   $w = 20$ m

3. $l = 20.6$ cm
   $w = 13$ cm

4. $l = 18.7$ m
   $w = 1.3$ m

5. $l = 60$ m
   $w = 22$ m

6. $l = 45$ cm
   $w = 31$ cm

7. $l = 20.4$ m
   $w = 7.2$ m

8. $l = 51.7$ m
   $w = 46.1$ m

9. $l = 9.8$ m
   $w = 6.4$ m

10. $l = 17$ mm
    $w = 8$ mm

11. $l = 70$ cm
    $w = 40$ cm

12. $l = 3.7$ m
    $w = 2.8$ m

13. $l = 7.4$ cm
    $w = 3$ cm

14. $l = 4.5$ cm
    $w = 2.2$ cm

15. $l = 44$ mm
    $w = 20$ mm

Find the area of each parallelogram.

16. $b = 7.8$ m
    $h = 1.2$ m

17. $b = 26$ cm
    $h = 11$ cm

18. $b = 53$ cm
    $h = 10$ cm

19. $b = 37.1$ cm
    $h = 5.2$ cm

20. $b = 9.7$ cm
    $h = 3.6$ cm

21. $b = 84$ m
    $h = 30$ m

22. $b = 6.3$ m
    $h = 4.2$ m

23. $b = 4.6$ m
    $h = 2.7$ m

24. $b = 24$ m
    $h = 5$ m

25. $b = 17.2$ m
    $h = 4.5$ m

26. $b = 2.7$ m
    $h = 1.8$ m

27. $b = 8.6$ cm
    $h = 5.7$ cm

28. $b = 13.2$ m
    $h = 8.6$ m

29. $b = 5.9$ cm
    $h = 3.5$ cm

30. $b = 11.3$ m
    $h = 7.4$ m

Set A   For use after page 125

Find the area of each triangle.

1. $b = 36$ cm
   $h = 4$ cm

2. $b = 14$ cm
   $h = 6$ cm

3. $b = 32$ cm
   $h = 5$ cm

4. $b = 46$ cm
   $h = 31$ m

5. $b = 57$ m
   $h = 42$ m

6. $b = 10$ cm
   $h = 5$ cm

7. $b = 51$ m
   $h = 22$ m

8. $b = 16$ cm
   $h = 7$ cm

9. $b = 48$ cm
   $h = 15$ cm

10. $b = 107$ m
    $h = 36$ m

11. $b = 8$ m
    $h = 6$ m

12. $b = 15$ cm
    $h = 4$ cm

13. $b = 84$ cm
    $h = 13$ cm

14. $b = 12$ cm
    $h = 5$ cm

15. $b = 20$ cm
    $h = 8$ cm

16. $b = 38$ cm
    $h = 4$ cm

17. $b = 45$ cm
    $h = 4$ cm

18. $b = 37$ cm
    $h = 26$ cm

19. $b = 50$ m
    $h = 20$ m

20. $b = 15$ cm
    $h = 20$ cm

Set B   For use after page 129

Find the circumference of each circle. Use $\pi = 3.14$.

1. $r = 3.1$ cm
2. $d = 5.6$ cm
3. $d = 4.8$ cm
4. $r = 2.7$ cm
5. $d = 5.2$ cm

6. $r = 5.5$ cm
7. $d = 6.8$ cm
8. $r = 4.9$ cm
9. $r = 7.3$ cm
10. $d = 4.5$ cm

11. $r = 3.7$ cm
12. $d = 6.5$ cm
13. $d = 12.2$ m
14. $r = 0.7$ cm
15. $r = 2.2$ cm

16. $r = 20.5$ m
17. $r = 50$ cm
18. $d = 0.1$ m
19. $d = 15.5$ m
20. $r = 25.5$ m

Set C   For use after page 131

Find the area of each circle. Use $\pi = 3.14$.

1. $r = 3$ m
2. $r = 0.4$ m
3. $r = 2.1$ m
4. $r = 30$ cm
5. $r = 100$ m

6. $r = 0.6$ m
7. $r = 7$ cm
8. $r = 10$ m
9. $r = 3.1$ cm
10. $r = 20$ cm

11. $r = 4.2$ cm
12. $r = 0.3$ cm
13. $r = 8$ m
14. $r = 12$ m
15. $r = 6.6$ cm

16. $r = 7.2$ cm
17. $r = 9$ m
18. $r = 0.5$ m
19. $r = 50$ cm
20. $r = 13$ cm

Find the quotients and remainders.

1. 5)182   2. 3)175   3. 7)203   4. 2)169   5. 8)371

6. 3)376   7. 5)2107   8. 9)2829   9. 4)2408   10. 6)1952

11. 7)3041   12. 6)3044   13. 8)2225   14. 3)2742   15. 2)1727

16. 4)2190   17. 9)1976   18. 6)2629   19. 7)4258   20. 5)2866

21. 8)3154   22. 7)3654   23. 2)1952   24. 6)2749   25. 4)3046

Find the quotients and remainders.

1. 21)843   2. 54)1743   3. 72)4072   4. 35)2576   5. 17)1029

6. 63)2438   7. 81)2209   8. 46)3772   9. 12)941   10. 91)4146

11. 33)2022   12. 48)1747   13. 74)15 188   14. 56)23 968   15. 27)14 668

16. 14)4503   17. 65)28 504   18. 88)19 148   19. 93)28 318   20. 32)23 762

21. 76)41 572   22. 31)26 805   23. 52)34 996   24. 47)43 556   25. 19)15 034

Find the quotients and remainders.

1. 256)21 619   2. 183)13 808   3. 415)93 790   4. 721)35 031

5. 634)319 574   6. 822)78 226   7. 549)403 211   8. 377)106 778

9. 152)128 666   10. 294)40 572   11. 738)289 747   12. 563)293 415

13. 573)345 042   14. 467)437 763   15. 358)271 749   16. 262)212 069

17. 914)432 649   18. 856)340 688   19. 659)538 829   20. 493)358 052

Find each quotient. Continue annexing zeros and dividing until the remainder is zero.

1. $5\overline{)13}$ 2. $8\overline{)34}$ 3. $2\overline{)31}$ 4. $4\overline{)3}$ 5. $6\overline{)5.1}$

6. $4\overline{)27}$ 7. $12\overline{)1.8}$ 8. $15\overline{)6}$ 9. $8\overline{)23.6}$ 10. $5\overline{)3.8}$

11. $20\overline{)75.4}$ 12. $5\overline{)41.2}$ 13. $40\overline{)376}$ 14. $32\overline{)1232}$ 15. $16\overline{)6.96}$

16. $54\overline{)148.5}$ 17. $62\overline{)461.9}$ 18. $26\overline{)1.17}$ 19. $18\overline{)63}$ 20. $25\overline{)0.9}$

21. $135\overline{)280.8}$ 22. $226\overline{)33.9}$ 23. $50\overline{)3.55}$ 24. $148\overline{)643.8}$ 25. $156\overline{)101.4}$

Round each quotient to the nearest hundredth.

1. $3\overline{)4.9}$ 2. $7\overline{)17}$ 3. $5\overline{)7.43}$ 4. $6\overline{)15.79}$ 5. $9\overline{)13}$

6. $17\overline{)14}$ 7. $14\overline{)15.6}$ 8. $18\overline{)32}$ 9. $12\overline{)46}$ 10. $16\overline{)11}$

11. $38\overline{)21}$ 12. $41\overline{)94.87}$ 13. $67\overline{)125}$ 14. $24\overline{)32}$ 15. $83\overline{)163}$

16. $29\overline{)24.7}$ 17. $95\overline{)47}$ 18. $46\overline{)84}$ 19. $58\overline{)35.6}$ 20. $71\overline{)243}$

21. $44\overline{)32.6}$ 22. $36\overline{)51}$ 23. $27\overline{)58.3}$ 24. $76\overline{)43.9}$ 25. $52\overline{)168}$

Find the quotients to the nearest hundredth.

1. $3.4\overline{)11.06}$ 2. $0.04\overline{)0.2968}$ 3. $5.26\overline{)7.04}$ 4. $0.213\overline{)0.1704}$

5. $41.3\overline{)59}$ 6. $0.007\overline{)0.504}$ 7. $0.82\overline{)3.034}$ 8. $29.2\overline{)10.07}$

9. $11.1\overline{)14.8}$ 10. $19.1\overline{)5.08}$ 11. $0.043\overline{)0.121}$ 12. $5.75\overline{)1.84}$

13. $0.09\overline{)0.716}$ 14. $0.06\overline{)0.162}$ 15. $4.2\overline{)48.6}$ 16. $7.8\overline{)4.368}$

17. $0.082\overline{)1.29}$ 18. $0.138\overline{)5.6}$ 19. $6.7\overline{)8.4}$ 20. $3.07\overline{)73}$

Give the prime factorization of each number.

1. 33
2. 18
3. 20
4. 40
5. 24
6. 54

7. 38
8. 36
9. 80
10. 27
11. 45
12. 64

13. 78
14. 42
15. 72
16. 90
17. 76
18. 48

19. 96
20. 52
21. 26
22. 88
23. 68
24. 50

Find the greatest common factor for each pair of numbers.

1. 6, 10
2. 48, 36
3. 80, 200
4. 45, 36
5. 48, 72

6. 75, 100
7. 28, 35
8. 10, 45
9. 51, 39
10. 24, 36

11. 8, 27
12. 25, 20
13. 90, 120
14. 108, 24
15. 150, 270

16. 50, 15
17. 24, 180
18. 48, 80
19. 52, 24
20. 56, 38

Find the least common multiple for each pair of numbers.

1. 8, 3
2. 2, 7
3. 15, 25
4. 8, 12
5. 30, 45

6. 5, 8
7. 7, 10
8. 12, 15
9. 4, 10
10. 20, 25

11. 7, 6
12. 3, 5
13. 16, 24
14. 25, 10
15. 26, 39

16. 40, 60
17. 12, 9
18. 49, 21
19. 8, 6
20. 36, 48

Set A   For use after page 197

Write a decimal for each fraction.

1. $\frac{7}{20}$ 2. $\frac{3}{8}$ 3. $\frac{3}{2}$ 4. $\frac{3}{4}$ 5. $\frac{5}{8}$ 6. $\frac{7}{10}$

7. $\frac{6}{25}$ 8. $\frac{7}{4}$ 9. $\frac{11}{20}$ 10. $\frac{9}{5}$ 11. $\frac{2}{3}$ 12. $\frac{4}{5}$

13. $\frac{9}{15}$ 14. $\frac{19}{20}$ 15. $\frac{9}{16}$ 16. $\frac{5}{11}$ 17. $\frac{17}{6}$ 18. $\frac{1}{6}$

Set B   For use after page 201

Find the lowest-terms fraction.

1. $\frac{10}{12}$ 2. $\frac{9}{15}$ 3. $\frac{12}{14}$ 4. $\frac{7}{21}$ 5. $\frac{3}{6}$ 6. $\frac{12}{15}$

7. $\frac{12}{20}$ 8. $\frac{10}{20}$ 9. $\frac{6}{18}$ 10. $\frac{36}{48}$ 11. $\frac{15}{24}$ 12. $\frac{16}{28}$

13. $\frac{9}{21}$ 14. $\frac{7}{28}$ 15. $\frac{15}{25}$ 16. $\frac{24}{64}$ 17. $\frac{20}{28}$ 18. $\frac{30}{100}$

19. $\frac{15}{60}$ 20. $\frac{8}{20}$ 21. $\frac{10}{45}$ 22. $\frac{18}{60}$ 23. $\frac{21}{35}$ 24. $\frac{28}{32}$

25. $\frac{32}{72}$ 26. $\frac{30}{36}$ 27. $\frac{26}{39}$ 28. $\frac{15}{80}$ 29. $\frac{70}{100}$ 30. $\frac{60}{96}$

Set C   For use after page 205

Write a mixed numeral or whole number for each improper fraction.

1. $\frac{10}{4}$ 2. $\frac{22}{5}$ 3. $\frac{26}{2}$ 4. $\frac{75}{8}$ 5. $\frac{58}{7}$ 6. $\frac{35}{6}$

7. $\frac{17}{3}$ 8. $\frac{43}{6}$ 9. $\frac{49}{4}$ 10. $\frac{31}{3}$ 11. $\frac{27}{4}$ 12. $\frac{61}{8}$

13. $\frac{33}{4}$ 14. $\frac{75}{8}$ 15. $\frac{7}{7}$ 16. $\frac{59}{6}$ 17. $\frac{16}{1}$ 18. $\frac{23}{3}$

Write an improper fraction for each mixed numeral.

19. $3\frac{1}{5}$ 20. $4\frac{1}{3}$ 21. $7\frac{1}{4}$ 22. $2\frac{5}{9}$ 23. $6\frac{1}{2}$ 24. $9\frac{1}{4}$

25. $8\frac{2}{3}$ 26. $7\frac{1}{8}$ 37. $6\frac{2}{5}$ 28. $5\frac{1}{3}$ 29. $4\frac{1}{6}$ 30. $5\frac{1}{7}$

31. $2\frac{5}{8}$ 32. $3\frac{2}{3}$ 33. $6\frac{1}{9}$ 34. $4\frac{3}{4}$ 35. $2\frac{5}{8}$ 36. $6\frac{3}{5}$

Add.

1. $5\frac{1}{3}$
   $+7\frac{1}{12}$

2. $3\frac{1}{2}$
   $+8\frac{3}{8}$

3. $2\frac{5}{6}$
   $+6\frac{1}{3}$

4. $4\frac{1}{2}$
   $+2\frac{1}{10}$

5. $5\frac{3}{4}$
   $+7\frac{1}{2}$

6. $23\frac{1}{4}$
   $+15\frac{5}{6}$

7. $41\frac{2}{3}$
   $+55\frac{3}{4}$

8. $38\frac{1}{10}$
   $+45\frac{2}{5}$

9. $74\frac{3}{8}$
   $+29\frac{1}{4}$

10. $61\frac{1}{10}$
    $+38\frac{1}{4}$

11. $37\frac{1}{2}$
    $+58\frac{2}{3}$

12. $76\frac{1}{4}$
    $+56\frac{2}{3}$

13. $46\frac{1}{4}$
    $+87\frac{1}{3}$

14. $68\frac{1}{4}$
    $+17\frac{1}{5}$

15. $46\frac{1}{2}$
    $+98\frac{7}{8}$

16. $\frac{1}{3}$
    $\frac{5}{6}$
    $+\frac{1}{2}$

17. $\frac{3}{8}$
    $\frac{1}{2}$
    $+\frac{3}{4}$

18. $15\frac{3}{8}$
    $36\frac{1}{4}$
    $+58\frac{1}{6}$

19. $57\frac{1}{2}$
    $72\frac{5}{6}$
    $+23\frac{2}{3}$

20. $74\frac{1}{16}$
    $36\frac{1}{8}$
    $+82\frac{3}{4}$

Subtract.

1. $54\frac{1}{6}$
   $-27\frac{2}{3}$

2. $28\frac{1}{2}$
   $-9\frac{7}{12}$

3. 18
   $-15\frac{3}{5}$

4. $47\frac{3}{8}$
   -28

5. $76\frac{1}{2}$
   $-28\frac{3}{4}$

6. $35\frac{1}{2}$
   $-18\frac{1}{8}$

7. $71\frac{2}{3}$
   $-46\frac{1}{4}$

8. $80\frac{1}{6}$
   $-51\frac{3}{8}$

9. $63\frac{1}{2}$
   $-29\frac{3}{10}$

10. $52\frac{1}{2}$
    $-35\frac{3}{4}$

11. $92\frac{2}{3}$
    $-34\frac{1}{5}$

12. $84\frac{5}{8}$
    $-29\frac{3}{4}$

13. $33\frac{1}{2}$
    $-18\frac{5}{6}$

14. $45\frac{3}{4}$
    $-38\frac{2}{5}$

15. 74
    $-24\frac{7}{8}$

16. $147\frac{2}{3}$
    $-86\frac{3}{4}$

17. $64\frac{3}{4}$
    $-34\frac{3}{10}$

18. 365
    $-98\frac{1}{9}$

19. $72\frac{1}{3}$
    $-37\frac{3}{8}$

20. $86\frac{3}{4}$
    $-49\frac{1}{8}$

21. $76\frac{1}{8}$
    $-17\frac{3}{5}$

22. $83\frac{1}{10}$
    $-46\frac{1}{2}$

23. $251\frac{3}{5}$
    $-150\frac{2}{3}$

24. $57\frac{5}{6}$
    $-29\frac{7}{8}$

25. $63\frac{3}{10}$
    $-4\frac{2}{3}$

Find the products.

1. $1\frac{1}{3} \times 1\frac{1}{5} = a$ 2. $8 \times 2\frac{3}{4} = d$ 3. $2\frac{3}{7} \times 14 = f$ 4. $9 \times 1\frac{2}{3} = g$

5. $8 \times 3\frac{1}{2} = c$ 6. $3\frac{1}{3} \times 4\frac{1}{2} = e$ 7. $\frac{3}{8} \times 4\frac{1}{3} = g$ 8. $6 \times 3\frac{1}{2} = c$

9. $2\frac{1}{8} \times 1\frac{1}{3} = h$ 10. $4\frac{2}{3} \times \frac{3}{7} = k$ 11. $\frac{3}{5} \times 1\frac{3}{4} = m$ 12. $8 \times 6\frac{1}{8} = x$

13. $9 \times 6\frac{2}{3} = s$ 14. $5\frac{1}{3} \times \frac{1}{4} = r$ 15. $4\frac{2}{3} \times 3\frac{1}{2} = b$ 16. $3\frac{3}{8} \times 3\frac{1}{3} = b$

17. $\frac{4}{5} \times 3\frac{1}{4} = t$ 18. $2\frac{2}{3} \times 7\frac{1}{2} = j$ 19. $8\frac{1}{2} \times 4 = n$ 20. $6 \times 3\frac{2}{3} = v$

21. $\frac{5}{8} \times \frac{2}{3} = z$ 22. $\frac{4}{5} \times \frac{3}{8} = p$ 23. $6\frac{2}{5} \times \frac{3}{4} = a$ 24. $1\frac{2}{3} \times 8\frac{1}{2} = d$

Find the quotients.

1. $\frac{3}{4} \div \frac{1}{2} = r$ 2. $\frac{4}{9} \div \frac{2}{3} = a$ 3. $\frac{1}{3} \div \frac{1}{12} = d$ 4. $\frac{1}{10} \div \frac{2}{5} = s$

5. $1\frac{1}{3} \div \frac{3}{4} = u$ 6. $\frac{5}{6} \div \frac{3}{8} = x$ 7. $3\frac{1}{4} \div 2\frac{5}{8} = w$ 8. $3\frac{5}{6} \div 3 = c$

9. $3\frac{3}{4} \div 5 = e$ 10. $3\frac{5}{8} \div \frac{3}{16} = g$ 11. $4\frac{1}{2} \div \frac{1}{3} = k$ 12. $5\frac{1}{3} \div 8 = f$

13. $\frac{6}{7} \div \frac{5}{14} = b$ 14. $4 \div 3\frac{1}{5} = h$ 15. $\frac{9}{10} \div \frac{3}{4} = j$ 16. $7 \div 1\frac{2}{3} = m$

17. $1\frac{1}{3} \div 1\frac{1}{2} = p$ 18. $3 \div 1\frac{1}{5} = q$ 19. $1\frac{1}{4} \div \frac{2}{3} = a$ 20. $1\frac{5}{6} \div 3\frac{1}{2} = d$

21. $3\frac{1}{6} \div 3\frac{1}{3} = f$ 22. $4\frac{1}{6} \div \frac{1}{3} = w$ 23. $4\frac{1}{2} \div 1\frac{7}{8} = x$ 24. $3\frac{1}{3} \div \frac{1}{10} = r$

Solve each proportion.

1. $\frac{2}{3} = \frac{x}{15}$ 2. $\frac{1}{2} = \frac{x}{20}$ 3. $\frac{7}{8} = \frac{35}{x}$ 4. $\frac{5}{9} = \frac{20}{x}$ 5. $\frac{3}{4} = \frac{x}{24}$

6. $\frac{5}{6} = \frac{x}{42}$ 7. $\frac{15}{24} = \frac{x}{32}$ 8. $\frac{9}{30} = \frac{12}{x}$ 9. $\frac{7}{14} = \frac{x}{42}$ 10. $\frac{12}{18} = \frac{x}{21}$

11. $\frac{12}{20} = \frac{15}{x}$ 12. $\frac{21}{24} = \frac{14}{x}$ 13. $\frac{4}{6} = \frac{x}{18}$ 14. $\frac{21}{49} = \frac{x}{28}$ 15. $\frac{10}{16} = \frac{20}{x}$

16. $\frac{20}{24} = \frac{x}{36}$ 17. $\frac{15}{20} = \frac{21}{x}$ 18. $\frac{6}{24} = \frac{x}{32}$ 19. $\frac{6}{9} = \frac{x}{15}$ 20. $\frac{6}{8} = \frac{x}{24}$

21. $\frac{14}{16} = \frac{x}{32}$ 22. $\frac{6}{10} = \frac{x}{15}$ 23. $\frac{3}{27} = \frac{5}{x}$ 24. $\frac{16}{20} = \frac{12}{x}$ 25. $\frac{3}{12} = \frac{x}{28}$

26. $\frac{8}{12} = \frac{12}{x}$ 27. $\frac{15}{18} = \frac{x}{30}$ 28. $\frac{18}{20} = \frac{x}{40}$ 29. $\frac{6}{14} = \frac{12}{x}$ 30. $\frac{15}{25} = \frac{x}{10}$

Write each fraction as a percent. Use mixed numerals when necessary.
Example: $\frac{5}{8} = 62\frac{1}{2}\%$

1. $\frac{3}{5}$ 2. $\frac{1}{8}$ 3. $\frac{5}{6}$ 4. $\frac{7}{8}$ 5. $\frac{5}{11}$

6. $\frac{4}{9}$ 7. $\frac{9}{40}$ 8. $\frac{3}{8}$ 9. $\frac{7}{15}$ 10. $\frac{5}{16}$

11. $\frac{7}{32}$ 12. $\frac{2}{9}$ 13. $\frac{17}{20}$ 14. $\frac{5}{9}$ 15. $\frac{17}{25}$

16. $\frac{32}{40}$ 17. $\frac{8}{15}$ 18. $\frac{15}{16}$ 19. $\frac{12}{27}$ 20. $\frac{13}{16}$

21. $\frac{17}{30}$ 22. $\frac{9}{20}$ 23. $\frac{45}{48}$ 24. $\frac{7}{25}$ 25. $\frac{27}{40}$

26. $\frac{2}{15}$ 27. $\frac{13}{40}$ 28. $\frac{3}{20}$ 29. $\frac{8}{9}$ 30. $\frac{7}{13}$

Find the percent of each number.

1. 3% of 62	2. 5% of 45	3. 25% of 30	4. 60% of 130
5. 10% of 73.8	6. 30% of 52	7. 18% of 46	8. 83% of 10
9. 61% of 25	10. 7% of 100	11. 50% of 15	12. 43% of 73
13. 40% of 81	14. 52% of 3.8	15. 95% of 41	16. 36% of 20
17. 56% of 30	18. 75% of 41	19. 42% of 250	20. 62% of 300
21. 32% of 78	22. 45% of 200	23. 10% of 5.7	24. 80% of 23
25. 71% of 10	26. 82% of 54	27. 35% of 26	28. 51% of 84
29. 41% of 70	30. 63% of 30	31. 57% of 100	32. 75% of 35

Solve the equations.

1. $20\% \times n = 1$	2. $7\% \times n = 0.35$	3. $11\% \times n = 2.2$
4. $35\% \times n = 3.15$	5. $50\% \times n = 50$	6. $75\% \times n = 15.75$
7. $8\% \times n = 2.4$	8. $15\% \times n = 9$	9. $10\% \times n = 9$
10. $30\% \times n = 13.8$	11. $43\% \times n = 8.6$	12. $60\% \times n = 27$
13. $25\% \times n = 4$	14. $12\% \times n = 8.4$	15. $65\% \times n = 22.1$
16. $71\% \times n = 35.5$	17. $70\% \times n = 26.6$	18. $42\% \times n = 10.5$
19. $3\% \times n = 2.79$	20. $54\% \times n = 18.9$	21. $62\% \times n = 9.3$
22. $80\% \times n = 52$	23. $71\% \times n = 21.3$	24. $90\% \times n = 45$
25. $45\% \times n = 23.4$	26. $56\% \times n = 14$	27. $40\% \times n = 23.2$
28. $33\% \times n = 9.24$	29. $50\% \times n = 23$	30. $48\% \times n = 16.8$
31. $63\% \times n = 12.6$	32. $82\% \times n = 615$	

Find the volume of each prism.

1. $l = 8$ m
   $w = 4$ m
   $h = 2$ m

2. $l = 9.5$ m
   $w = 6$ m
   $h = 3.2$ m

3. $l = 12$ m
   $w = 9$ m
   $h = 8$ m

4. $l = 10.4$ m
   $w = 6.5$ m
   $h = 4$ m

5. $l = 7$ m
   $w = 4.5$ m
   $h = 9$ m

6. $l = 23$ cm
   $w = 15$ cm
   $h = 8$ cm

7. $l = 15$ cm
   $w = 12$ cm
   $h = 20$ cm

8. $l = 75$ cm
   $w = 50$ cm
   $h = 50$ cm

9. $l = 25$ cm
   $w = 20$ cm
   $h = 30$ cm

10. $l = 32$ cm
    $w = 18$ cm
    $h = 28$ cm

11. $l = 4$ m
    $w = 1.5$ m
    $h = 3$ m

12. $l = 3.5$ m
    $w = 2$ m
    $h = 2$ m

13. $l = 35$ cm
    $w = 24$ cm
    $h = 30$ cm

14. $l = 20$ cm
    $w = 15$ cm
    $h = 40$ cm

15. $l = 65$ cm
    $w = 30$ cm
    $h = 45$ cm

16. $l = 10$ m
    $w = 5$ m
    $h = 8$ m

17. $l = 62$ cm
    $w = 41$ cm
    $h = 50$ cm

18. $l = 13$ m
    $w = 9.5$ m
    $h = 4$ m

19. $l = 200$ cm
    $w = 10$ cm
    $h = 10$ cm

20. $l = 15$ m
    $w = 4$ m
    $h = 7.5$

Find the volume of each cylinder. Use 3.14 for π.

1. $r = 8$ m
   $h = 20$ m

2. $r = 4$ m
   $h = 12$ m

3. $r = 2$ m
   $h = 1$ m

4. $r = 3$ m
   $h = 2.5$ m

5. $r = 10$ m
   $h = 10$ m

6. $r = 30$ cm
   $h = 15$ cm

7. $r = 22$ cm
   $h = 45$ cm

8. $r = 15$ cm
   $h = 20$ cm

9. $r = 20$ cm
   $h = 12$ cm

10. $r = 5$ cm
    $h = 10$ cm

11. $r = 12$ m
    $h = 8.5$ m

12. $r = 3$ m
    $h = 1.5$ m

13. $r = 3$ m
    $h = 5$ m

14. $r = 7$ m
    $h = 5.5$ m

15. $r = 8$ m
    $h = 10$ m

16. $r = 44$ cm
    $h = 13$ cm

17. $r = 25$ cm
    $h = 12$ cm

18. $r = 15$ cm
    $h = 30$ cm

19. $r = 10$ cm
    $h = 20$ cm

20. $r = 12$ cm
    $h = 30$ cm

21. $r = 9$ m
    $h = 14$ m

22. $r = 150$ cm
    $h = 80$ cm

23. $r = 95$ cm
    $h = 125$ cm

24. $r = 85$ cm
    $h = 100$ cm

25. $r = 75$ cm
    $h = 150$ cm

Find the sums.

1. $6 + {}^-2 = n$ 2. $9 + {}^-6 = n$ 3. $4 + {}^-3 = n$ 4. ${}^-5 + 2 = n$

5. ${}^-7 + {}^-3 = n$ 6. $8 + {}^-2 = n$ 7. $5 + {}^-1 = n$ 8. ${}^-13 + 6 = n$

9. ${}^-20 + 7 = n$ 10. $17 + {}^-6 = n$ 11. $25 + {}^-9 = n$ 12. ${}^-32 + {}^-2 = n$

13. ${}^-8 + 6 = n$ 14. ${}^-45 + 5 = n$ 15. ${}^-15 + 9 = n$ 16. ${}^-12 + 7 = n$

17. $\begin{array}{r} {}^-7 \\ +\ 4 \\ \hline \end{array}$ 18. $\begin{array}{r} 3 \\ +\ {}^-8 \\ \hline \end{array}$ 19. $\begin{array}{r} {}^-6 \\ +\ 5 \\ \hline \end{array}$ 20. $\begin{array}{r} {}^-1 \\ +\ {}^-9 \\ \hline \end{array}$ 21. $\begin{array}{r} {}^-8 \\ +\ 14 \\ \hline \end{array}$

22. $\begin{array}{r} 5 \\ +\ {}^-11 \\ \hline \end{array}$ 23. $\begin{array}{r} {}^-7 \\ +\ 23 \\ \hline \end{array}$ 24. $\begin{array}{r} 31 \\ +\ {}^-8 \\ \hline \end{array}$ 25. $\begin{array}{r} 6 \\ +\ {}^-16 \\ \hline \end{array}$ 26. $\begin{array}{r} {}^-3 \\ +\ {}^-2 \\ \hline \end{array}$

27. $\begin{array}{r} 4 \\ +\ {}^-10 \\ \hline \end{array}$ 28. $\begin{array}{r} 17 \\ +\ {}^-8 \\ \hline \end{array}$ 29. $\begin{array}{r} {}^-20 \\ +\ 9 \\ \hline \end{array}$ 30. $\begin{array}{r} {}^-7 \\ +\ 27 \\ \hline \end{array}$ 31. $\begin{array}{r} 8 \\ +\ {}^-34 \\ \hline \end{array}$

32. $\begin{array}{r} {}^-7 \\ +\ 12 \\ \hline \end{array}$ 33. $\begin{array}{r} {}^-37 \\ +\ 9 \\ \hline \end{array}$ 34. $\begin{array}{r} {}^-9 \\ +\ 8 \\ \hline \end{array}$ 35. $\begin{array}{r} {}^-5 \\ +\ 10 \\ \hline \end{array}$ 36. $\begin{array}{r} {}^-11 \\ +\ 9 \\ \hline \end{array}$

Find the differences.

1. $3 - {}^-5 = n$ 2. ${}^-4 - 6 = n$ 3. ${}^-3 - {}^-2 = n$ 4. $7 - {}^-3 = n$

5. $2 - 7 = n$ 6. ${}^-5 - 8 = n$ 7. $1 - 9 = n$ 8. $3 - {}^-8 = n$

9. ${}^-5 - 10 = n$ 10. ${}^-6 - {}^-2 = n$ 11. ${}^-11 - 2 = n$ 12. ${}^-8 - 7 = n$

13. ${}^-1 - 4 = n$ 14. ${}^-12 - 9 = n$ 15. $6 - {}^-9 = n$ 16. ${}^-5 - 4 = n$

17. $0 - {}^-3 = n$ 18. ${}^-4 - 7 = n$ 19. ${}^-8 - {}^-3 = n$ 20. $9 - 14 = n$

21. ${}^-3 - {}^-7 = n$ 22. $4 - 9 = n$ 23. $9 - {}^-4 = n$ 24. ${}^-2 - {}^-8 = n$

25. ${}^-12 - {}^-8 = n$ 26. ${}^-6 - {}^-9 = n$ 27. $0 - 2 = n$ 28. ${}^-6 - 7 = n$

29. $6 - {}^-5 = n$ 30. $7 - 12 = n$ 31. ${}^-12 - {}^-15 = n$ 32. $8 - 15 = n$

Find the products.

1. -3×7
2. -4×-6
3. -7×2
4. -5×5
5. 9×-6

6. -2×-8
7. -7×6
8. 4×-5
9. -8×-7
10. 0×-3

11. 5×-7
12. -1×2
13. 6×-8
14. -3×5
15. 7×-7

16. -8×9
17. -3×4
18. 12×-3
19. -4×-9
20. -6×5

21. 2×-6
22. -8×-4
23. -23×-4
24. 8×-11
25. 26×-5

26. -10×-2
27. -36×2
28. 15×-7
29. -8×5
30. -4×4

31. -43×6
32. -7×4
33. -4×30
34. -8×-11
35. -52×6

36. -49×8
37. -9×5
38. -5×-63
39. -2×93
40. -3×8

41. -7×38
42. -71×-5
43. 2×-5
44. -42×-7
45. -66×3

46. -9×7
47. 14×-9
48. -4×-81
49. 6×-6
50. -8×75

1. $-16 \div 4$
2. $-10 \div -2$
3. $18 \div -3$
4. $30 \div -5$
5. $-24 \div 8$

6. $-28 \div 7$
7. $12 \div -4$
8. $-36 \div 6$
9. $-54 \div -9$
10. $-6 \div 3$

11. $-14 \div -2$
12. $48 \div -8$
13. $-56 \div -7$
14. $-20 \div 5$
15. $32 \div -4$

16. $64 \div -8$
17. $-24 \div 6$
18. $35 \div -5$
19. $-49 \div 7$
20. $-8 \div 2$

21. $-27 \div -3$
22. $-40 \div 5$
23. $-27 \div 9$
24. $-18 \div -6$
25. $-42 \div 7$

26. $30 \div -6$
27. $-14 \div -7$
28. $-56 \div 8$
29. $20 \div -4$
30. $81 \div -9$

31. $-45 \div -5$
32. $-9 \div 3$
33. $28 \div -4$
34. $-72 \div 8$
35. $-48 \div -6$

36. $-36 \div 9$
37. $54 \div -6$
38. $-16 \div 2$
39. $-15 \div -3$
40. $-25 \div -5$

41. $32 \div -8$
42. $-63 \div 9$
43. $-35 \div -7$
44. $10 \div -5$
45. $-36 \div 4$

46. $-63 \div -7$
47. $40 \div -8$
48. $-24 \div -4$
49. $-72 \div 9$
50. $-21 \div 3$

Table of Measures

Metric System*   U.S. Customary Units

Length

Metric		U.S.	
1 millimeter (mm)	0.1 centimeter (cm) 0.001 meter (m)	1 foot (ft)	12 inches (in.)
1 centimeter (cm)	10 millimeters (mm)	1 yard (yd)	36 inches (in.) 3 feet (ft)
1 decimeter (dm)	100 millimeters (mm) 10 centimeters (cm)	1 mile (mi)	5280 feet (ft) 1760 yards (yd)
1 meter (m)	1000 millimeters (mm) 100 centimeters (cm) 10 decimeters (dm)	1 nautical mile	6076 feet (ft) 1852 meters (m)
1 kilometer (km)	1000 meters (m)		

Area

Metric		U.S.	
1 square meter (m²)	100 square decimeters (dm²) 10 000 square centimeters (cm²)	1 square foot	144 square inches (in.²)
1 hectare (ha)	0.01 square kilometer (km²) 10 000 square meters (m²)	1 square yard (yd²)	9 square feet (ft²) 1296 square inches (in.²)
1 square kilometer (km²)	1 000 000 square meters (m²) 100 hectares (ha)	1 acre (A)	43 560 square feet (ft²) 4 840 square yards (yd²)
		1 square mile (mi²)	640 acres (A)

Volume

Metric		U.S.	
1 cubic decimeter (dm³)	0.001 cubic meter (m³) 1000 cubic centimeters (cm³) 1 liter (ℓ)	1 cubic foot (ft³)	1728 cubic inches (in.³)
1 cubic meter (m³)	1 000 000 cubic centimeters (cm³) 1 000 cubic decimeters (dm³)	1 cubic yard (yd³)	27 cubic feet (ft³) 46 656 cubic inches (in.³)

Capacity

Metric		U.S.	
1 teaspoon	5 milliliters (ml)	1 cup (c)	8 fluid ounces (fl oz)
1 tablespoon	12.5 milliliters (ml)	1 pint (pt)	16 fluid ounces (fl oz) 2 cups (c)
1 liter (ℓ)	1000 milliliters (ml) 1000 cubic centimeters (cm³) 1 cubic decimeter (dm³) 4 metric cups	1 quart (qt)	32 fluid ounces (fl oz) 4 cups (c) 2 pints (pt)
1 kiloliter (kl)	1000 liters (ℓ)	1 gallon (gal)	128 fluid ounces (fl oz) 16 cups (c) 8 pints (pt) 4 quarts (qt)

Mass

Metric		U.S.	
1 gram (g)	1000 milligrams (mg)	1 pound (lb)	16 ounces (oz)
1 kilogram (kg)	1000 grams (g)	1 ton (T)	2000 pounds (lbs)
1 metric ton (t)	1000 kilograms (kg)		

*For meaning of prefixes see page 117 or 396

Mathematical Symbols

$=$	Is equal to		$\overleftrightarrow{AB}$	Line through points A and B
$\neq$	Is not equal to		$\overrightarrow{AB}$	Ray AB
$>$	Is greater than		$\overline{AB}$	Segment with endpoints A and B
$<$	Is less than		$\angle ABC$	Angle ABC
$\leq$	Is less than or equal to		$m(\angle ABC)$	Measure of angle ABC
$\approx$	Is approximately equal to		$m(\overline{AB})$	Measure, or length, of segment AB
$\cong$	Is congruent to		$\triangle ABC$	Triangle ABC
$\sim$	Is similar to		$\overarc{RS}$	Arc with endpoints R and S
$\%$	Percent		$35°$	Thirty-five *degrees,*
π	Pi		$14'$	fourteen *minutes,*
			$20''$	twenty *seconds*

Metric System Prefixes

tera	T	one trillion		deci	d	one tenth
giga	G	one billion		centi	c	one hundredth
mega	M	one million		milli	m	one thousandth
kilo	k	one thousand		micro	μ	one millionth
hecto	h	one hundred		nano	n	one billionth
deka	da	ten		pico	p	one trillionth

Formulas

$P = a + b + c$	Perimeter of triangle		$C = \pi \cdot d$	Circumference of circle
$P = 2(l + w)$	Perimeter of rectangle		$A = \pi \cdot r^2$	Area of circle
$A = l \cdot w$	Area of rectangle		$V = \frac{1}{3} \cdot \pi \cdot r^3$	Volume of sphere
$A = b \cdot h$	Area of parallelogram		$V = \pi \cdot r^2 \cdot h$	Volume of cylinder
$A = \frac{B+b}{2} \cdot h$	Area of trapezoid		$V = \frac{1}{3} \cdot \pi \cdot r^2 h$	Volume of cone
$A = \frac{1}{2} \cdot b \cdot h$	Area of triangle		$V = B \cdot h$	Volume of prism
$a^2 + b^2 = c^2$	Pythagorean Theorem			(B = base area)
$V = l \cdot w \cdot h$	Volume of rectangular solid		$V = \frac{1}{3} \cdot B \cdot h$	Volume of pyramid

Glossary

accuracy The *more accurate* of two measures is the measure with the smaller relative error.

acute angle An angle smaller than a right angle.

addend Any one member of a set of numbers to be added. In the equation $7 + 9 = 16$, 7 and 9 are addends.

additive inverse Each of two numbers whose sum is zero is said to be the additive inverse of the other.

adjacent angles Two angles with a common vertex, a common side, and no common interior points. In the figure, $\angle 1$ and $\angle 2$ are adjacent angles.

adjacent sides Two sides of a polygon with a common vertex.

algorithm (algorism) A computational procedure. For example, the algorithm for finding the quotient of two numbers.

alternate exterior angles A transversal of two lines forms eight angles as shown. Angles 1, 2, 7, and 8 are exterior angles. Angles 1 and 7, on alternate sides of the transversal, are a pair of alternate exterior angles, as are angles 2 and 8.

alternate interior angles Two of the four interior angles (3, 4, 5, and 6) shown above which are on alternate sides of the transversal. Angles 3 and 5 form such a pair, as do angles 4 and 6.

altitude (of a triangle) The segment from any vertex perpendicular to the opposite side. Also, see *height*.

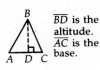

$\overline{BD}$ is the altitude. $\overline{AC}$ is the base.

angle Two rays which have a common vertex (endpoint).

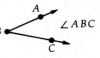

$\angle ABC$

angle bisector The ray which divides an angle into two congruent angles. In the figure $\overrightarrow{DB}$ bisects $\angle ADC$.

approximation A number that is suitably "close" to another number. For example, a decimal approximation for $\frac{2}{9}$ is 0.22. The symbol "$\approx$" denotes "is approximately"; for example $\pi \approx 3.14$.

arc A part of a circle. Note that three points, instead of two, are used to denote a specific arc since $\overarc{AB}$ could denote a *minor* arc $\overarc{ACB}$ or a *major* arc $\overarc{ADB}$.

area The measure of a plane region in terms of a chosen unit, usually a square.

arithmetic mean The sum of a list of numbers divided by the number of addends in the list. (Often called the "average")

associative (grouping) principle The principle which states that the sum (or product) of three or more numbers is the same regardless of grouping:
$(a + b) + c = a + (b + c)$
or $(a \cdot b) \cdot c = a \cdot (b \cdot c)$

average See *arithmetic mean*.

base (of numeration) The term "base" refers to the type of grouping involved in a system of numeration. For example, in base eight: $25_{(8)}$ means 2 eights and 5, and $346_{(8)}$ means 3 sixty-fours, 4 eights, and 6.

base (of a polygon) Any side of a polygon may be referred to as a base. See figure for *altitude of a triangle*.

base (of a space figure) See examples below.

Bases of a cylinder   Base of a cone   Base of a pyramid

bisect To divide into two congruent parts.

center A (fixed) point of symmetry for a geometric figure. See the figure for *circle*.

centi- A prefix meaning *one hundredth*.

centimeter A unit of length that is $\frac{1}{100}$ of a meter.

central angle An angle with its vertex at the center of the circle.

chord A segment with both endpoints on a circle.

circle The set of all points in a plane which are a specified distance from a fixed point called the *center*.

circumference The distance around a circle. For each circle, the number is the product of its diameter and the number π. The formula is $C = \pi d$.

circumscribed circle A circle drawn through the vertices of a polygon. A circle can be circumscribed about any triangle but only about certain other polygons.

circumscribed polygon If the sides of a polygon are tangent to a circle, then the polygon is circumscribed about the circle. Also, see *inscribed circle*.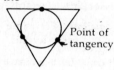

Point of tangency

common factor A number that is a factor of each of two or more given numbers. For example, 3 is a common factor of 6 and 9.

common multiple A number that is a multiple of each of two or more given numbers. For example, 18 is a common multiple of 2, 3, and 9.

commutative (order) principle The principle which states that the sum (or product) of any two numbers is the same regardless of the order in which they are added (or multiplied): $a + b = b + a$ or $a \cdot b = b \cdot a$

complementary angles Two angles whose measures have a sum of 90°.

composite number Any whole number greater than 1 which is not prime. Composite numbers have more than two different factors.

concave figure A non-convex figure.

concentric circles Two or more circles that have the same center.

cone A space figure formed by a closed plane curve and all line segments from a point not in the plane of the curve to all the points of the curve.

congruent angles Angles which have the same measure.

congruent polygons Two figures are congruent if they can be matched so that corresponding angles are congruent and corresponding sides are congruent.

congruent segments Segments which have the same length. We write $\overline{AB} \cong \overline{CD}$.

convex figure A figure is convex if every segment joining any two points on the boundary of the figure contains only points on the figure or in its interior.

coordinate axes Two intersecting perpendicular number lines used for graphing ordered number pairs (*coordinates*).

$\bullet\,(2.3)$

coordinates An ordered number pair matched with a point in the coordinate plane. See the figure for *coordinate axes*.

correspondence A matching of elements in one set with those of another set.

corresponding segments Two segments matched by any one-to-one correspondence between segments of two figures.

cross products In the equation $\frac{a}{b} = \frac{c}{d}$, the products ad and bc are called cross products. Two ratios $\frac{a}{b}$ and $\frac{c}{d}$ are equal if and only if $ad = bc$.

cross section The intersection of a space figure and a plane.

cube (geometry) A regular polyhedron each of whose six faces are squares.

cube (numeration) A number raised to the third power. 8 is the cube of 2 because $2^3 = 8$. Also, to raise a number to the third power.

cylinder The space figure formed by two congruent curves in parallel planes and the parallel segments connecting corresponding points of the curves.

decagon A 10-sided polygon.

deci- A prefix meaning *one tenth*.

decimal (numeral) Any base-ten numeral written using a decimal point.

decimal point The dot that is used in a decimal numeral.

decimal system of numeration A system of numeration in which powers of ten and place value are used.

decimeter A unit of length that is $\frac{1}{10}$ of a meter, or 10 centimeters.

degree A unit angle that is $\frac{1}{90}$ of a right angle.

deka- A prefix meaning *ten*.

dekameter A unit of length that is 10 meters.

denominator For each fraction $\frac{a}{b}$, b is the denominator.

diagonal A segment connecting two nonconsecutive vertices of a polygon.

diameter Any chord that contains the center of a circle.

difference The number resulting from subtraction.

digits The basic symbols used in a place-value system of numeration. In base ten, the symbols are 0, 1, 2, 3, 4, 5, 6, 7, 8, and 9.

distributive principle The fundamental principle connecting addition and multiplication.
$a \cdot (b + c) = a \cdot b + a \cdot c$.

dividend The number to be divided in a division problem.

$$3 \leftarrow \text{Quotient}$$
$$5\overline{)17} \leftarrow \text{Dividend}$$
$$\underline{15}$$
$$\text{Divisor} \quad 2 \leftarrow \text{Remainder}$$

divisible A given number is divisible by a second number if the remainder is zero. If $a = b \cdot c$ with $b \neq 0$ and $c \neq 0$, then a is divisible by either b or c.

division The inverse of the operation of multiplication.

$$\begin{array}{ccc} \text{F} & \text{F} & \text{P} \\ 3 \cdot 4 & = & 12 \end{array}$$

$$\begin{array}{ccc} \text{P} & \text{F} & \text{F} \\ 12 \div 4 & = & 3 \\ 12 \div 3 & = & 4 \end{array}$$

divisor See *dividend*.

dodecahedron A polyhedron which has 12 faces. A regular dodecahedron has 12 congruent pentagonal faces.

edge A segment that is a side of any face of a space figure. A cube has 12 edges.

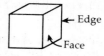

element Any member of a set.

ellipse A closed plane curve generated by a point (P) moving in such a way that the sum of the distances from two fixed focal points $(F_1$ and $F_2)$ is constant.

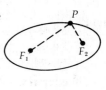

equality The relation of identity. A statement of equality asserts that two symbols name the same object or number.

equally likely outcomes Outcomes or results that have the same chance of occurring.

equation A mathematical sentence using the equality symbol $(=)$ $7 + n = 9$ is an equation.

equiangular triangle A triangle all of whose angles have the same measure.

equilateral triangle A triangle having all sides the same length.

equivalent decimals Decimals which represent the same number. For example, 0.5, 0.50, and 0.500 are equivalent decimals.

equivalent fractions Fractions which represent the same number such as $\frac{1}{2}$, $\frac{5}{10}$, and $\frac{50}{100}$.

equivalent ratios Two ratios which represent the same fractional number. For example, the ratio 5:10 is the same as 1:2. $\frac{5}{10} = \frac{1}{2}$

estimate An approximation for a given number. Often used in the sense of a rough calculation.

even number A whole-number multiple of 2. The set of even numbers is $\{0, 2, 4, 6, \ldots\}$.

expanded notation A representation of a number as a sum of powers of ten such as:
$3425 = 3 \cdot 10^3 + 4 \cdot 10^2 + 2 \cdot 10^1 + 5 \cdot 10^0$.

exponent A numeral written above and to the right of a mathematical expression to indicate how many times a number is to be used as a factor. For example, in the expression 5^4, the 4 indicates that 5 is to be used as a factor 4 times: $5 \cdot 5 \cdot 5 \cdot 5 = 5^4$

extremes The first and last terms in a proportion written in the form $a : b = c : d$. The numbers *a* and *d* are extremes and *b* and *c* are called the *means*.

face   Any one of the bounding polygonal regions of a space figure. See the figure for *edge*.

factor   Any one member of a set of numbers to be multiplied. In the equation $5 \cdot 7 = 35$, 5 and 7 are factors.

factor tree   A diagram suggestive of a tree showing the prime factorization of a number.

flow chart   A diagram which gives instructions in a logical order.

formula   A general fact or rule expressed by using symbols. For example, the area of any parallelogram with base *b* and height *h* is given by $b \cdot h$. The formula is usually presented with the equation $A = b \cdot h$.

fraction   A symbol for a fractional number of the form $\frac{a}{b}$ such that $b \neq 0$.

fractional number   The set of non-negative rational numbers.

function   A correspondence that associates each element in a first set with a unique element of a second set. Different elements in a first set may possibly be matched with the same element of the second set.

gram   A unit of mass. The mass of a one cubic centimeter of water at 4°C.

graph   A set of points associated with a given set of numbers or number pairs showing a relation or function.

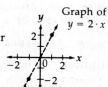

Graph of $y = 2 \cdot x$

graph (statistical)   A picture used to illustrate a given collection of data. It may be in the form of a bar graph, a circle graph, a line-segment graph, or a pictograph.

greatest common factor (GCF)   The largest, or greatest, number that is a factor of each of a set of numbers.

greatest possible error   Half of the basic unit in which a measurement is given. For example, if a length is given as 18 centimeters to the nearest centimeter, then the basic unit is the centimeter and the greatest possible error is 0.5 centimeter.

hectare   A unit of area that is 10 000 square meters.

hecto-   A prefix meaning *one hundred*.

height (of a prism)   The perpendicular distance between the planes of the parallel faces.

hexagon   A 6-sided polygon.

hypotenuse   The side of a right triangle opposite the right angle.

icosahedron   A polyhedron of 20 faces. A regular icosahedron has equilateral triangles for its faces.

identity element   For addition, zero is the identity element since $a + 0 = a$ for any number *a*. Similarly, for multiplication, 1 is the identity element since $a \cdot 1 = a$.

identity principles   For any number $a, a + 0 = a$ and $a \cdot 1 = a$.

improper fraction   A fraction whose numerator is greater than or equal to its denominator.

inequality   A mathematical statement using either of the symbols $<$ or $>$ such as $\frac{3}{4} < \frac{7}{8}$.

inscribed angle   An angle that contains three points of the circle and has its vertex on the circle.

inscribed polygon   See *circumscribed circle*.

integers   The set consisting of the natural numbers $\{1, 2, 3, \ldots\}$, the negatives of the natural numbers $\{^-1, ^-2, ^-3, \ldots\}$, and zero.

intersecting lines   Two lines which have a common point.

inverse (operation)   Operations which are opposite in effect such as addition and subtraction or multiplication and division.

isosceles triangle   A triangle with at least two congruent sides.

kilo-   A prefix meaning *one thousand*.

kilogram   The basic unit of mass in the metric system. 1000 grams.

kilometer A unit of length that is 1000 meters.

least common denominator The least common multiple of the denominators of two or more fractions. For example, the least common denominator of $\frac{5}{6}$ and $\frac{3}{4}$ is 12.

least common multiple (LCM) The smallest non-zero number that is a multiple of each of two or more given numbers. The LCM of 4 and 6 is 12.

legs (of a right triangle) The perpendicular sides of a right triangle.

length The measure of a segment (or curve) in terms of a chosen unit.

line segment A set of points consisting of two points A and B and all points between them. The symbol $\overline{AB}$ is used to denote a segment.

liter (cubic decimeter) The basic unit of capacity in the metric system. 1000 cubic centimeters.

lowest-terms (simplest) fraction A fraction is in lowest terms if the numerator and denominator of the fraction have no common factor other than 1.

mean See *arithmetic mean.*

means The second and third terms in a proportion written in the form $a:b = c:d$. See *extremes.*

median (of a set) The middle number of a set containing an odd number of elements that are arranged in order. If a set contains an even number of elements, the average of the two middle numbers is the median.

median (of a triangle) The segment from the vertex to the midpoint of the opposite side of a triangle.

meter The basic unit of length in the metric system approximately 1 650 763.73 times the wave length of the orange-red spectral emission line of krypton-86.

midpoint (middle point) A point which divides a segment into two congruent segments.

milli- A prefix meaning *one thousandth.*

minute A unit of angular measure that is $\frac{1}{60}$ of a degree.

mixed decimal numeral A combination of a decimal and a fraction such as $0.4\frac{1}{3}$ and read as "four and one-third tenths."

mixed numeral A numeral such as $4\frac{2}{3}$ indicating the sum of a whole number and a fractional number; $4\frac{2}{3} = 4 + \frac{2}{3}$.

mode The most frequently occurring element of a set. There may be more than one mode of a set.

multiple A first number is a multiple of a second number if there is a whole number that multiplies by the second number to give the first number. For example, 24 is a multiple of 4 and 6 since $4 \times 6 = 24$.

multiplication An operation that combines a first number (*factor*) and a second number (*factor*) to give another number (this result is called the *product* of the two factors).

multiplicative inverse See *reciprocal.*

natural numbers The set of numbers $\{1, 2, 3, \ldots\}$.

negative integers The set of numbers $\{^-1, ^-2, ^-3, \ldots\}$.

number pair An ordered pair of numbers such as $(3, 4)$, often coordinates of a point in a plane.

numeral A symbol for a number.

numerator For each fraction $\frac{a}{b}$, a is the numerator.

obtuse angle An angle greater than a right angle and smaller than a straight angle.

octagon An 8-sided polygon.

octahedron A polyhedron having eight faces. Each face of a regular octahedron is an equilateral triangle.

odd number Any number in the set $\{1, 3, 5, 7, \ldots\}$.

one principle For any number a, $a \cdot 1 = a$. See *identity principle* for multiplication.

operation A binary operation like "multiplication" associates each ordered pair of numbers with one number. Usually we speak of the four fundamental operations: addition, subtraction, multiplication, and division.

opposites principle For any integer a, $a + {}^-a = 0$.

origin The intersection of the coordinate axes; the point associated with the number pair $(0, 0)$.

outcome A possible result in a probability experiment.

parallel lines Lines in the same plane which do not intersect.

parallelogram A quadrilateral whose opposite sides are parallel.

pentagon A 5-sided polygon.

percent (%) Literally means "per hundred." A symbol such as 3% is an abbreviation for "3 per 100" or 0.03.

perimeter The sum of the lengths of the sides of a polygon.

period In writing numerals, each set of three digits separated by a space is called a period.

perpendicular bisector A line which bisects a segment as well as being perpendicular to it.

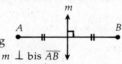

$m \perp$ bis $\overline{AB}$

perpendicular lines Two intersecting lines that form right angles.

pi (π) The ratio of the circumference of a circle to its diameter. $\pi \approx 3.14$.

place value A system used for writing numerals for numbers, using only a definite number of symbols or digits. In the decimal system of numeration each place of a numeral has ten times the value of the place to its right.

plane figure A set of points in one plane.

point of tangency If a line and circle intersect in just one point, the intersection is the point of tangency.

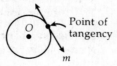

polygon A closed plane figure whose boundary is made up of segments.

polyhedron A space figure each of whose faces is a polygonal region.

positive integer Any number in the set $\{1, 2, 3, \ldots\}$.

power In the statement $a = b^n$, a is the nth power of b. For example, for $1000 = 10^3$, 1000 is the third power of 10.

prime factorization An expression of a composite number as a product of prime factors.

prime number A whole number greater than 1 whose only factors are itself and 1.

prism A 3-dimensional (space) figure whose bases are congruent polygonal regions in parallel planes and whose faces are parallelograms.

probability The ratio of the number of times a certain outcome can occur to the number of total possible outcomes.

product The number $a \cdot b$ which results from applying the multiplication operation to the numbers a and b.

proportion An equation stating that two ratios are equal: $a:b = c:d$ or $\frac{a}{b} = \frac{c}{d}$.

protractor An instrument for measuring angles.

pyramid A 3-dimensional (space) figure with a polygonal base and triangular lateral faces.

Pythagorean Theorem In any right triangle, the sum of the areas of the squares on the legs is equal to the area of the square on the hypotenuse.

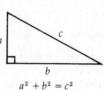

$a^2 + b^2 = c^2$

quadrilateral A 4-sided polygon.

quotient The number $a \div b$ (or $b \div a$) which results from applying the division operation to the numbers a and b.

radius Any segment from the center of a circle to a point on the circle.

Radius OA

ratio The ratio of two numbers a and b is their quotient, $\frac{a}{b}$.

rational number The quotient of two integers, the divisor not being zero.

ray A half-line together with the point determining it (endpoint).

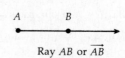

Ray AB or $\overrightarrow{AB}$

reciprocal If $a \cdot b = 1$, each of the numbers a and b is the reciprocal (multiplicative inverse) of the other. Each non-zero real number has a unique reciprocal. Zero has no reciprocal.

rectangle A parallelogram with four right angles.

reflection A rigid motion that maps the points of a plane onto itself. If point P is reflected in a line with a reflection image P_1, then the line is the perpendicular bisector of $\overline{PP_1}$.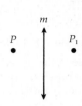

region All the points in the part of a plane bounded by a simple closed curve. The interior of this curve is a region.

regular polygon A polygon that is equiangular and equilateral; for example, a square.

remainder In whole-number division, if dividend D is divided by divisor d and the relation $D = (q \cdot d) + r$ is obtained where $0 < r < d$, then r is called the remainder. Note that $r = 0$ if d is a factor of D (see *dividend*). Also, the difference in a subtraction problem.

repeating decimal A decimal whose digits from some point on repeat periodically. Examples: 6.2835835 . . . and 0.3333333 . . . . These examples may also be written 6.2$\overline{835}$ and 0.$\overline{3}$ respectively.

rhombus An equilateral parallelogram which is not a square.

right angle An angle whose measure is 90°.

right triangle A triangle that has one right angle.

rigid motion A transformation of the points of the plane that preserves all distances.

Roman numerals The numerals I, V, X, L, C, D, M, and combinations of these numerals used in the Roman numeration system.

rotation A rigid motion in which the points of the plane are turned about a fixed point.

rounding A process of replacing a number by an approximation (another number) with fewer significant digits. For example, 456 789 rounded to the nearest thousand would be 457 000.

scale drawing A drawing of an object made so that distances in the drawing are proportional to actual distances. A scale of 1:10 indicates that distances in the drawing are $\frac{1}{10}$ of the actual distances.

scalene triangle A triangle with no pair of congruent sides.

scientific notation A notation used for writing any number as the product of a power of ten and a number between 1 and 10 (including 1).

second A unit of angular measure that is $\frac{1}{60}$ of a minute.

segment A set of points consisting of two points A and B and all points between them.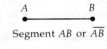

Segment AB or $\overline{AB}$

semicircle An arc that is exactly half a circle. One of two arcs cut off by a diameter.

set A group or collection of objects.

similar polygons Two figures are similar if they can be matched so that corresponding angles are congruent and corresponding sides have the same ratio.

skew lines Lines that are not in the same plane. They do not intersect, yet they are not parallel.

space The set of all points. This term usually denotes a 3-dimensional quality. We also refer to a plane as 2-dimensional space and a line as a 1-dimensional space.

space figure A geometric figure whose points are not all in the same plane.

sphere The set of all points in space at a fixed distance from a given point.

square root If $x^2 = y$, then x is the square root of y.

statistics The science of analyzing numerical information.

straightedge An unmarked ruler.

subtend Literally means "to be opposite to." For example, central angles and inscribed angles in a circle are said to subtend the arcs they cut off. Also, chords and arcs in a circle subtend the angles of a circle.

$\overarc{AB}$ subtends $\angle AOB$ or $\overarc{AB}$ is subtended by $\angle AOB$

subtraction The operation that is the inverse of the addition operation.

A	A	S		S	A	A
5	+ 6	= 11		11	− 5	= 6
				11	− 6	= 5

sum The number $a + b$ which results when the operation of addition is applied to the numbers a and b.

supplementary angles Two angles whose measures have a sum of 180°.

surface area The total area of the polygonal regions (faces) of a polyhedron.

symmetric figure A plane figure which can be divided into two congruent parts by a line (of symmetry).

tangent A line which intersects a circle in just one point.

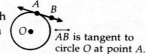

$\overrightarrow{AB}$ is tangent to circle O at point A.

terminating decimal A decimal such as 0.5, 1.0, 1.24, 0.0307, and so on, that represents the quotient of a whole number and a power of 10.

$$0.5 = \frac{5}{10}, \quad 1.24 = \frac{124}{10^2}, \quad 0.0307 = \frac{307}{10^4}$$

tessellation A repeated pattern of geometric figures which will completely "cover a plane" without any gaps or overlapping.

tetrahedron A polyhedron having 4 faces.

translation A rigid motion in which each point of the plane is moved the same distance and in the same direction.

transversal A line which intersects two or more lines.

trapezoid A quadrilateral with one pair of parallel sides.

bases, or parallel sides

triangle A 3-sided polygon.

unit The object adopted as a standard of measurement. For length, we choose a *unit* segment; for area, we choose a *unit square*; and for volume, a *cube*.

variable A symbol, usually a letter, used to represent any number in a given set. For example, we may say: "If x is a whole number, then $2 \cdot x$ is an even number."

vertex A point that two rays of an angle have in common. Also, the common point of any two sides of a polygon.

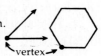

vertex

vertical angles Two pairs of angles formed by two intersecting lines. Angles 1 and 3 (and 2 and 4) are vertical angles.

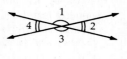

volume The measure of a space figure in terms of a chosen unit.

whole numbers Any number in the set $\{0, 1, 2, 3, \ldots\}$.

zero principle The principle which states that for any number a, $a + 0 = a$. Also, see *identity element* for addition.

Index